Sophomore Organic Chemistry 2 By Inquisition

Kevin Burgess
Texas A & M University

By Inquisition Press

This edition first published in 2016.

Authors and publishers do not warrant the information contained in this book to be free of errors; data, illustrations, procedural details, or other items may inadvertently be inaccurate.

Publisher: *By Inquisition Press*.

Outside cover art by Kevin Burgess.

Library of Congress Cataloging-in-Publication Data is available.

ISBN 978-0-692- 78246-0

Preface

This is the second of two books intended to accompany courses in sophomore organic chemistry in The United States and anywhere else using similar curricula. They are intended as workbooks for "flipped" settings where instructors and students may solve problems from this book in an interactive way, or as study guides for students wanting to check their understanding as they take a conventional class.

I thank the friends who have already looked at some of these questions, and have given valuable suggestions for improvements. Special thanks to Dr Anyanee Kamkaew who solved all the problems, hence suggested numerous corrections and improvements, and generated a set of answers that can be found on the web page for By Inquisition Press (www.byinquisition.org). Dr Evamarie Capareda also reviewed the content carefully and gave much help and encouragement. Dr Aurore Loudet, a phenomenal eagle-eyed checker, weeded out many of my stupid mistakes. Then there were many others who helped including many students in my research group and, in alphabetical order, Dr Ivana Fleischer, Verena Lehner, Santos Pagire, Julietta Yedoyan, all from the University of Regensburg where I stayed for two months towards the end of this project, courtesy of Dr Oliver Reiser and The Humboldt Foundation. At TAMU over the years that it took to compose these texts there were many graduate and undergraduate students who checked parts, and some professors, Kenn Harding, GG, and Patricio Santander in particular, also gave help and encouragement. Dana Choe contributed two of the cartoons, and the rest were composed with a little help from my friends.

Thank you all.

All the errors in this book are mine. I welcome constructive criticism (burgess@tamu.edu) that points to errors in the text or in the answers online, confusing questions, or material to include or exclude.

Kevin Burgess
Rachal Professor of Chemistry
Department of Chemistry
Texas A & M University

www.chem.tamu.edu/rgroup/burgess/

www.byinquisition.org

What This Book Offers Instructors

Summary

This workbook is designed to:

- form a framework for flipping second semester sophomore organic chemistry classes;

- provide students with a set of questions and answers that they need to learn how to study organic chemistry effectively;

- steer students towards important chemical concepts necessary to major in biological sciences including medicine, dentistry, plant sciences, veterinary science, food science, as well as chemistry; and,

- enable students to avoid having to buy expensive textbook/online bundled resources.

Philosophy

The emphasis of the *Sophomore Organic Chemistry By Inquisition* workbooks, of which this is the second, is *how students should study organic chemistry*, more than on organic chemistry itself. These workbooks are designed to enable an instructor to flip a sophomore organic chemistry class by working a fraction of the problems in class, and leaving the students to solve the rest (I share experiences on how to flip sophomore organic classes in the preamble to the first book in the series). Alternatively, students may work through the problems presented here to complement classes taught using conventional lecture styles.

Book 1 in this series covers essential concepts for the first semester of sophomore organic chemistry. This workbook, the second in the series, covers many of the essential concepts for the second semester of organic chemistry, but *with a particular emphasis on those which apply to carbohydrates, nucleic acids, proteins and peptides*. Those issues are dealt with first because they are the most important to students who are not chemistry majors.

Some advanced concepts that are important to chemical or biochemical syntheses of small molecule natural products are dealt with *after* the chemistry needed to understand carbohydrates, nucleic acids, proteins and peptides. This is not because syntheses of natural products are not important, they are. It is because chemical and biochemical syntheses of natural products involve such a huge array of reactions that it is almost impossible to comprehensively teach the fundamentals of those in two semesters without overwhelming a significant fraction of the audience. More importantly, few academics expect majors in the biological sciences outside of chemistry to learn and retain that specialized synthetic information from a sophomore organic chemistry class.

Inevitably, most instructors will realize there is some material they might expect to be covered that is not found in these workbooks. However, this is a workbook not a syllabus, and part of the appeal of flipping classes, teaching students to take the initiative for learning, is that instructors can augment the material in this workbook with other problems and reading assignments to produce optimal syllabi for their particular environment. Instructors may also use online homework selected from resources like Sapling Learning (http://www2.saplinglearning.com); there is no web-based package bundled with this book.

Students need to compare their answers against model solutions. Consequently, answers for this workbook are available via the *By Inquisition* website (www.byinquisition.org) and will also be covered in some videos online (details on the byinquisition.org web site).

Students will need access to textbooks and online materials to aid their understanding. They can use any decent textbook with these notes, including editions other than the latest, *ie* ones which can be bought relatively inexpensively.

What This Book Offers Students

Summary

This is the bad news:

- it is going to take at least 40 – 0 hours of *focused, targeted* practice per semester to get a good grade in sophomore organic chemistry 2
- this book probably will not cover absolutely everything your instructor wants you to know
- material covered in this book does not follow that in any particular textbook, so there will be some effort involved in correlating chapters in a textbook with sections in this workbook
- there is repetition in the problems (with slight changes) to drive home the key points
- all students will find some questions in this book which they feel could have been phrased better (but I have done my best to make them crystal clear)

The good news is:

- students of sophomore organic chemistry who solve the problems in this book following the guidelines below, will significantly improve, irrespective of the exact course content and the order in which it is presented.

How To Use This Book

(i)   Revise Org. Chem. 1 (using *Sophomore Organic Chemistry 1 By Inquisition*?).

(ii)   Gain a basic understanding of the new material covered in the appropriate section of this book.

(ii)   Attempt the problems *without looking at the ideal answers provided on the website for this book*.

(iii)   When unable to solve a problem, determine if it is probing for a fact or testing understanding of a key concept.

(iv)   If a problem requires memorization of a fact, but that memory is not available, look up the answer in the text, from the web, anywhere *except the ideal answers provided on the website for this book*.

(v)   If a problem requires application of a concept but the required understanding is not there yet, learn more about the concept, then try again *without looking at the ideal answers on the website for this book*.

(vi)   Crosscheck your answers with friends, and discuss if necessary.

(vii)   Finally, check the ideal solutions provided on the web if there is any uncertainty about the correct ones.

It is impossible to solve all the problems in this book without learning some organic chemistry first [see (ii) above]. These are ways to learn enough organic chemistry to begin to solve the problems in this book:

- going to lectures
- reading a textbook
- targeted web research
- talking to friends or instructors about organic chemistry
- watching appropriate videos online

The best way to gain that understanding is to do all these things, as necessary.

Contents

Part 2: Towards Understanding Esterases And Proteases

Part 3: Towards Understanding Peptides And Proteins

in·qui·si·tion (ĭn′kwĭ-zĭsh′ən, ĭng′-) *n.*

1. The act of inquiring into a matter; an investigation. See Synonyms at **inquiry**.

2. *Law* An inquest.

3.

a. Inquisition A tribunal formerly held in the Roman Catholic Church and directed at the suppression of heresy.

b. An investigation that violates the privacy or rights of individuals, especially through rigorous or harsh interrogation.

c. A rigorous or severe questioning.

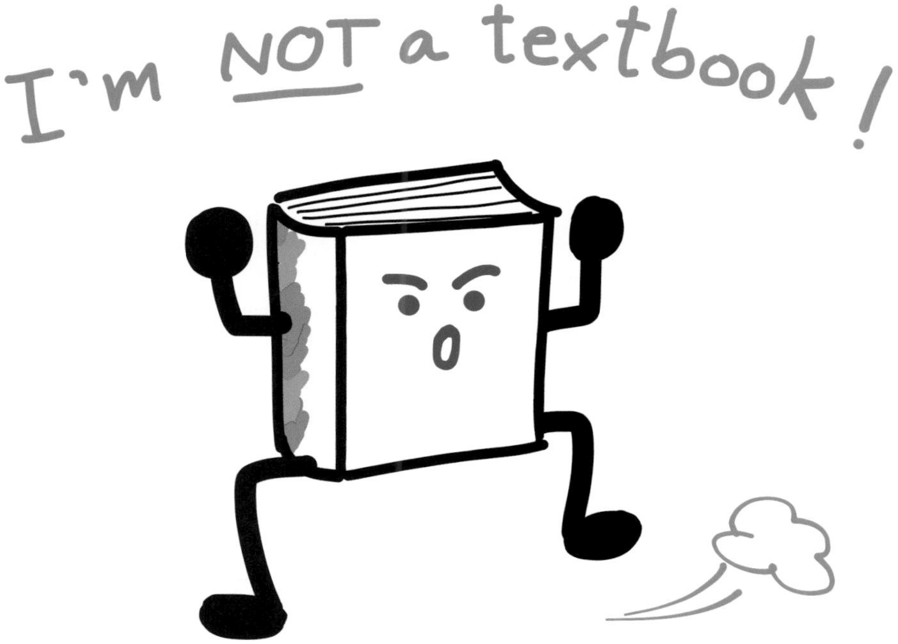
I'm NOT a textbook!

Part 1:
Towards Understanding Sugars And Nucleic Acids

1   Nucleophilic Addition Of Hard Anions To Aldehydes And Ketones

from chapter(s) _____ in the recommended text

A Introduction

Focus

This chapter is about combining electrophilic carbons with nucleophiles, particularly, *C*-nucleophiles. In some cases, reactions are represented with full structures of the reagents and readers must be able to recognize the nucleophilic carbon involved, but most of the examples in this section present reactions in the simplest possible way.

Reasons To Care

Synthesis of organic molecules generally involves building up carbon frameworks. Most often $C - C$ construction is achieved by adding electrophilic carbon fragments to nucleophilic ones.
For instance, hypothetically pentane might be prepared via formation of the bond broken by the jagged line, hence it might be approached in the two ways represented below.

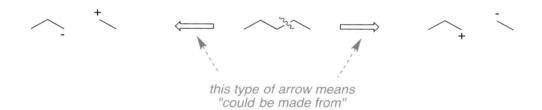

this type of arrow means "could be made from"

Most organic reactions are ionic processes that can be visualized in simple terms like this. When interpreting how an organic reaction works, look first for likely nucleophiles combining with electrophiles, then worry about details (*eg* by-products, stoichiometry, and reaction conditions), just like when buying a used car it is a good idea to check the engine before the heater, radio and fuzzy dice hanging from the mirror.

Concepts

ionization • curly arrows to depict combinations of cations and anions • retrosynthesis and fundamentals of how organic molecules are formed by making $C - C$ bonds • *Re*- and *Si*-face attack

Objective

This part of the *Inquisition* encourages the people to identify and follow true path and towards overall goals, while avoiding temptations to deviate towards the superficial.

B Types Of Additions To Carbonyls

Polarity Of Carbonyls

Draw an arrow of style **A** aligned with the carbonyl group such that the crossed end is near the positive end of the dipole and the arrow-tip is near the negative end.

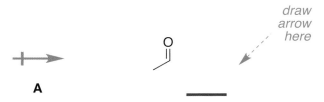

The carbon of a carbonyl group is *positively / negatively* polarized.

A

Nucleophiles add to carbonyl *carbons / oxygens* and, when they do, the electrons flow towards the most electronegative atom, which is the *oxygen / carbon*.

Reactivity Of Nucleophiles And Carbonyls At Different pH Values

Circle the best nucleophile and put a square around the best electrophile given the selection below.

CH_3^- NH_3

In carbonyl (CO) addition reactions, negatively charged nucleophiles tend to be *more / less* reactive than otherwise similar neutral ones.

Carbonyls that are protonated on the oxygen tend to be *more / less* reactive than ones that are not.

Anions like CH_3^- and H^- are called *hard / soft* because the charge on these is concentrated in one place, making them highly reactive.

Protonated carbonyls *are / are not* likely to donate H^+ to anions that are basic; therefore, protonations of carbonyls *can / cannot* be used to enhance their reactivity of basic anions.

It is *normal / completely wrong* to show hard, reactive basic anions adding to aldehydes and ketones under acidic conditions.

It follows that reactions of aldehydes and ketones with reactive basic anions are performed under *acidic / neutral or basic* conditions.

Additions of reactive basic anions to carbonyl compounds *can / cannot* be reversible if the anion involved is very stable.

Formation Of Tetrahedral Intermediates

Draw the products of these additions of anions to carbonyl compounds, using curly arrows to indicate electron flow.

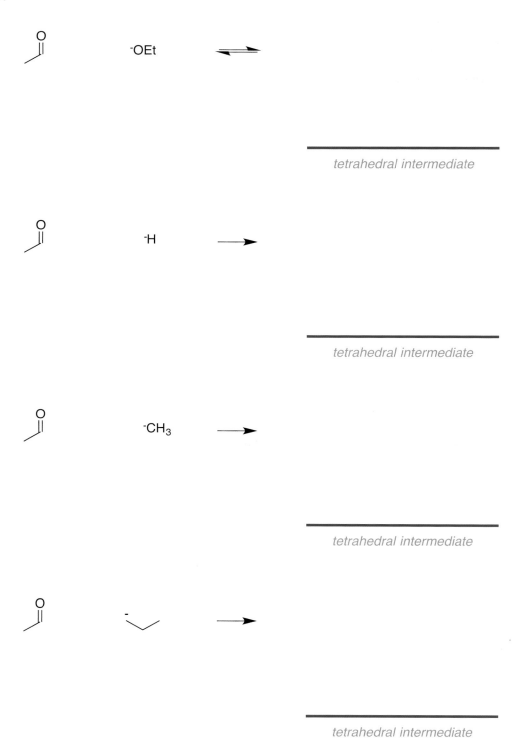

_____

tetrahedral intermediate

_____

tetrahedral intermediate

_____

tetrahedral intermediate

_____

tetrahedral intermediate

Central carbons in these tetrahedral intermediates are *sp / sp² / sp³* hybridized.
Protonation of these tetrahedral intermediates would give *aldehydes / alcohols / alkanes*.

Addition of alkoxides to aldehydes or ketones is reversible because the reactants can surmount the energy barriers involved (this is *kinetics / thermodynamics*), but the product and the reactants are of comparable energy (*kinetics / thermodynamics*).

Addition of alkoxides to aldehydes or ketones forms *one / two* C–O bond(s) between the nucleophile and the carbonyl carbon, and breaks *one / two* bond(s) of the C=O.

Negatively charged nucleophiles that are too stable, and do not give particularly stable products may add to aldehyde and ketone carbonyls, but the equilibrium will favor the *starting materials / products*.

If a nucleophile is stable but reactive it *will / will not* be inclined to add reversibly, whereas unstable and reactive nucleophiles will tend to move "energetically downhill" to product, and stay there, *ie irreversible / reversible* addition.

Divide the following anions into relatively stable or unstable, respectively: Cl⁻, Br⁻, Me⁻, Ph⁻, CN⁻, MeO⁻, CH₂CH⁻ where methoxide is a mid-point.

MeO⁻

relatively stable	*relatively unstable*

In general, anions that are weak bases tend to add *reversibly / irreversibly* to ketones. This chapter is mainly about nucleophiles that add irreversibly under basic conditions.

C Reactions of Aldehydes And Ketones With Hydridic Reducing Agents

In each of the following reactions, assume the reagent H⁻ is completely nucleophilic and only adds to the carbonyl. The products are formed after aqueous work-up procedures (adding water, then extraction). Show the products and indicate curly arrows to show how they are formed.

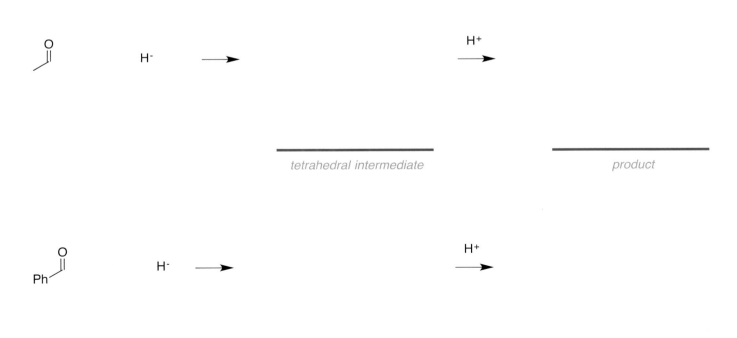

tetrahedral intermediate   *product*

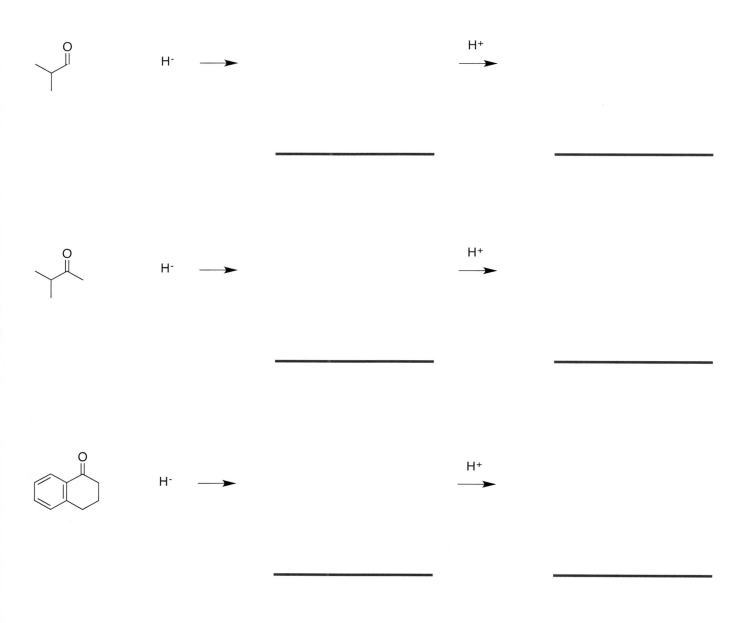

In fact, not all sources of hydride are equal. Name the following common sources of hydride. Two of them are nucleophilic, but one is *only* basic: indicate which is which.

NaBH$_4$ NaH   LiAlH$_4$

name: _____   _____   _____

nucleophilic / basic   *nucleophilic / basic*   *nucleophilic / basic*

The nucleophilic reagents add hydride to the carbonyl of aldehydes and ketones to form an alkoxide that is protonated to form an alcohol on addition of acid. The basic one *does / does not* do this efficiently.

Predict the products of the following reactions, and show the alkoxide intermediate in the first one.

NaBH₄

H₂O

_____   _____

(i) NaBH₄

(ii) H⁺

+

_____
two diastereomers

(i) LiAlH₄

(ii) H⁺

_____

(i) NaBD₄

(ii) H⁺

+

_____
two diastereomers

Reactions that involve addition of hydride to carbonyl compounds are *oxidation / reduction* processes.
Draw aldehydes or ketones that could be used to make the following alcohols via reduction with hydrides.

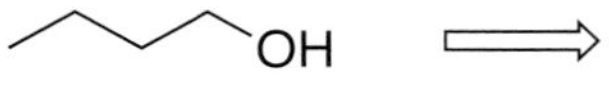

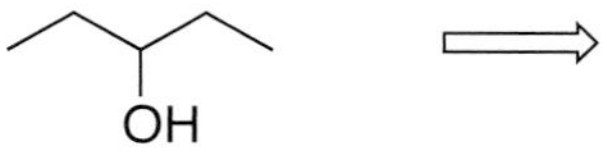

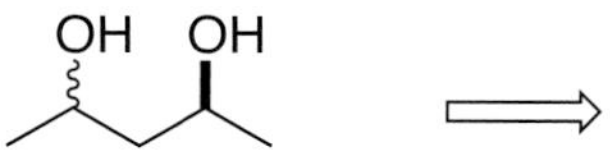

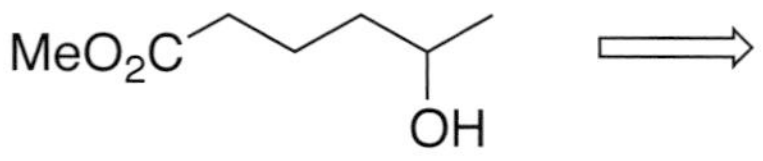

~~~OH ⟹

_____

OH ⟹

_____

OH OH ⟹

_____

MeO_2C~~~OH ⟹

_____

Only sodium borohydride can be used for the last reaction because:

_____
_____.

Only one of the following alcohols can be formed by sodium borohydride reduction; circle that one.

All the following compounds except one can be formed via sodium borohydride reduction of aldehydes or ketones, circle that one.

D Addition Of Carbanions

Anions that would be formed in deprotonation of alkanes, alkenes, and alkynes are relatively *stable / reactive*, hence they tend to add to carbonyls *reversibly / irreversibly*.

Moreover, this tendency is reinforced since the C–C bond formed is *weaker / stronger* than the C–O π-bond that is broken.

These anions tend to react instantly with water, so they are formed and used under *aqueous / anhydrous* conditions.

When they add to aldehydes or ketones, the product alkoxide *does / does not* equilibrate with starting material and remains until protons are added to the system.

Show the following mechanism with clear curly arrows.

tetrahedral intermediate

Show similar mechanisms for the following reactions.

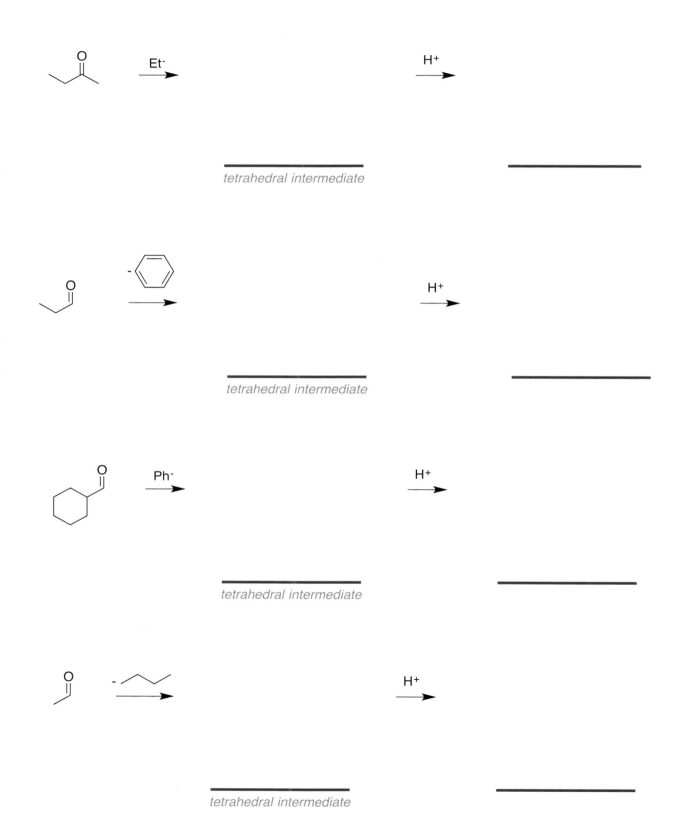

tetrahedral intermediate

tetrahedral intermediate

tetrahedral intermediate

tetrahedral intermediate

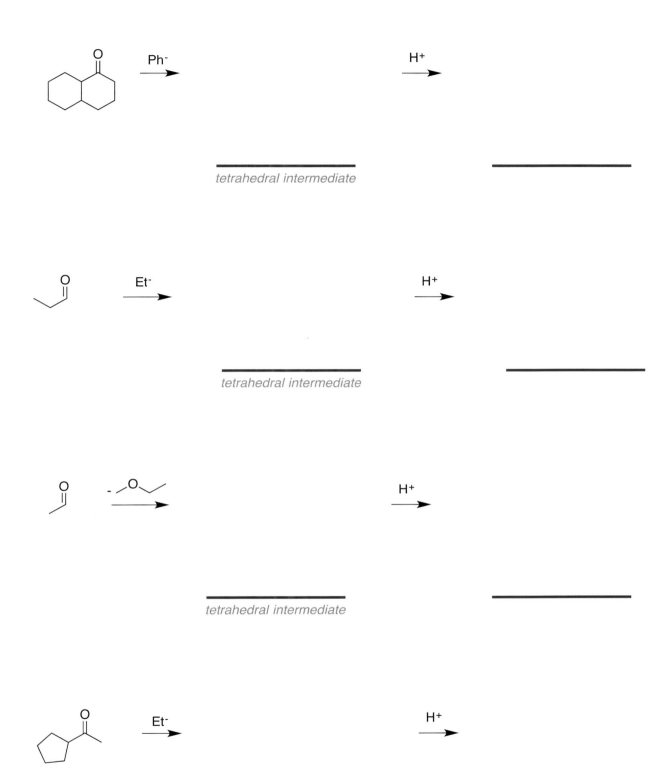

tetrahedral intermediate

tetrahedral intermediate

tetrahedral intermediate

tetrahedral intermediate

E Reactions Of Carbonyl Compounds With Acetylide Anions

Circle those of the following bases that could be used to deprotonate terminal alkynes (refer to a text?)

NEt$_3$ NaNH$_2$ MeMgBr   HO$^-$ LiN^{i}Pr$_2$ LiBu   Na$_2$CO$_3$

Acetylide anions add to aldehydes or ketones to form *primary or secondary / secondary or tertiary* alcohols, respectively.

Predict the products of the following reactions.

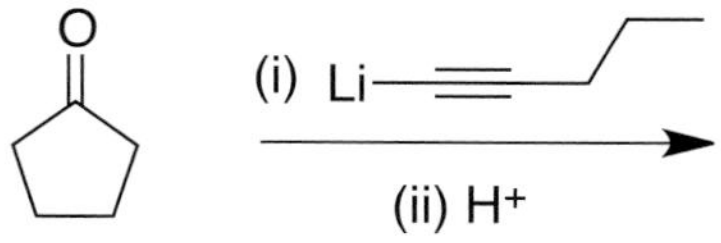

Ph~~~CHO   Li≡≡—Ph →   H$_3$O$^+$ →

_____   _____

cyclopentanone   (i) Li≡≡—~~~
(ii) H$^+$

_____

H$_2$CO   (i) H$_2$C$_2$, excess NaH →
(ii) H$^+$

_____

---

two diastereomers

Draw carbonyl compounds that could be used to make the following alcohols using acetylide anions or dianions.

---

two diastereomers

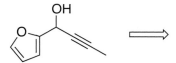

F *Si* And *Re* Faces Revisited

Reactions on different faces of a prochiral sp^2-hybridized carbon with no existing chiral centers can give different *diastereomers / enantiomers*.

Approach on the face displaying a clockwise ranking of the three substituents according to the priority rules is called *Re / Si*-face attack and addition to the other face is *Re / Si* -face attack.

Show the products of the following reactions in which the face selectivity is somehow controlled. Recall, addition of nucleophiles to aldehydes and ketones can give chiral alcohols after protonation.

$$\xleftarrow[\text{\textit{Re-face} addition}]{\text{Et}^-} \quad \text{Ph} \overset{O}{\underset{}{\diagup\!\!\!\diagdown}} \quad \xrightarrow[\text{\textit{Si-face} addition}]{\text{Et}^-}$$

$$\xrightarrow[\text{\textit{Re-face}}]{\text{LiAlH}_4}$$

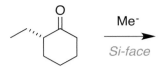

(R)-Alcohols *are / are not* always formed from *Re*-face attack, and (S)-alcohols *are / are not* always formed from *Si*-face attack.

Test your reasoning by drawing 4 hypothetical examples below.

2   Addition Of Grignard Reagents To Aldehydes And Ketones

from chapter(s) _____ in the recommended text

A Introduction

Focus

The last section features additions of negatively charged agents to carbonyl compounds. That concept is more important than learning reagent names and reaction conditions, but among the reagents for doing this reaction the most important are probably Grignard reagents. Grignard reagents can be formed from a wide range of alkyl or aryl chlorides, bromides, or iodides, and used to form a huge diversity of carbon frameworks.

This section is about Grignard reagents, and ways in which they complement hydride reduction chemistry.

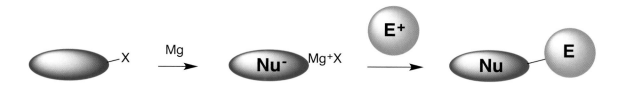

Reasons To Care

Grignard reagents react instantly with water or any other mildly acidic substance. Consequently, they do not exist in the body, and there is no close analog to these in biological chemistry. Grignard reagents are only directly useful in chemical laboratories and processes, but the concept of building organic molecules by matching reactive centers with opposite charges is uniformly useful, and reactions of Grignard reagents with aldehydes and ketones are a simple way to show this. These processes are also a primer for reactions of carbonyl compounds with nucleophiles under acid catalysis; those transformations *are* relevant to biological chemistry.

Concepts

curly arrows to depict reaction of carbanions with carbonyls • hydridic reduction chemistry • retrosynthesis

Objective

To understand how formation of Grignard reagents converts alkyl halides (electrophiles) or aryl halides into nucleophiles for $C - C$ bond construction.

B Grignard Reagents: A Type Of Carbanion Equivalents

Grignard reagents are made from alkyl halides (except fluorides) and *xenon / manganese / magnesium*; they are *strong / weak* bases.

Grignards *can / cannot* be formed from compounds with functional groups that would react immediately, especially acidic ones because these reagents protonate rapidly.

Grignards cannot be isolated from 1,2-dihaloalkanes because MgX_2 is eliminated immediately after a Grignard is formed liberating *propene / ethane / ethyne*.

Show the products of the following reactions, and their reactions with water that illustrate how they are destroyed if not kept in a dry medium.

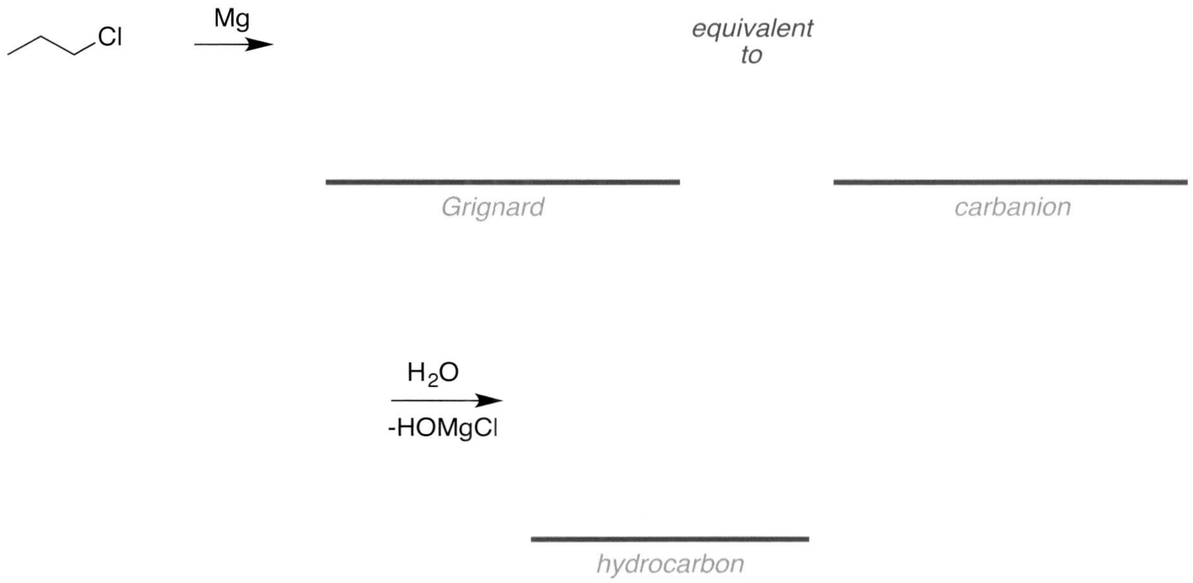

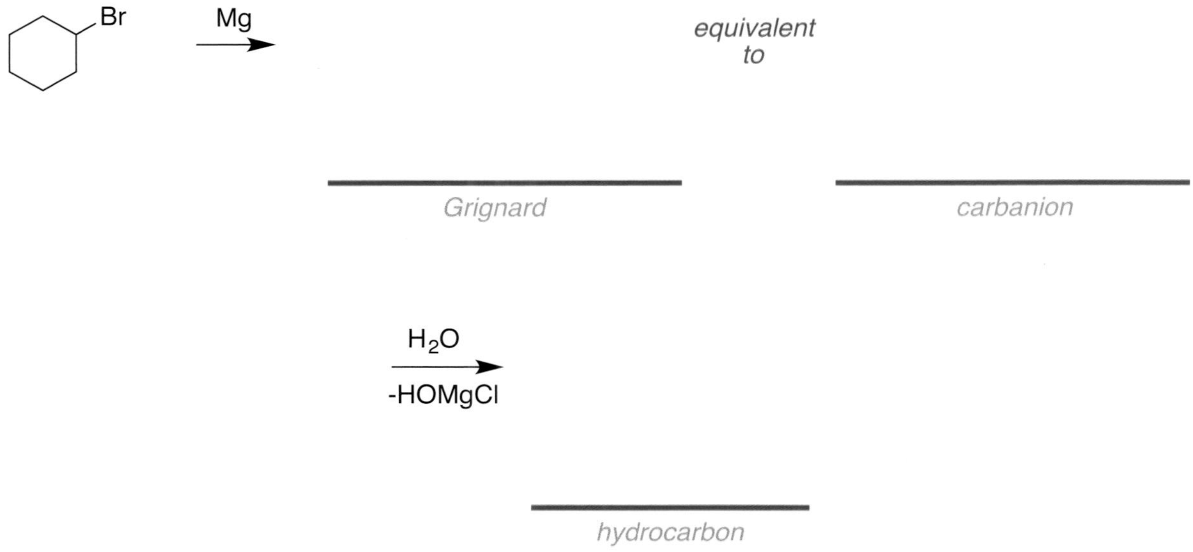

	equivalent to
Grignard	*carbanion*

$$\xrightarrow[\text{-HOMgCl}]{H_2O}$$

_____
hydrocarbon

	equivalent to
Grignard	*carbanion*

$$\xrightarrow[\text{-HOMgCl}]{H_2O}$$

_____
hydrocarbon

32

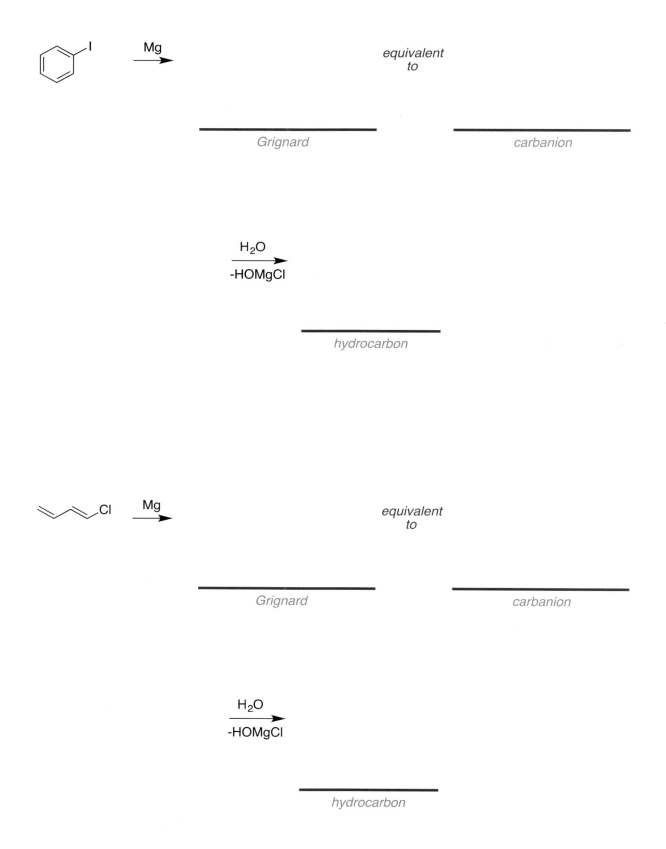

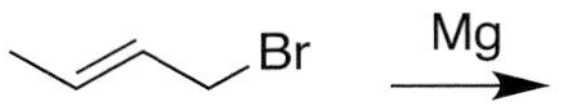

⌇⌇⌇Br $\xrightarrow{\text{Mg}}$

equivalent to

_____   _____
Grignard   carbanion

$\xrightarrow[\text{-HOMgCl}]{\text{H}_2\text{O}}$

_____
hydrocarbon

Only some of the following compounds can form Grignards; put a circle around those that *can*.

1,2-dichloroethane	bromobenzene	benzyl bromide	butane
allyl chloride	2-chloropropane	1,2-diiodopropane	2-chloroethanol
diethyl ether	fluoroethane	bromoethanal	3-iodopropanol
chloro(methoxy)methane	1-bromo-3-methoxy-ethanal		bromoethane

C Reactions Of Methanal With Grignard Reagents

Draw formaldehyde in three different ways (maybe one line diagram, and two formulae representations).

_____   _____   _____

Complete the following disconnections in the same style as the first one.

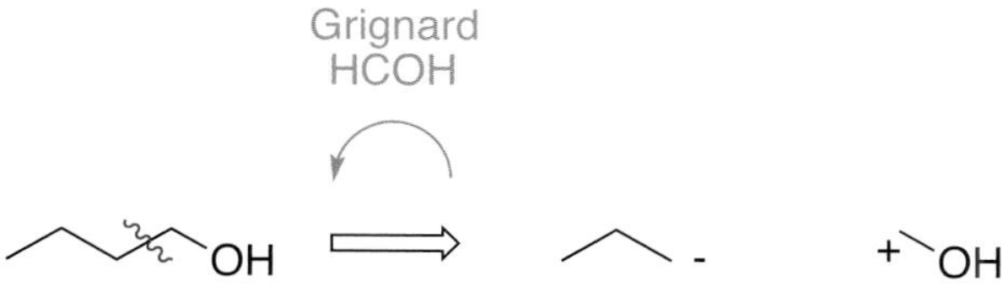

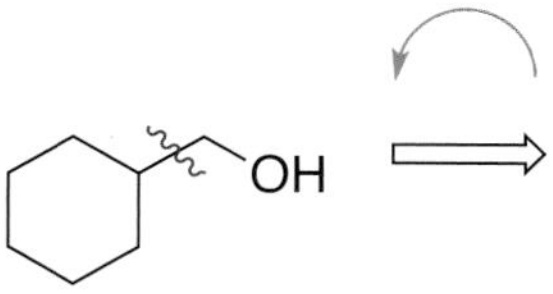

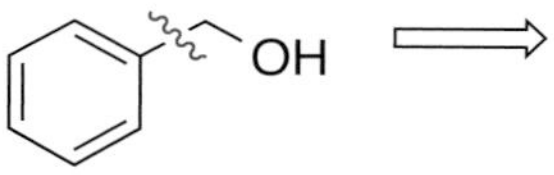

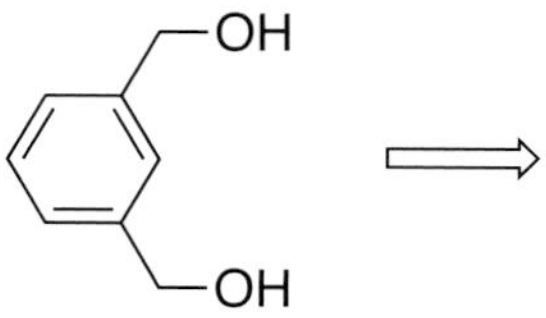

Grignard
HCOH

⌒

⟍⟍⟋⟍OH ⟹ ⟍⟋⟍ −   + ⟍OH   [cyclohexyl]⟍OH ⟹

_____

[phenyl]⟍OH ⟹   ⟍⟍⟋⟍OH ⟹

_____   _____

[benzene with two CH₂OH groups] ⟹   ⟍⟍⟋OH ⟹

_____   _____

Draw the products of the following reaction sequence showing curly arrows to depict the electron flow.

MgBr   +   =O   ⟶ $\xrightarrow[\text{-HOMgBr}]{\text{+H}_2\text{O}}$

_____   _____

Grignard reagents with *methanal* give *primary / secondary / tertiary* _____ (name the functional group) on protonation.

These products have *the same / one more / one less* carbon than the Grignard.

Predict the products of the following reactions.

MgBr   +   =O   ⟶ $\xrightarrow[\text{-HOMgBr}]{\text{+H}_2\text{O}}$

_____   _____

BrMg~~~~MgBr $\xrightarrow{\text{excess} =O}$ $\xrightarrow[\text{-HOMgBr}]{\text{+H}_2\text{O}}$

_____   _____

$\overset{/\!/O}{\longrightarrow}$

$\xrightarrow[\text{-HOMgBr}]{\text{+H}_2\text{O}}$

_____   _____

$\overset{/\!/O}{\longrightarrow}$

$\xrightarrow[\text{-HOMgBr}]{\text{+H}_2\text{O}}$

_____   _____

Show Grignards that could be used to make the following *primary / secondary / tertiary* alcohols from methanal.

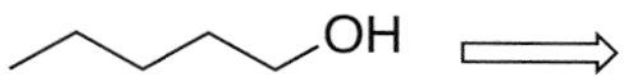

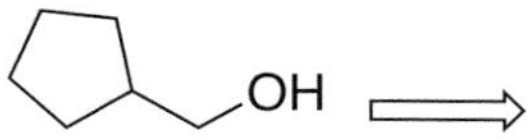

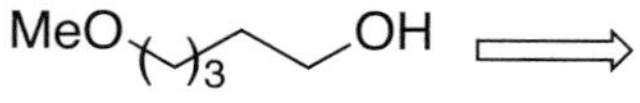

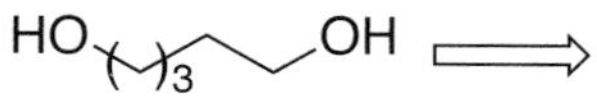

~~~OH $\Longrightarrow$

⬠~~OH $\Longrightarrow$

_____   _____

MeO(~)₃~OH $\Longrightarrow$

HO(~)₃~OH $\Longrightarrow$

_____   _____

a di-Grignard

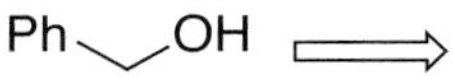

Ph⁀OH ⟹

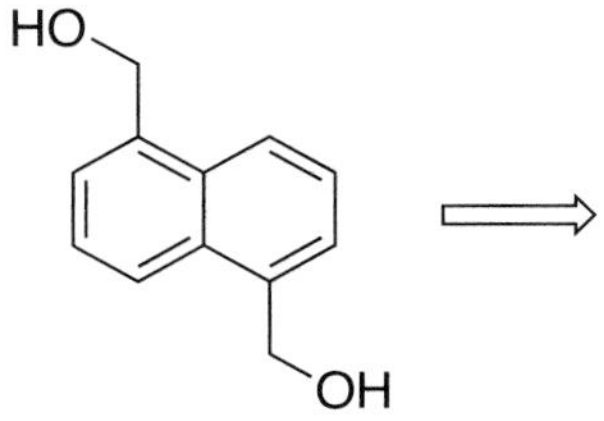

HO⁀ (naphthalene structure) OH ⟹

a di-Grignard

_____   _____

CD₃CH₂OH ⟹

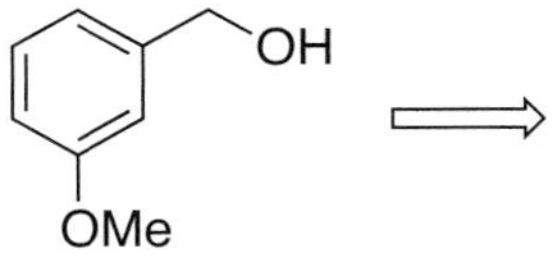

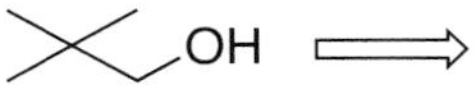

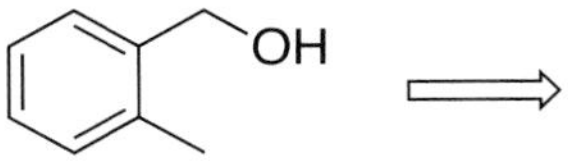

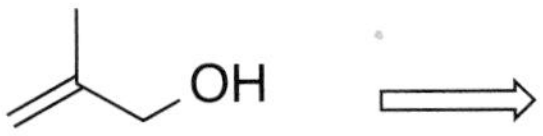

(benzene with CH₂OH and OMe) ⟹

_____   _____

✕OH ⟹

(benzene with CH₂OH and CH₃) ⟹

_____   _____

OH (cyclopropyl) ⟹

⁀OH ⟹

_____   _____

Grignard reagents are _more / less_ basic than nucleophiles like methoxide, and add to carbonyl compounds _reversibly / irreversibly_.

The alcohols formed from reactions of Grignards with methanal are _primary / secondary / tertiary_ because methanal has _one / two / three_ hydrogens attached to the carbonyl group.

Reactions of Grignards with other aldehydes must give _primary / secondary / tertiary_ alcohols; methanal _is / is not_ unique.

D Reactions Of Other Aldehydes With Grignards

Predict the products of the following sequence showing curly arrows for the reaction flow.

MeMgBr   + $\longrightarrow$ $\xrightarrow[-HOMgBr]{+H_2O}$

_____   _____

Grignard reagents react with aldehyde *homologs* of methanal to give *primary / secondary / tertiary* alcohols with *the same / more / less* carbon atoms as the combination of the Grignard and the aldehyde. Test this assertion by predicting the products of the following reactions (after protonation).

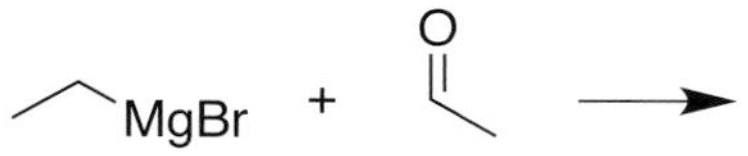

+ $\longrightarrow$ MeMgBr + EtCOH $\longrightarrow$

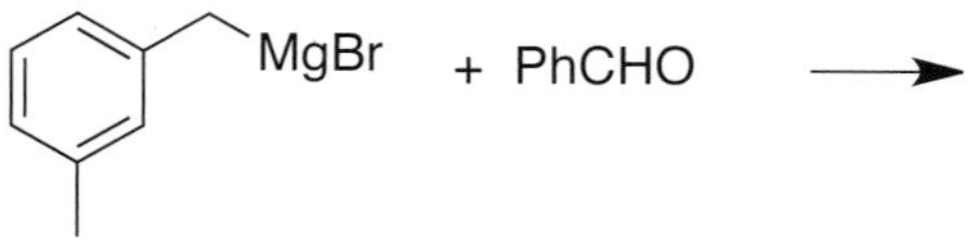

_____   _____

+ PhCHO $\longrightarrow$

_____

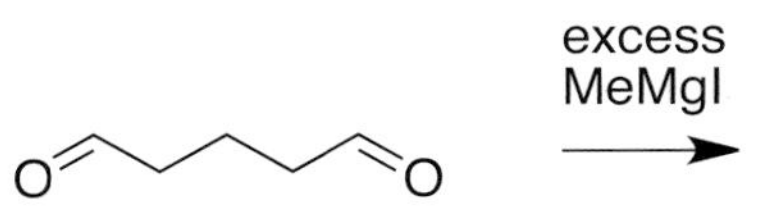

O=\/\/\=O + excess MeMgI →

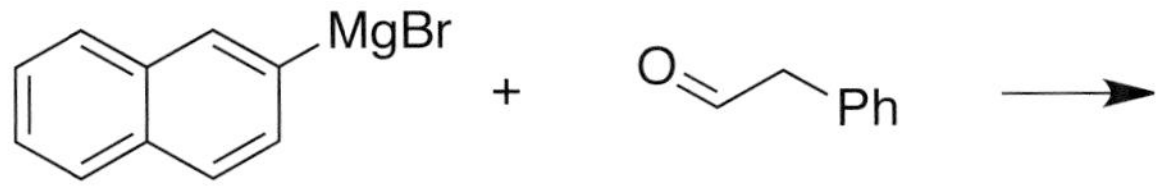

_____

[naphthyl]—MgBr + O=\/—Ph →

_____

Show the Grignards and aldehydes that could be used to make the following *primary / secondary / tertiary* alcohols. If there are two ways of doing this, indicate both.

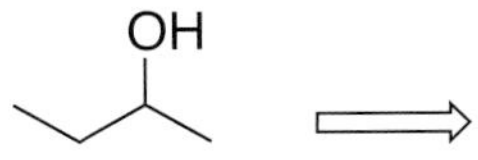

OH
\/\   ⟹   *or*

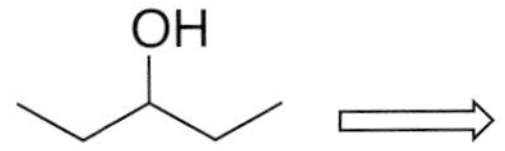

_____

OH
\/\/   ⟹

_____

Clue for the next problem: the Grignard must be a stable one in any synthesis proposed …..

E Reactions Of Ketones With Grignards

Predict the product of the following reaction sequence.

MeMgCl   +   (acetone structure)   ⟶   _____ $\xrightarrow[\text{-HOMgCl}]{\text{+H}_2\text{O}}$ _____

Grignards react with *ketones* to give *primary / secondary / tertiary* alcohols.

The products of the reaction of a Grignard with a ketone are alcohols with *the same / more / less* carbons than the combination of the Grignard and the ketone starting materials.

Two of the alcohol product substituents *must / cannot* be the same when symmetrical ketones are used.

Predict the products of the following reactions after protonation.

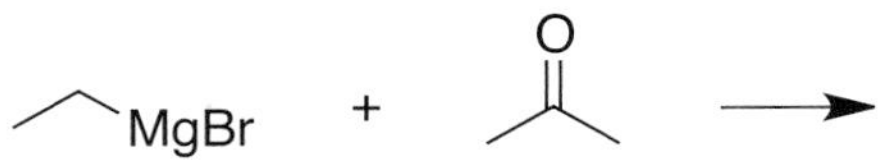

(propyl)MgBr   +   (acetone)   ⟶   _____

MeMgBr   +   EtCOEt   ⟶   _____

(diketone structure)   +   2PhMgI   ⟶   _____

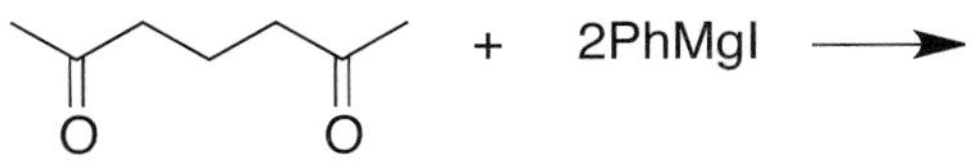

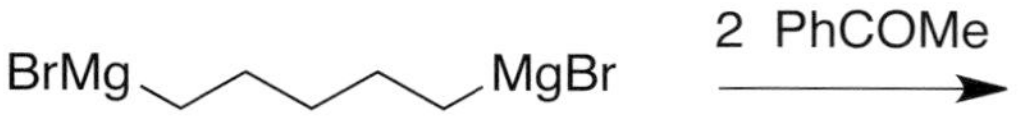

BrMg$\diagup\!\!\diagdown\!\!\diagup\!\!\diagdown\!\!\diagup$MgBr $\xrightarrow{\text{2 PhCOMe}}$

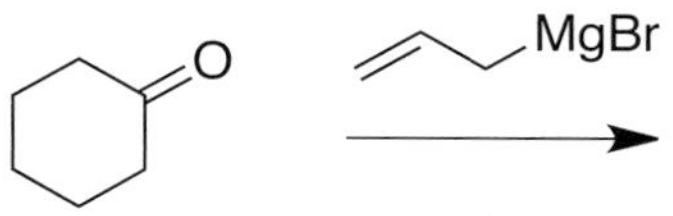

_____

$\diagup\!\!\diagdown$MgBr $\xrightarrow{\hspace{2cm}}$

_____

MeCOEt + PhMgCl $\longrightarrow$

_____

MeCOPh + EtMgBr $\longrightarrow$

_____

Indicate the components from which the following alcohols can be formed from *ketones* and Grignard reagents. If more than one way is possible, indicate all of them.

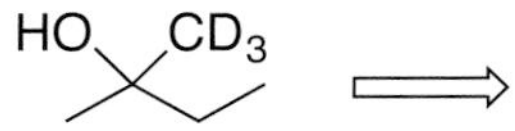

HO CD$_3$ ⟹   *or*   *or*

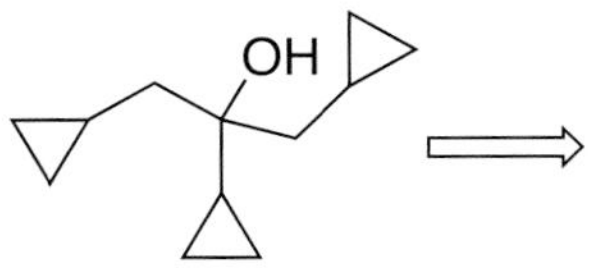

_____   _____   _____

OH ▷ ⟹   *or*

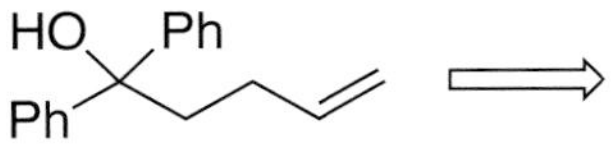

_____   _____

HO Ph
Ph   ⟹

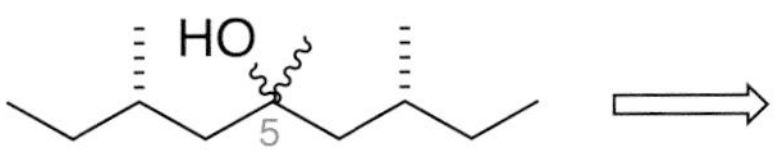

_____

HO   ⟹
5

_____

For the product above it *is / is not* possible to draw two diastereomers of this product by varying the stereochemistry at C.

It *is / is not* possible to draw two diastereomers of the product below by varying the stereochemistry at C.

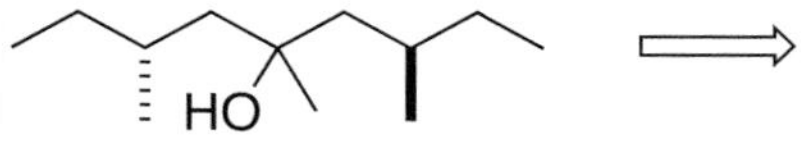

F Complimentary Grignard and Hydride Reductions

Draw two ways to access these alcohols in one step (after protonation): one through hydride reduction of a ketone or aldehyde, the other through a Grignard (show reagents).

a Grignard route   *hydride route*

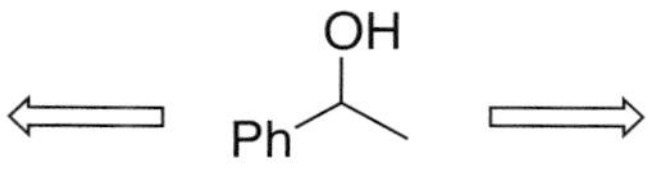

G Reactions Of Carbon Dioxide With Grignards

Carbon dioxide is similar to a ketone with respect to nucleophilic reactions with Grignards. Predict the products of the following reaction sequence, and use curly arrows to show the reaction mechanism.

H_2O

-HOMgBr

_____ _____

CO_2 adds to Grignard reagents to form the following functional group after protonation:
_____.

Products of addition of Grignard reagents to carbon dioxide have *the same / one more / one less* carbon than the Grignard.

Predict the products of the following reactions.

(i) CO_2

(ii) H_2O

_____

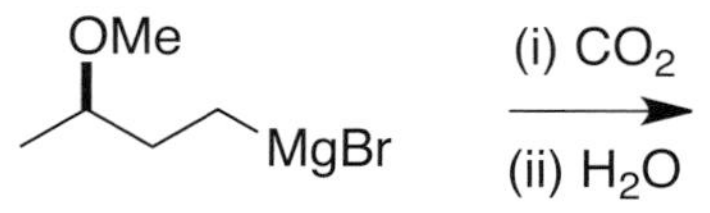

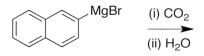

(i) CO$_2$

(ii) H$_2$O

(i) CO$_2$

(ii) H$_2$O

(i) CO$_2$

(ii) H$_2$O

Identify the Grignards that can be used to make the following carboxylic acids from carbon dioxide.

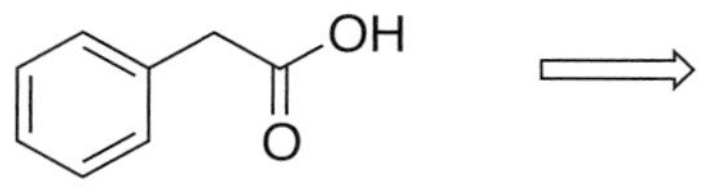

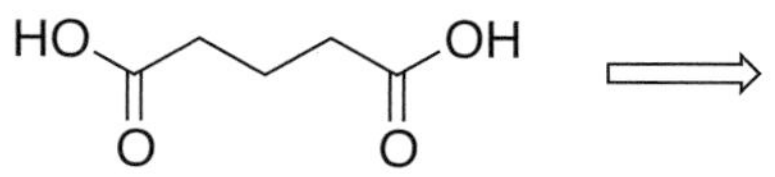

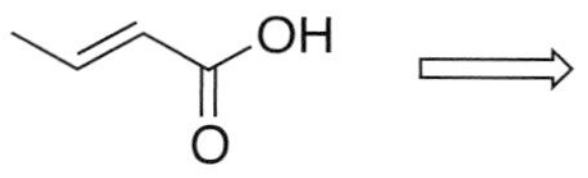

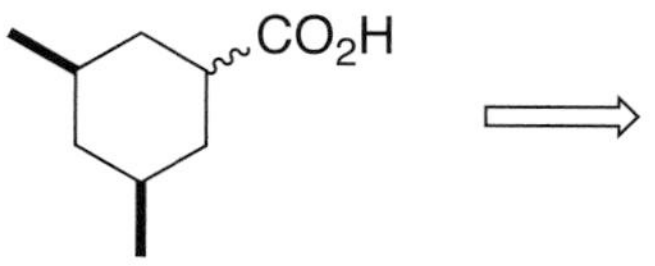

_____

_____

_____

_____

Grignard reagents with the magnesium attached directly to a chiral center *almost always / never* react with loss of stereochemistry at that center.

3 Addition Of Water And Alcohols To Aldehydes And Ketones

from chapter(s) _____ in the recommended text

A Introduction

Focus

Water adds to aldehydes and ketones to form hydrates. These reactions are reversible because water can be lost easily. Similarly, *alcohols* add to ketones and aldehydes in acid-mediated reactions that can be driven to completion, and which cannot reverse unless aqueous acid is present. In the absence of water and acid, acetals and ketals, unlike hydrates, are stable because there is no proton available to reform alcohols and the parent carbonyl. This section is on formation of acetals, ketals and hydrates.

Reasons To Care

Carbohydrates form rings via formation of hemiacetals, and join to form oligomers using acetal and ketal linkages (*eg* maltose and sucrose). Understanding the mechanisms by which these are formed *chemically* facilitates appreciation of their stabilities, and how these same types of bonds might be formed in Nature.

Some natural products that are not sugars also contain acetals or ketals, *eg* spirolaxine.

Concepts

acids and bases • curly arrows to depict electron flow under acidic conditions • entropy

Objective

Ketones and aldehydes can be activated by protonation to add nucleophiles (*eg* water, alcohol and amines), a series of proton transfer reactions occur, then water may leave. This generic description outlines a vast number of reactions in bioorganic chemistry.

B Relative Reactivities Of Aldehydes And Ketones

Hydrogen atoms are regarded as *more / less* electron withdrawing than alkyl groups.

Rank the reactivities of the following compounds towards nucleophiles (1 is most, 5 is least); to do this, take account of electronic *and* steric effects.

1 / 2 / 3 / 4 / 5 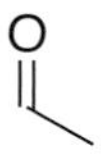   1 / 2 / 3 / 4 / 5 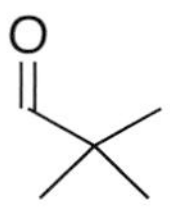   1 / 2 / 3 / 4 / 5 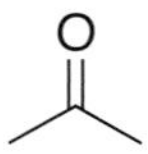   1 / 2 / 3 / 4 / 5 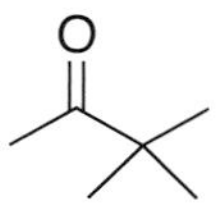   1 / 2 / 3 / 4 / 5

Addition of a nucleophile to a ketone or an aldehyde changes the carbon geometry from sp^2 planar to sp^3 tetrahedral, *ie* _____ ° to _____ °.

When forming tetrahedral intermediates from carbonyl compounds, the substituents become *closer / further apart* thus *accentuating / reducing* steric effects relative to the starting material.

Order the reactivities of the following carbonyl compounds towards nucleophiles by drawing their structures in the following diagram: benzaldehyde, diphenyl ketone, propanone, methanal, phenylethanone, 3,3-dimethylpropanal, ethanal, ethandial (glyoxal).

most reactive - ➤

- ➤ *least reactive*

C Proton Transfer Steps

Proton transfer, loss from one atom in an intermediate, followed by gain of a proton by another atom is *common / uncommon* in organic mechanisms.

Illustrate the following proton transfer steps by showing curly arrows for loss of a proton from the heteroatom with the positive charge, then addition of it to the neutral one.

It is common to abbreviate loss of proton and gain of proton in one step (without curly arrows). Show this in the following examples.

D Addition Of Water

Hydration of aldehydes and ketones is an *irreversible / equilibrium* process that involves protonation of the carbonyl group, addition of water, and deprotonation.

Hydrates of methanal, and of compounds with electron withdrawing carbonyl substituents, are *weakly / strongly* favored relative to the parent carbonyls.

Draw hydration of methanal using curly arrows to show electron flow.

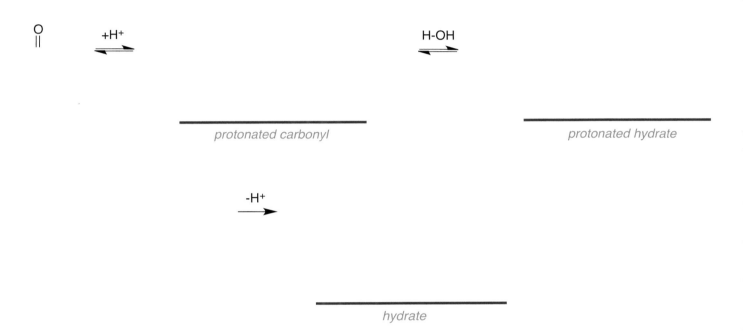

Draw the key intermediates for hydration of acetone using curly arrows to show electron flow.

The equilibrium constant for hydration of acetone is 2×10^{-3} so when mixed with 10 equivalents of water the amount of hydrate will be: *more than 2 % / exactly 2 % / less than 2 %*.
On adding water, the angle between carbonyl substituents of a ketone contracts from _____ ° to
_____ °; consequently, formation of a hydrate is *favored / disfavored* when the carbonyl substituents are *large*.
When aldehydes are mixed with $H_2^{18}O$, the heavy atom label *does / does not* become incorporated into the aldehyde C=O.

E Additions Of Alcohols
Draw the "hydration" of acetone but using H-OMe instead of H-OH as the nucleophile.

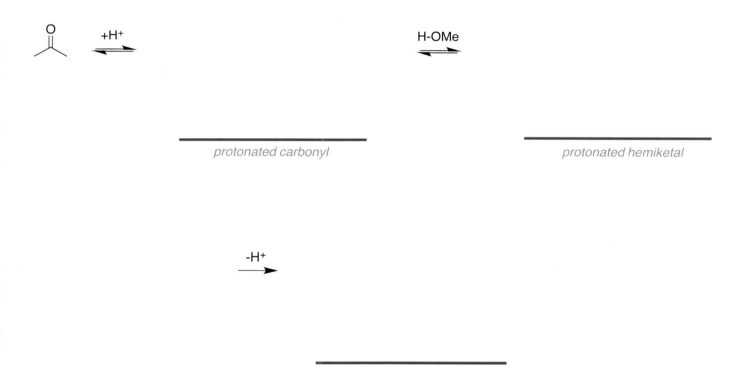

protonated carbonyl   protonated hemiketal

The product above with one OH and one OR group attached to the carbon that was the carbonyl group, is a(n) *acetal / hemiacetal / hemiketal* because it is half way to the $R_2C(OR')_2$ form and derived from a *ketone*.
The product formed from adding one alcohol to an aldehyde is called a(n) *acetal / hemiketal / hemiacetal*.

Draw a *reversible* sequence of events representing protonation on the OH group of the *hemiacetal / hemiketal* from hydration of *ethanal*, loss of water to give an *oxonium* intermediate, addition of another methanol nucleophile, and finally deprotonation to give *a ketal / an acetal*.

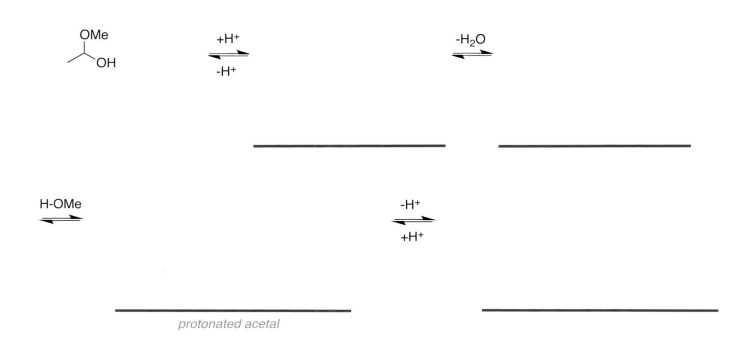

protonated acetal

Acetals and ketals *do / do not* react with excess aqueous acid to give aldehydes and ketones.

Complete the following mechanism for addition of methanol to *benzophenone* under acidic conditions to give a hemiketal by completing the structures and drawing in curly arrows.

hemiketal

Draw the same process for acid-catalyzed addition of methanol to butanone.

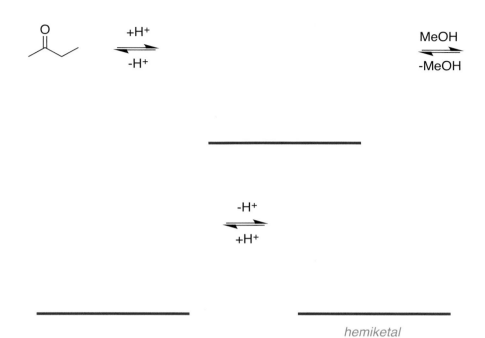

+H+
-H+

MeOH
-MeOH

-H+
+H+

hemiketal

Complete the following mechanism showing curly arrows.

+H+
-H+

MeOH
-MeOH

starting material?

-H+
+H+

HO   OMe

Complete the following diagram to show how *hemiacetals* and *hemiketals*, like those above, can be protonated on the hydroxyl, expel water, add another alcohol then lose a proton.

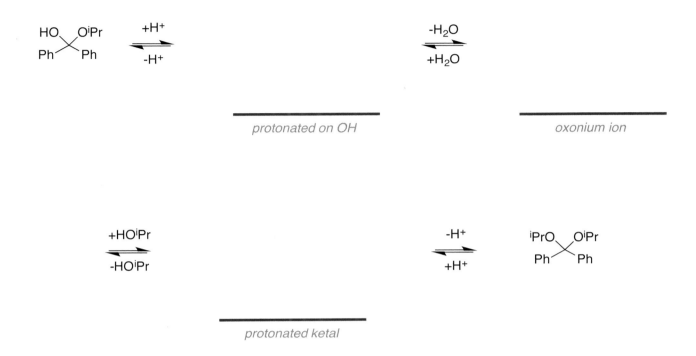

HO OiPr
Ph   Ph
+H+ / -H+

-H₂O / +H₂O

_____ *protonated on OH*   _____ *oxonium ion*

+HOiPr / -HOiPr

-H+ / +H+   iPrO OiPr
              Ph   Ph

_____ *protonated ketal*

The starting material in this sequence was formed from a ketone and *an alcohol / water / an ester*. Draw exactly the same sequence for the hemiacetal from ethanal and methanol.

+H+ / -H+

-H₂O / +H₂O

_____   _____ *protonated on OH*   _____ *oxonium ion*

+HOMe / -HOMe

-H+ / +H+

_____ *protonated acetal*   _____ *acetal*

Draw exactly the same sequence for the hemiacetal from benzaldehyde and *n*-butanol (introduce the alcohol over the appropriate arrow).

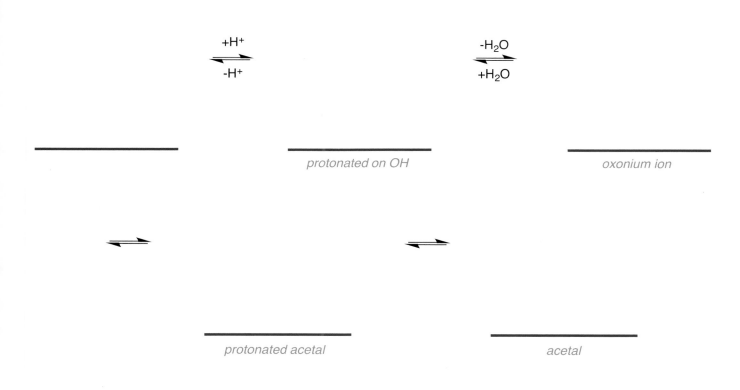

protonated on OH

oxonium ion

protonated acetal

acetal

Draw the same sequence for the hemiacetal from cyclopropane carboxaldehyde and ethanol, taking care to fill in the reactants around the arrows.

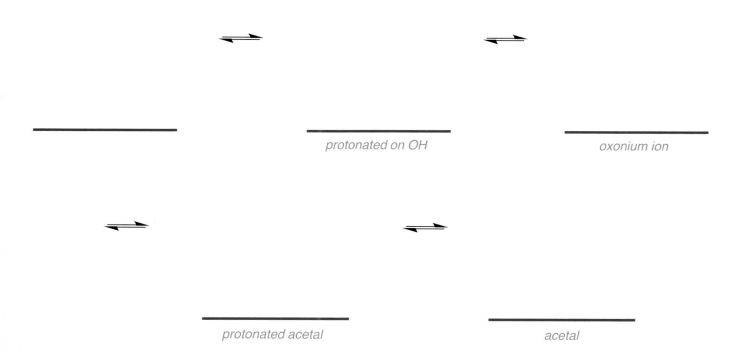

protonated on OH

oxonium ion

protonated acetal

acetal

Draw the same sequence for the hemiketal from 2-butanone and 1,2-ethanediol, taking care to fill in the reactants around the arrows. Draw the reagents above each arrow.

$\rightleftharpoons$

$\rightleftharpoons$

_____

_____ protonated on OH

_____ oxonium ion

$\rightleftharpoons$

$\rightleftharpoons$

_____ protonated ketal

_____ ketal

Write the complete mechanism for formation of 2,2-dimethoxypropane from acetone and methanol.

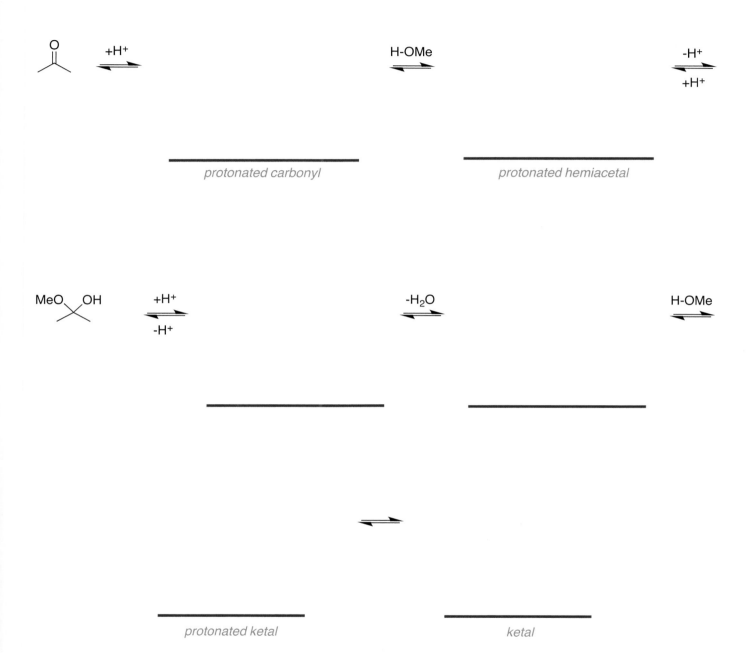

protonated carbonyl

protonated hemiacetal

protonated ketal

ketal

Write the complete mechanism for formation of a ketal from 1,2-dihydroxybenzene (show curly arrows, as usual) and cyclopentanone.

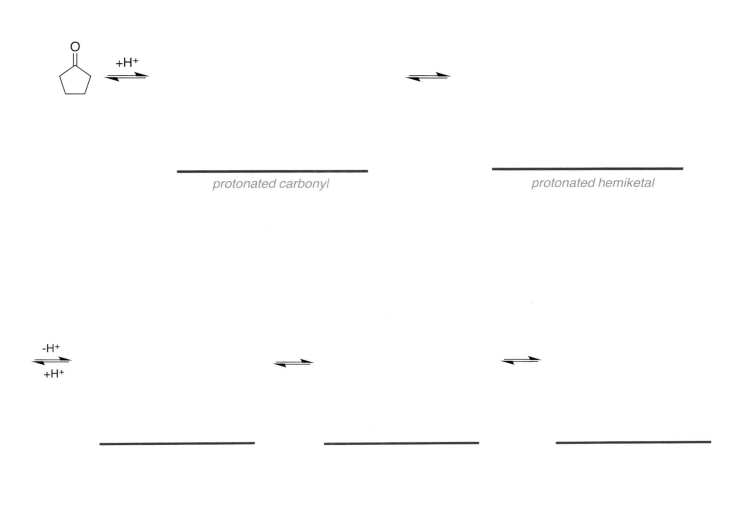

protonated carbonyl   protonated hemiketal

-H⁺
+H⁺

protonated ketal   ketal

62

The following diagrams show one compound in a chemically related set of aldehyde or ketone, hemiacetal or hemiketal, acetal or ketal. Predict the other two compounds in the series in each case and label each product as appropriate.

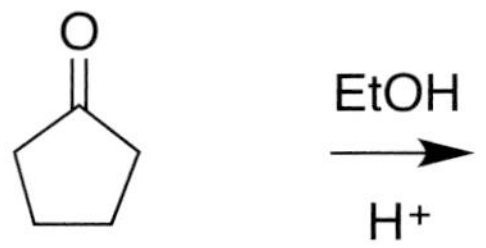

hemiacetal / hemiketal   _acetal / ketal_

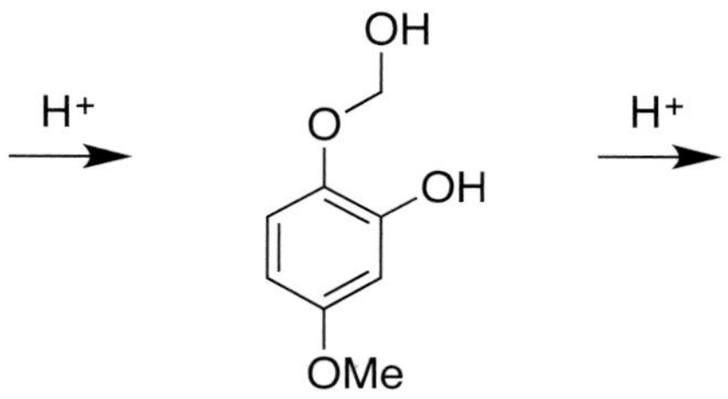

aldehyde + "diol"   _acetal / ketal_

ketone + "diol"   _hemiacetal / hemiketal_

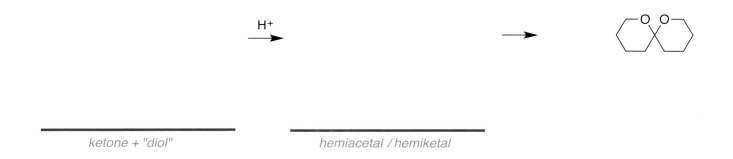

<u>**   **</u>
ketone + "diol"

<u>**   **</u>
hemiacetal / hemiketal

Indicate how many alcohol and ketone *molecules* it would take to make the following acetals and ketals, and the total number of *molecules* generated (do not forget the water lost in these reactions).

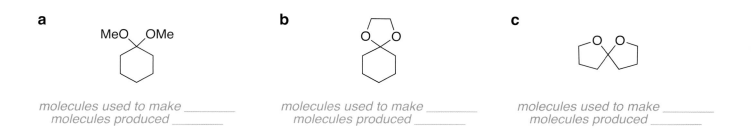

a

molecules used to make _____
    molecules produced _____

b

molecules used to make _____
    molecules produced _____

c

molecules used to make _____
    molecules produced _____

Based on entropic considerations alone, the ketal most stable to acid is *a / b / c*.

4 Formation Of Cyanohydrins, Imines, Enamines

from chapter(s) _____ in the recommended text

A Introduction

Focus

Addition of hydrogen cyanide to ketones and aldehydes follows a predictable route: protonation of the carbonyl then addition of the nucleophile, cyanide. Addition of ammonia and primary amines to aldehydes and ketones forms an intermediate very similar to hydrates, as illustrated here for methylamine. Like aldehyde and ketone hydrates, an OH group can be protonated, then water is displaced by the action of the lone pair on the other atom, now giving an enamine. Reactions of secondary amines follow the same pathway, but there is no proton left on the iminium nitrogen, so they lose a C-<u>H</u> to form an enamine.

hydration of a ketone:

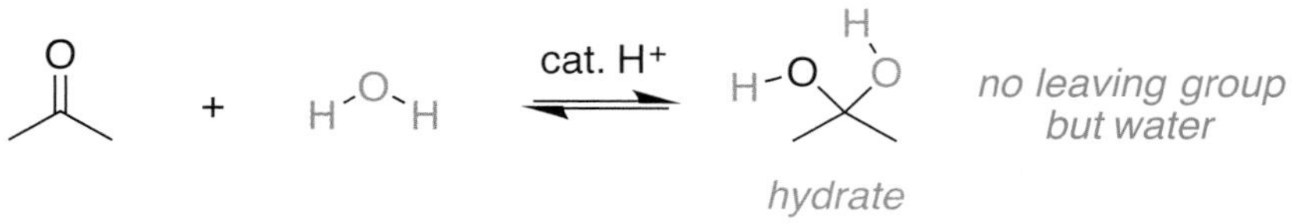

condensation with primary amine:

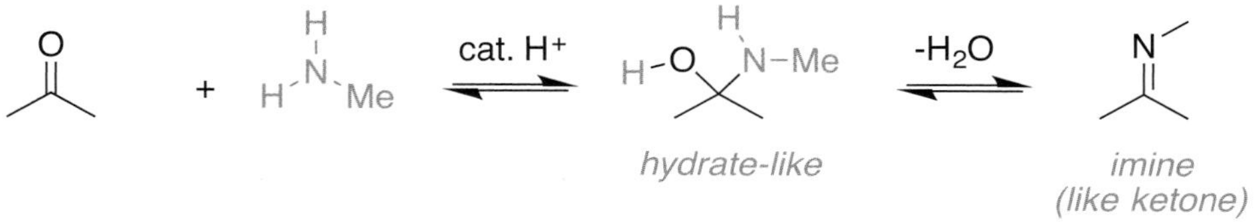

condensation with secondary amine:

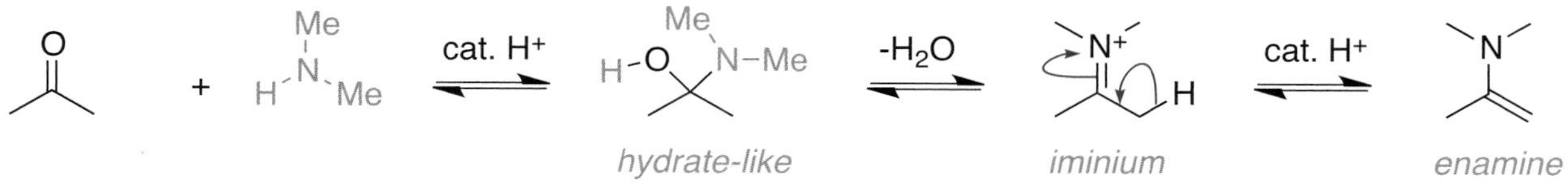

Reasons To Care

Condensations of amines with ketones are common in cell biology, *eg* in the biosynthesis of amino acids.

Concepts

acids and bases • electron flow • expulsion of water in condensation reactions

Objective

Learning reaction mechanisms in isolation is quite difficult, but it is much easier when the similarities and small differences of a series of related transformations are considered. Here the objective is to relate reactions of aldehydes and ketones to mechanisms for cyanohydrin, imine, and enamine formation.

B Tetrahedral Intermediates And Beyond

The four tetrahedral intermediates shown below are formed from 2-butanone and HCN, EtMgX, pyrrolidine (look up structure), or methylamine. Write the corresponding starting material below each structure.

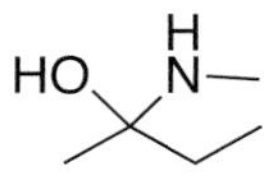

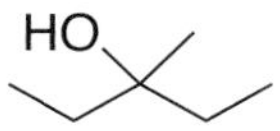

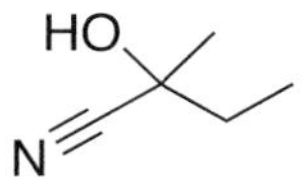

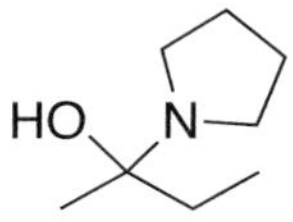

starting material?

Two of these intermediates would be inclined to lose water when protonated on the oxygen *because* a nitrogen is present to push in electrons from a lone pair. Put circles around those two intermediates.

C Reactions Of Aldehydes And Ketones With HCN

The pKa of HCN is 9.1; the cyanide anion is a *strong / weak* base because it is relatively stable, so, unsurprisingly, it adds *reversibly* to aldehydes or ketones. Show the mechanism of addition of HCN to acetone illustrated with clear curly arrows.

protonated carbonyl   _cyanohydrin adduct_

Show the same mechanism for the starting materials indicated below.

$\xrightleftharpoons{\text{H}^+}$

$\xrightleftharpoons{^-\text{CN}}$

_____   _____   _____
     4-nitrobenzaldehyde   *protonated carbonyl*   *cyanohydrin adduct*

$\xrightleftharpoons{\text{H}^+}$

$\xrightleftharpoons{^-\text{CN}}$

_____   _____   _____
     cyclohexanone

$\xrightleftharpoons{\text{H}^+}$

$\xrightleftharpoons{^-\text{CN}}$

_____   _____   _____
     phenylethanone

D Condensations Of Aldehydes Or Ketones With Amines

Primary Amines Form Imines

Imines (Schiff bases) form when *primary* amines or ammonia condense (*lose / gain* water) with aldehydes or ketones.

Show the mechanism of condensation of cyclopentanone with phenylamine.

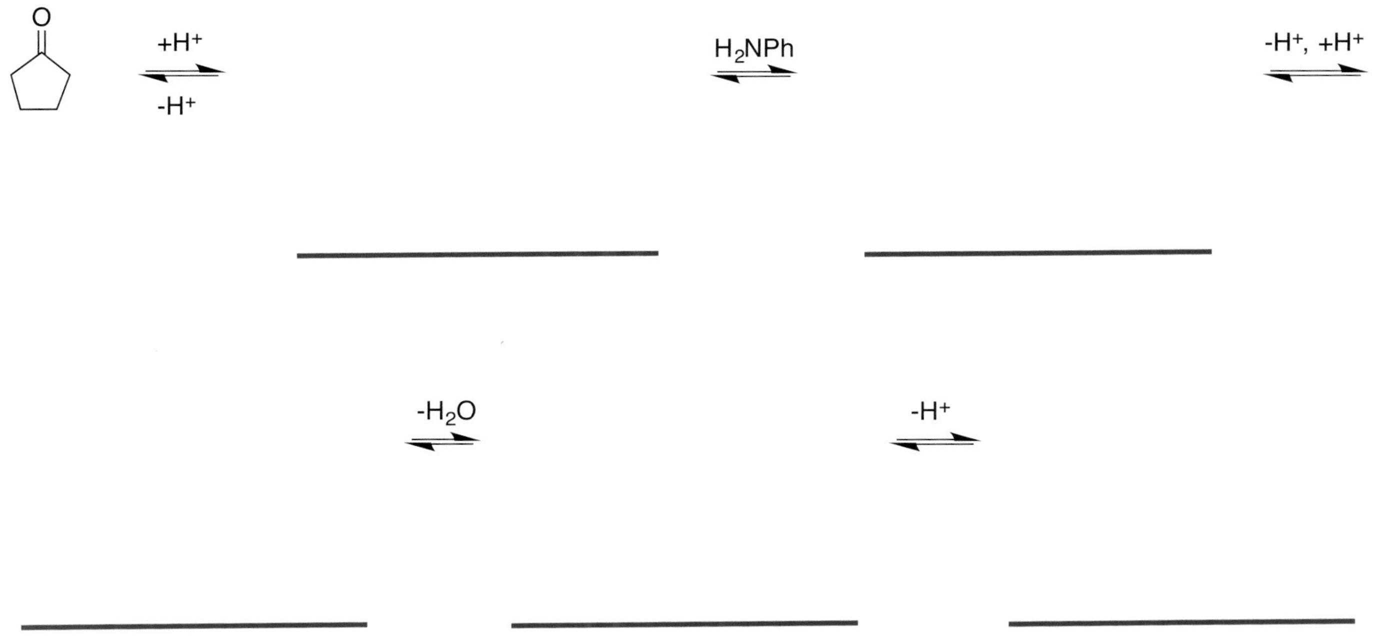

+H+

-H+

H₂NPh

-H+, +H+

-H₂O

-H+

Show the same mechanism for cyclohexane carboxaldehyde.

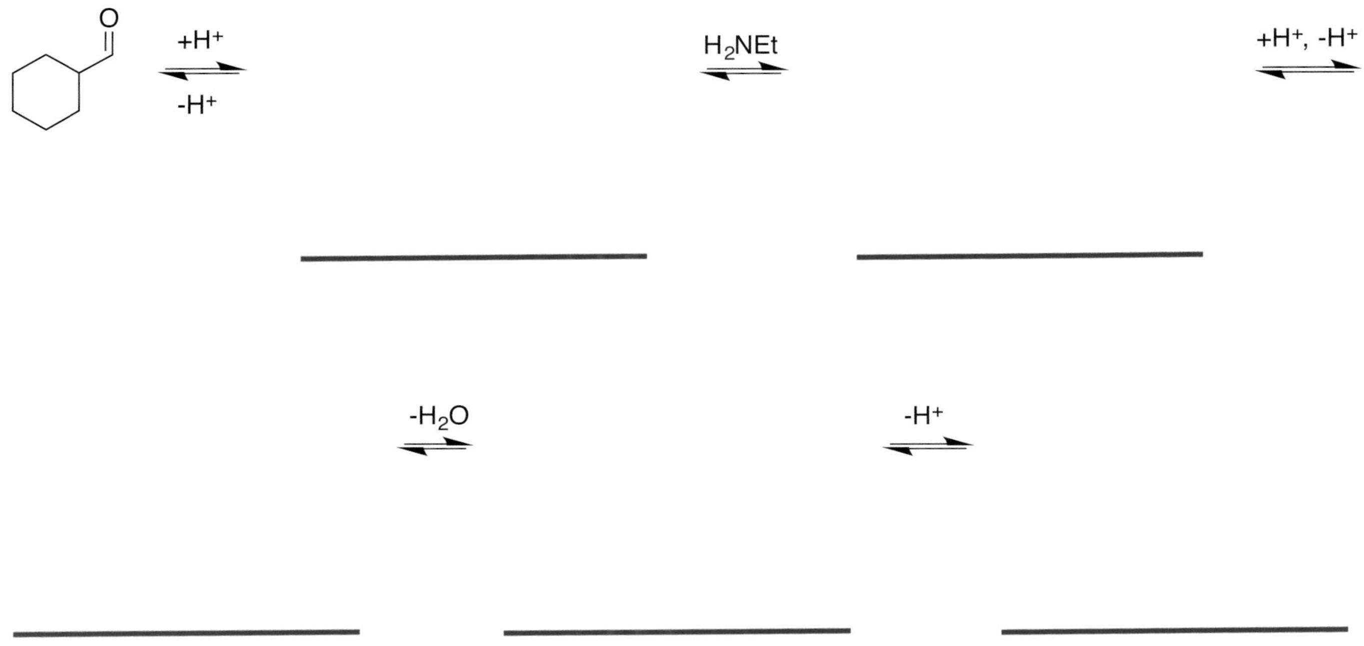

+H+

-H+

H₂NEt

+H+, -H+

-H₂O

-H+

The rate of this reaction reaches a maximum at about pH 4. because: _____
_____.

Draw the mechanism for reaction of benzaldehyde with phenylamine at pH 4. to form the corresponding imine.

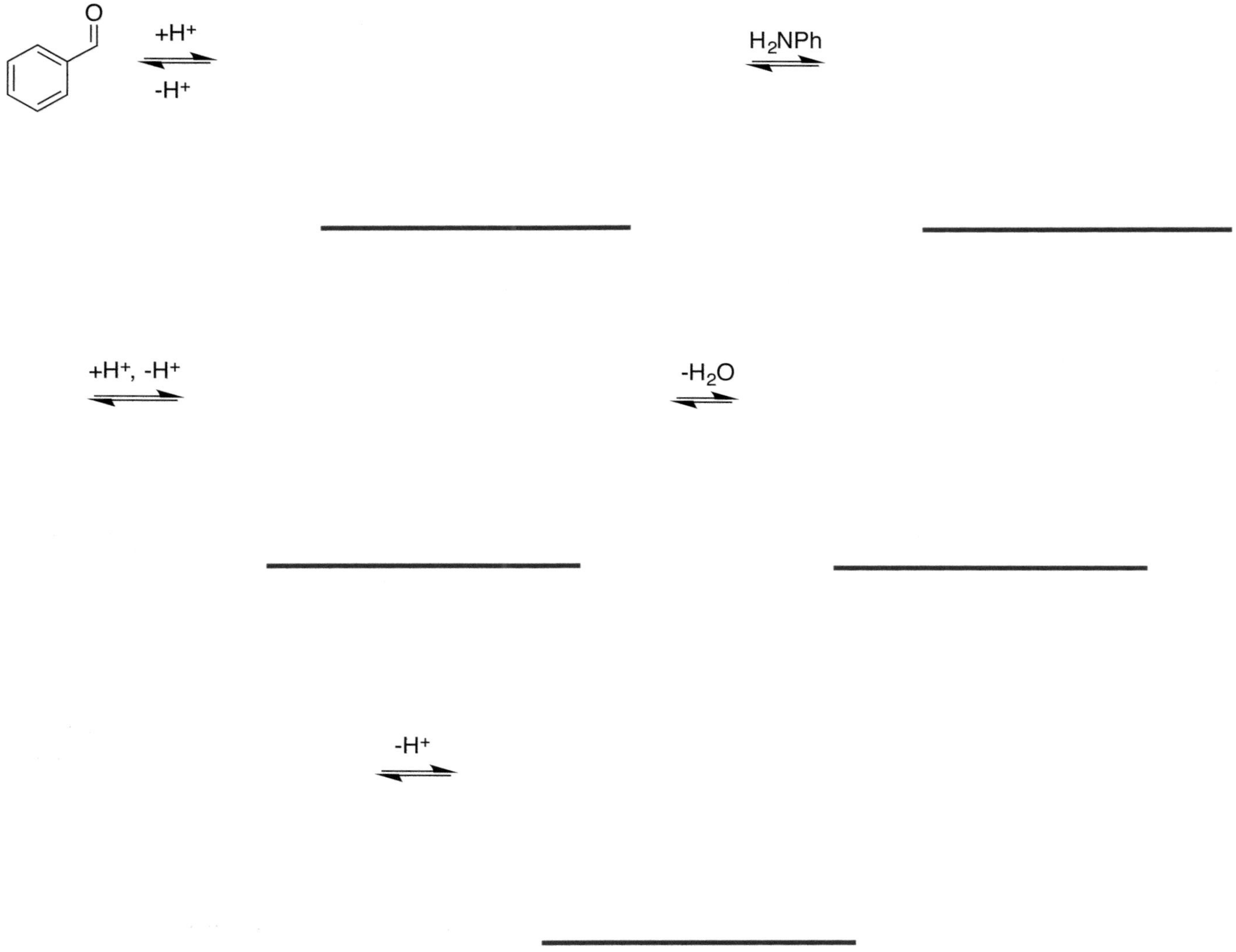

+H+   ⇌   -H+

H₂NPh   ⇌

_____   _____

+H+, -H+   ⇌

-H₂O   ⇌

_____   _____

-H+   ⇌

_____

Secondary Amines Form Iminium Ions Then, Perhaps, Enamines

Secondary amines condense with aldehydes and ketones to give *enamines* because deprotonation of the iminium intermediates must proceed through loss of protons from the *α-carbon / nitrogen*.

All the steps in enamine formation are *reversible / irreversible*.

Show the mechanism of enamine formation from phenylethanone and pyrrolidine.

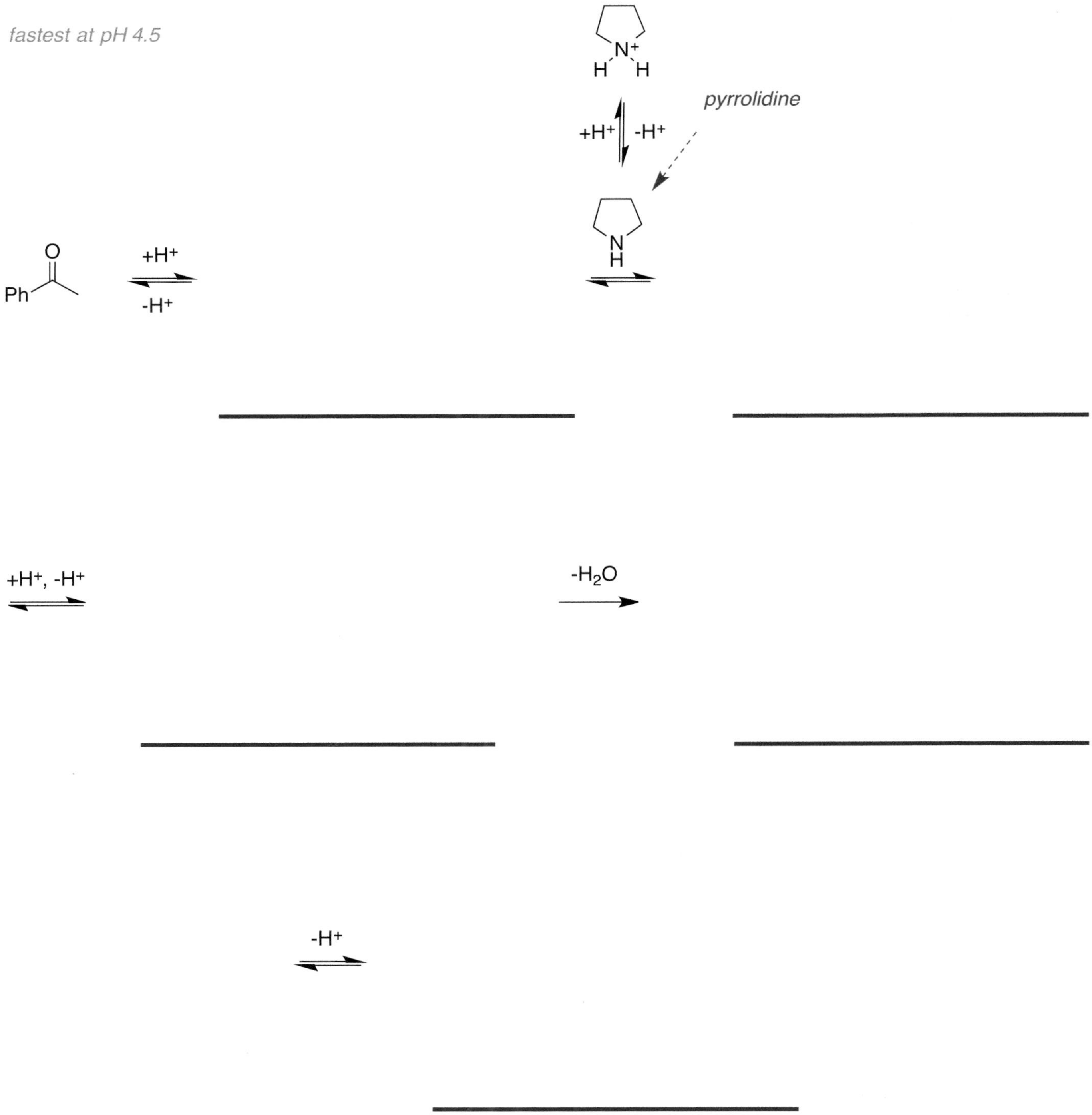

fastest at pH 4.5

pyrrolidine

+H⁺ | -H⁺

O
Ph

+H⁺

-H⁺

+H⁺, -H⁺

-H₂O

-H⁺

The 6-membered ring analog of pyrrolidine is called *piperidine / piperazine / pyran* (check Wiki).

Show a mechanism similar to the one above but for enamine formation from cyclopentanone and piperidine.

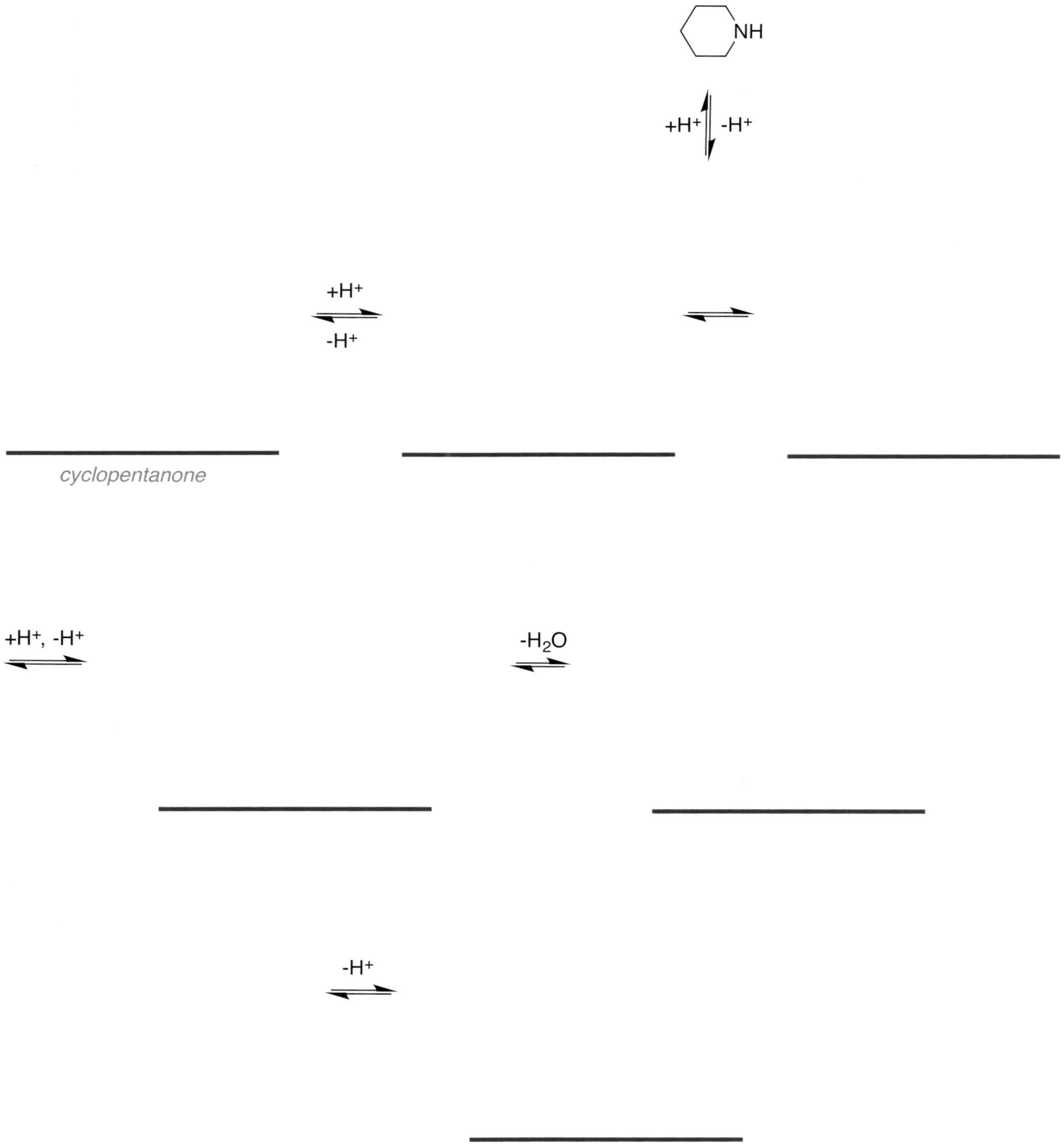

NH

+H⁺ ‖ -H⁺

+H⁺
⇌
-H⁺

⇌

_____   _____   _____
     cyclopentanone

+H⁺, -H⁺   -H₂O
⇌   ⇌

_____   _____

                    -H⁺
                    ⇌

                    _____

Water and acids *do / do not* hydrolyze enamines back to the ketones and amines.

Each of the following reactions involve formation of *imines* or *enamines*; show the products.

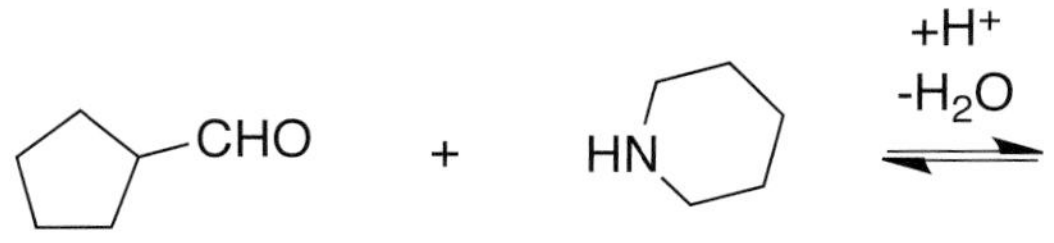

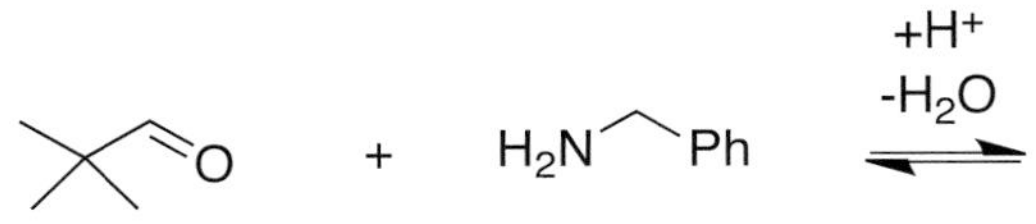

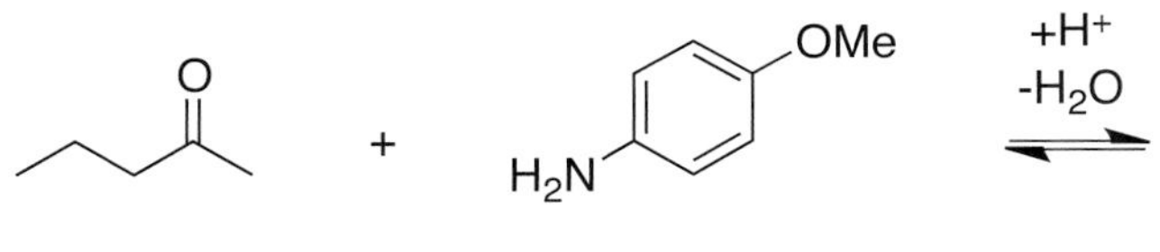

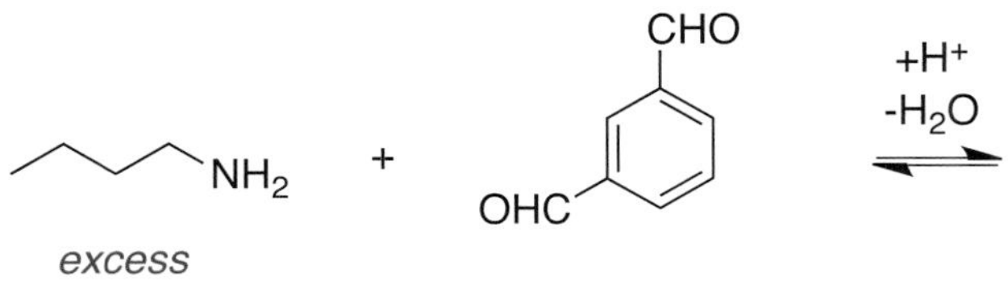

CHO + HN(ring) $\xrightarrow{+H^+ \; -H_2O}$

_____

(ketone) + H$_2$N–Ph $\xrightarrow{+H^+ \; -H_2O}$

_____

(ketone) + H$_2$N–C$_6$H$_4$–OMe $\xrightarrow{+H^+ \; -H_2O}$

_____

NH$_2$ (excess) + OHC–C$_6$H$_4$–CHO $\xrightarrow{+H^+ \; -H_2O}$

_____

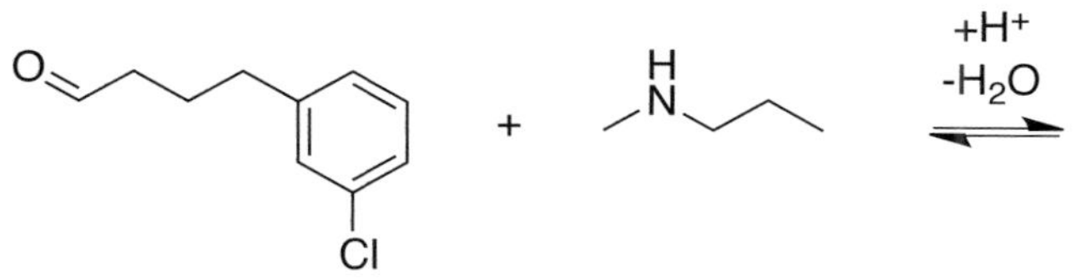

Review the mechanisms in this chapter, then state the reason why primary and secondary amines react differently in condensations (to give imines and enamines, respectively):

_____

_____ .

E Transamination

Abbreviate the following imine as indicated, then draw a mechanism for addition of aspartic acid, then loss of the Lys side-chain from the enzyme (ie loss of N-enz).

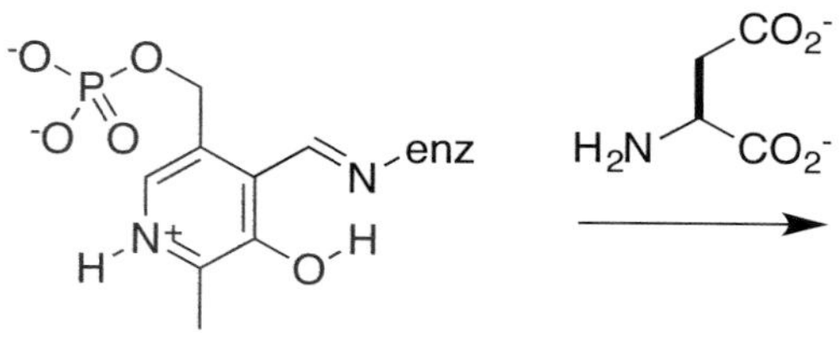

= R

-H+, +H+

_____

tetrahedral intermediate

-H₃N+enz

_____   _____
        tetrahedral intermediate   *imine products*

The following reaction involves a deprotonation that neutralizes the charge of the pyridinium-*N*, protonation on the benzylic carbon, then imine hydrolysis to give a product in which the amine group of Asp has been replaced by a ketone. Complete the mechanism, showing highlights of the electron flow.

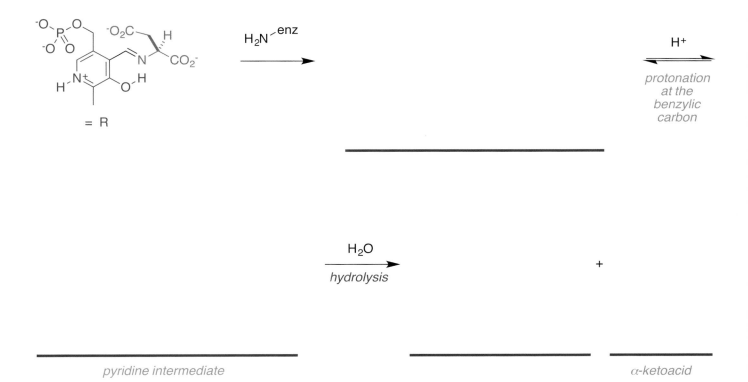

H_2N–enz

H^+

protonation at the benzylic carbon

H_2O

hydrolysis

+

_____
pyridine intermediate

_____   _____
                                    α-ketoacid

Transamination, as illustrated above, is an enzyme-mediated process for degradation of amino acids *in vivo*. Shown above is the *reduction / oxidation* of aspartic acid.

The amine formed in the process above is recycled back to the enzyme bound imine via reaction with the *α-keto acid / amine* derived from another amino acid.

Transamination reactions *remove amino acids completely / degrade one and form another*.

5   Stereochemistry Illustrated By Carbohydrates

from chapter(s) _____ in the recommended text

A Introduction

Focus

Some aspects of stereochemistry were covered in the first phase of this *Inquisition*, *eg* priority rules, assigning configurations, and definitions of terms like "diastereomers" and *"meso"*. However, these fundamentals are not as difficult to master as drawing complex chiral molecules in different ways without accidentally changing their stereochemistries. This, coincidentally, is one of the hardest aspects of carbohydrate chemistry so both together form a single focus in this chapter.

Reasons To Care

Stereochemistry in carbohydrates is important. Most carbon atoms in carbohydrates are chiral, and their configurations distinguish the different monomers (*eg* glucose, galactose, *etc*). However, the hemiacetal (or ketal) centers in carbohydrates can sometimes open and re-form in different ways. Aldose monomers with six carbon atoms can cyclize intramolecularly to form five- or six-membered hemiacetals (furanose and hexanose forms) and other different anomeric configurations.   Acetal or ketal units link monosaccharide building blocks in oligosaccharides, and these can also have different configurations.

cellulose, and other oligosaccharides, are monosaccharides linked by acetal groups

Understanding carbohydrate chemistry requires the ability to manipulate complex stereochemical information.

Concepts

drawing chiral molecules accurately • Fischer projections • optical rotations • nomenclature in carbohydrate chemistry • hydrolysis of acetals and ketals • formation of hemiketals

Objective

This section probes and stretches minds around the torturous ways carbohydrates can equilibrate between different conformers and cyclic hemiacetals/hemiketals, then different oligomeric forms.

B Assigning *R*- and *S*-Configurations

"Breakdown" representations of the following functional groups that could be used to assess their relative priorities.

Prioritize the following fragments according to the rules for assigning configuration.

highest priority   *lowest*

Circle which of the following compounds can be optically active

76

Assign the configurations of the following molecules if they are chiral. Circle any of these compounds that will not have an optical rotation, but instead use a square around those that are *meso*.

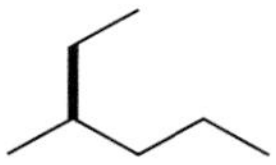

R / S 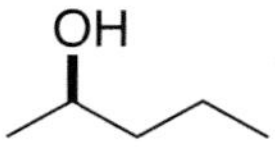   R / S 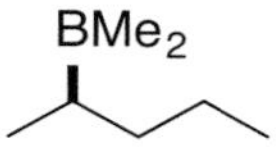   R / S 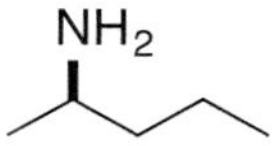   R / S 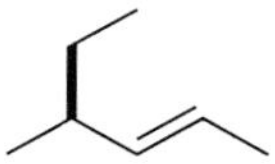   R / S 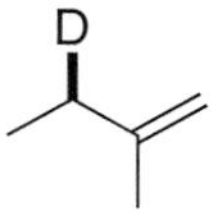   R / S 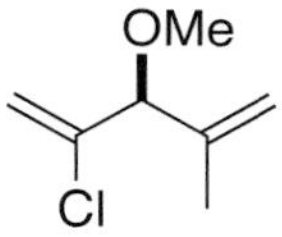   R / S 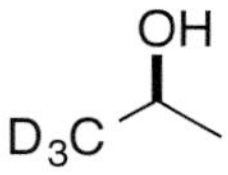   R / S

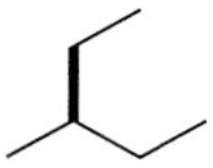

R / S 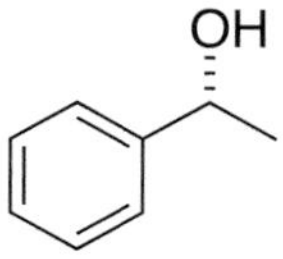   R / S 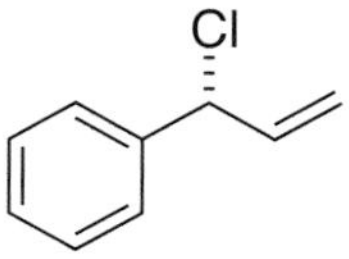   R / S 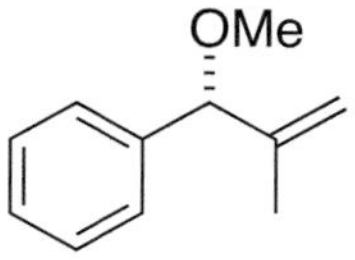   R / S 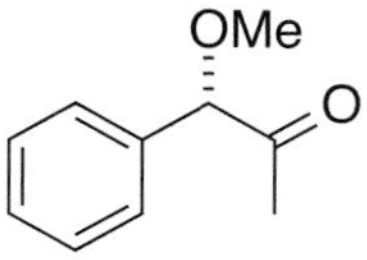   R / S 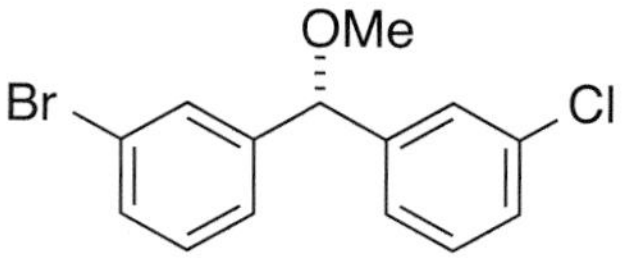   R / S

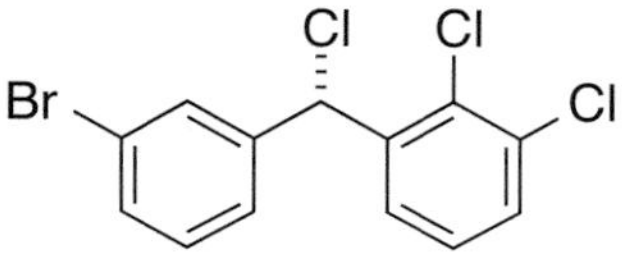

R / S 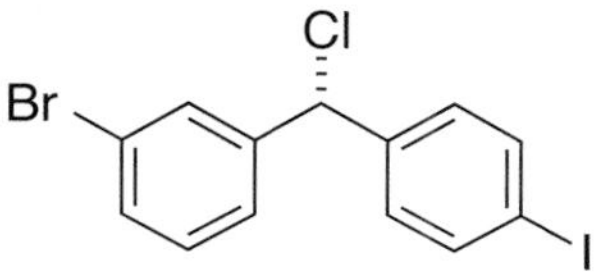   R / S 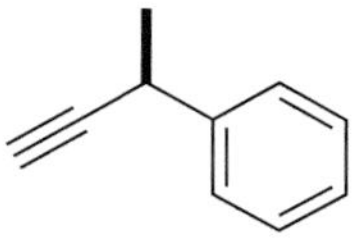   R / S 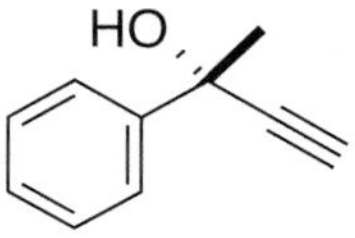   R / S 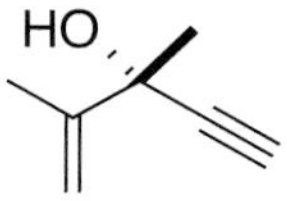   R / S

R / S 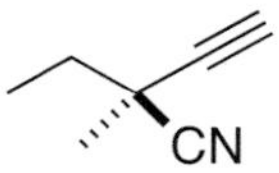   R / S 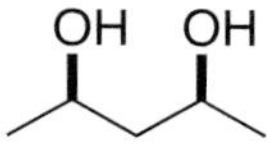   R / S   R / S 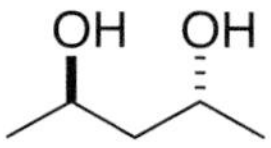   R / S   R / S 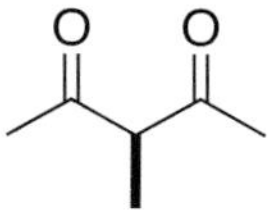   R / S

_____   _____

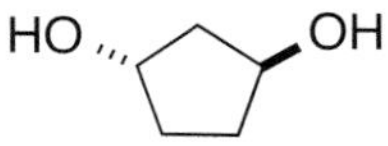

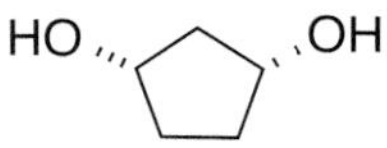

write assignments

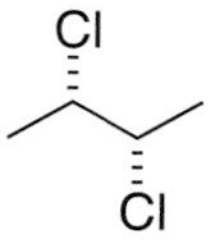

_____   _____   _____   _____   _____   _____

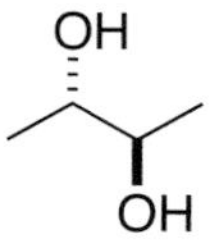

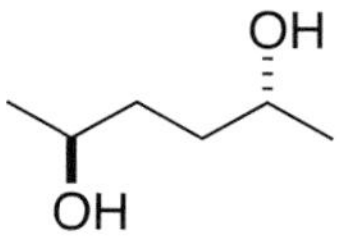

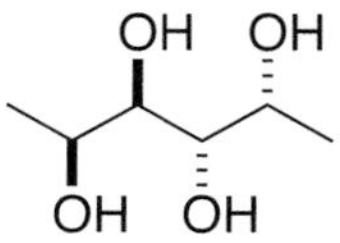

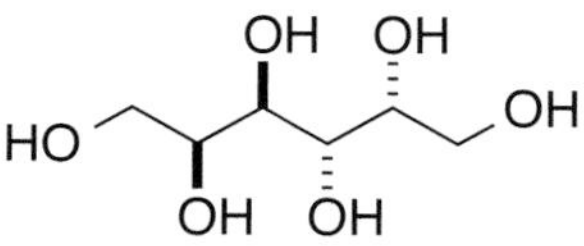

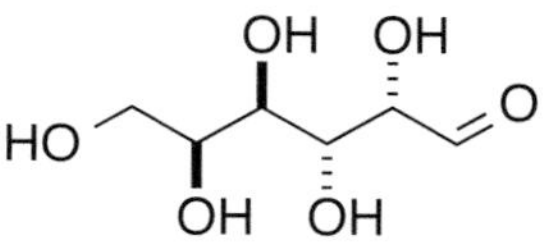

write assignments

C Stereochemical Representations Of Carbohydrates

Nomenclature

The terms *carbohydrate*, *saccharide*, and *sugar* *are all used to describe compounds in this series / have different meanings*.

Carbohydrates can be complicated structures formed from repeating units. These units are mostly named with the suffix *"ose"* (eg _____): if they contain an aldehyde they are called *aldoses / ketoses* and if they contain ketones they are called *aldoses / ketoses*. Classify each of these sugars as ketoses or aldoses.

D-glucose
aldose / ketose

D-ribose
aldose / ketose

D-fructose
aldose / ketose

dihydroxyacetone
aldose / ketose

Fischer Projections

Stereochemistries of monomeric sugars can be represented as Fischer projections with the aldehyde at the *top / bottom* by convention.

The simplest aldose is glyceraldehyde, CHO-CH(OH)-CH$_2$OH. D-Glyceraldehyde has the OH group on the chiral center on D-*right* (and the less common enantiomer stammers about having it on the L-, L-, L-*left*). Draw D-glyceraldehyde in the Fischer projection form, then as a zigzag representation.

_____

D-glyceraldehyde Fischer projection

_____

L-glyceraldehyde Fischer projection

_____

D-glyceraldehyde Fischer projection

_____

L-glyceraldehyde Fischer projection

78

Glyceraldehyde is a *triose / tetrose / pentose / hexose* because it contains three carbons.
Monosaccharides with five carbons are *trioses / tetroses / pentoses / hexoses*, and glucose (a six carbon sugar) is a *triose / tetrose / pentose / hexose*.

Aldoses that share the same configuration as D-glyceraldehyde *at the end nearest the primary alcohol* are also D-. Assign these sugars as D- or L- and circle the parts that define them as such.

```
   CHO          CHO              CHO          CHO                  CHO          CHO
 H—OH       HO—H            HO—H         H—OH               HO—H         H—OH
HO—H         H—OH           HO—H         H—OH               HO—H         H—OH
 H—OH       HO—H             H—OH       HO—H                HO—H         H—OH
 H—OH       HO—H             H—OH       HO—H               CH₂OH        CH₂OH
  CH₂OH        CH₂OH         CH₂OH        CH₂OH

        glucose                        mannose                        ribose

  D- or L-      D- or L-        D- or L-      D- or L-          D- or L-      D- or L-
```

D- Glucose and its L-isomer are *enantiomers / epimers*. D-Mannose and D-glucose are *enantiomers / epimers*. Draw enantiomers of the following monosaccharides by completing these Fischer projections:

```
   CHO              CHO                  CHO
 H—OH           HO—H                 HO—H
 H—OH           HO—H                  H—OH
 H—OH            H—OH                  H—OH
 H—OH            H—OH                  H—OH
  CH₂OH            CH₂OH                CH₂OH
 _____        _____          _____
  enantiomer        enantiomer          enantiomer


   CHO              CHO                  CHO
 H—OH           HO—H                 HO—H
 H—OH           HO—H                  H—OH
HO—H            HO—H                 HO—H
 H—OH            H—OH                  H—OH
  CH₂OH            CH₂OH                CH₂OH
 _____        _____          _____
  enantiomer        enantiomer          enantiomer
```

Transposing Fischer Projections Into Zigzag Structures

Naturally occurring sugars tend to be *D- / L-*.

Amino acids can be related to glyceraldehyde in the same way as monosaccharides. Genetically encoded amino acids are *D- / L-*.

Complete the following zigzag representations of the Fischer projections indicated (*hard?* use models to check your answer).

Without models it is sometimes essential to draw carbohydrates in different conformations to transpose their configurations onto other conformations. Problems like those above are much more difficult otherwise.

D Carbohydrates Can Cyclize To Hemiacetals Or Hemiketals

Draw tetrahydrofuran (THF) and 4*H*-pyran (six-membered ring, CH_6O with saturated carbon opposite the ring *O*-atom), and tetrahydropyran.

THF | *4H-pyran* | *tetrahydropyran*

Much of carbohydrate chemistry relies upon being able to accurately transform a diagram of a chiral molecule into an alternative representation. This can be difficult and requires practice. Shown below are molecules drawn in an extended form, and parts of their structures re-drawn in other conformations. Complete the drawings of the molecules in the other conformations.

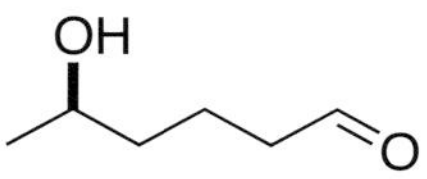

is the same as

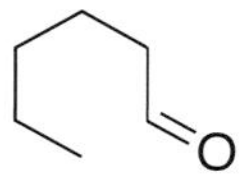

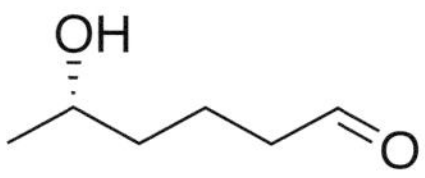

is the same as

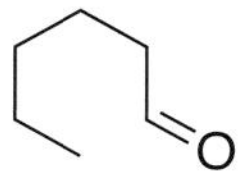

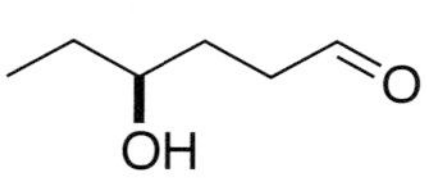

is the same as

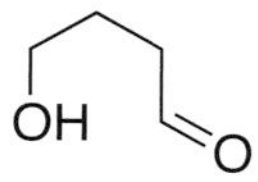

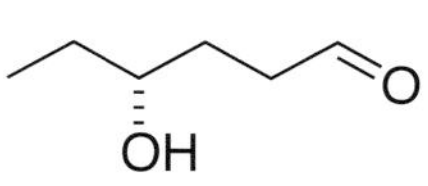

is the same as

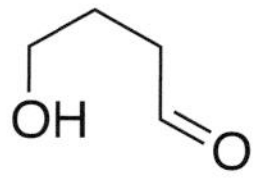

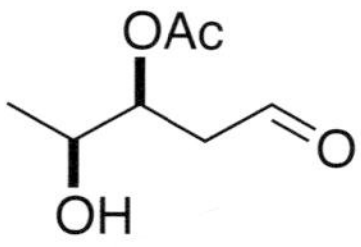

is the same as

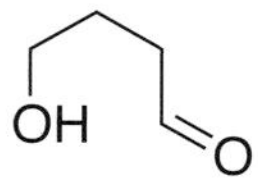

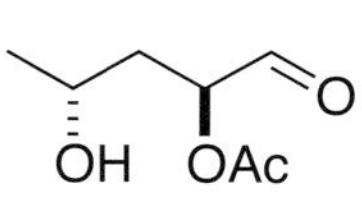

is the same as

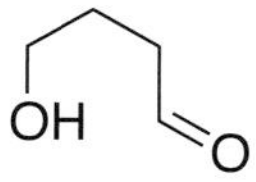

Many aldoses can cyclize into hemiacetals that resemble pyrans (*six / five*-membered ring) and to one that resemble furans (*six / five*-membered ring). Isomerization of carbohydrates between furanose and pyranose forms proceeds via the typical mechanism for acid-mediated hydrolyses of hemiacetals: protonation of the endocyclic, anomeric, -O, ring opening, then ring closure using another hydroxyl. Draw this mechanism for the equilibrium below, showing clear curly arrows for each step.

_____
protonated pyranose form

ring closing   ring opening

_____
protonated furanose form

ring closing   ring opening

_____
protonated aldehyde

_____
protonated aldehyde redrawn poised for 5-membered ring formation

Glucose *and / but not* ribose can exist as a mixture of furanose and pyranose forms, hence the optical rotation of this material (or these materials) is sensitive to pH and temperature.

Pyranose forms tend to exist in chair conformations, but it is best to re-draw them in artificial flat conformations to relate them to Fischer projections. Complete the following diagrams.

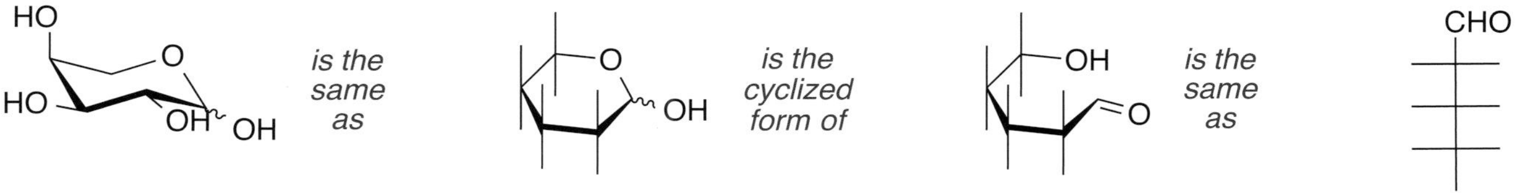

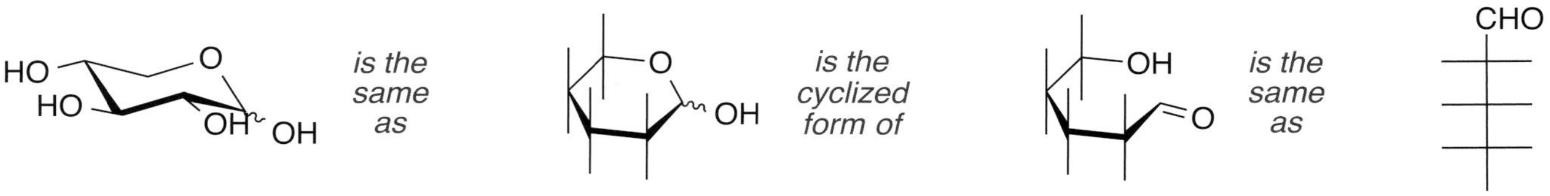

is the
same
as

is the
cyclized
form of

is the
same
as

is the
same
as

is the
cyclized
form of

is the
same
as

Complete the following diagrams relating *furanose / pyranose* forms of *hexoses / pentoses* to Fischer projections.

is the
same
as

is the
cyclized
form of

is the
same
as

glucose

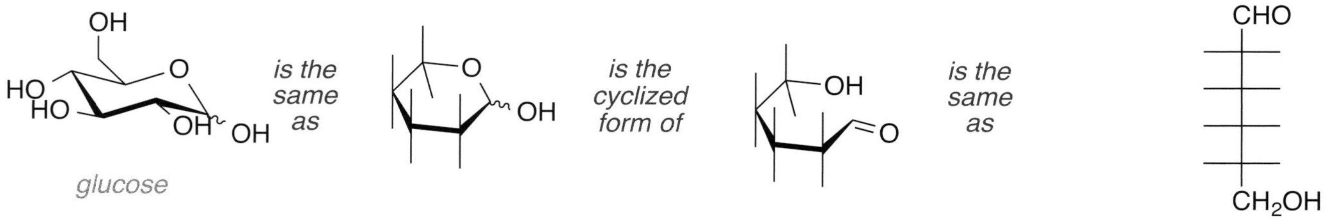

The anomer of D-glucopyranose that has all substituents in an equatorial position is α- / β-.

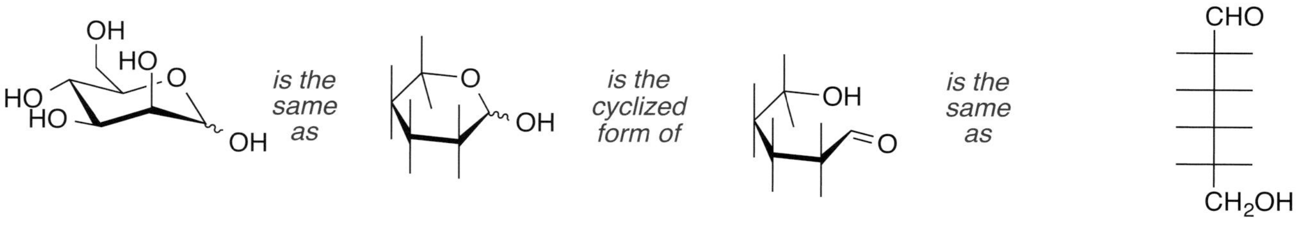

is the
same
as

is the
cyclized
form of

is the
same
as

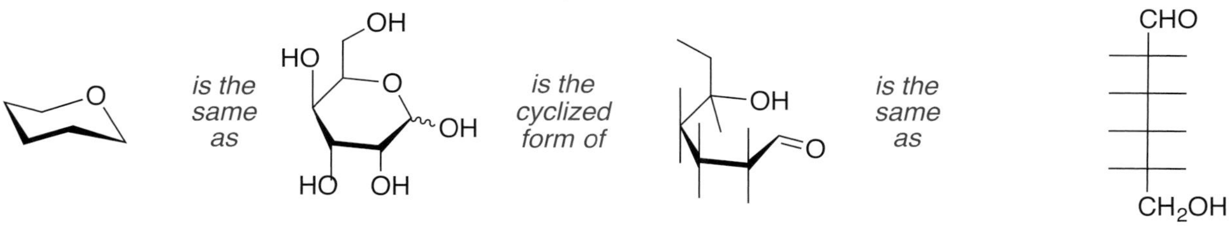

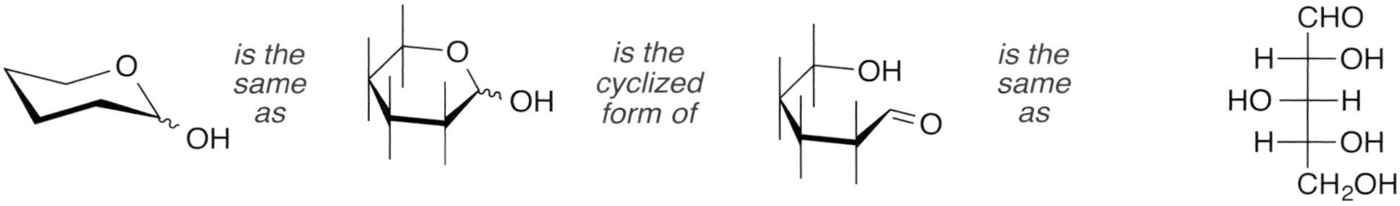

is the same as

is the cyclized form of

is the same as

CHO
—
—
—
—
CH₂OH

is the same as

is the cyclized form of

is the same as

CHO
H——OH
HO——H
H——OH
CH₂OH

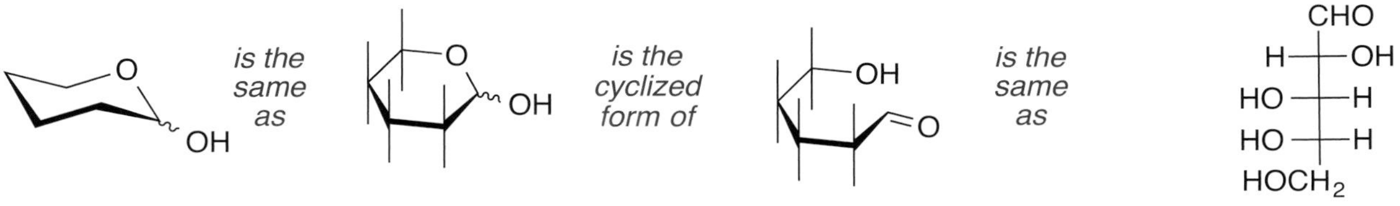

is the same as

is the cyclized form of

is the same as

CHO
H——OH
HO——H
HO——H
HOCH₂

Use a similar approach to relate the following monosaccharides to their cyclic hemiketal forms. Note how α- and β-anomers are defined in the first example. By definition, the α-anomer is the one with the anomeric-*OH cis / trans* to the -CH₂OH ring substituent.

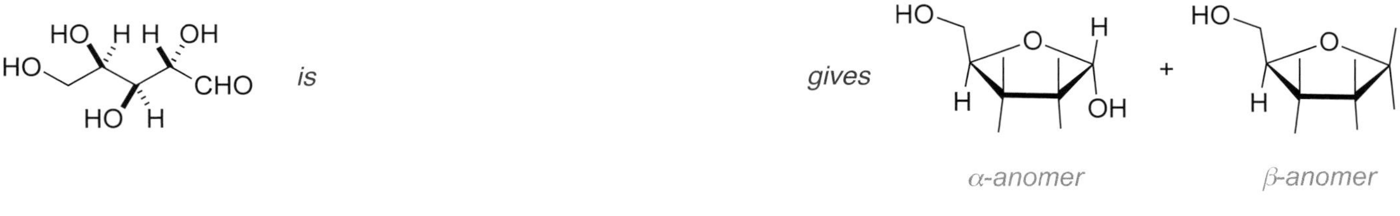

is

gives

+

α-anomer   *β-anomer*

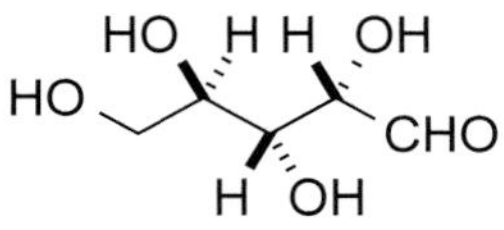

is _____ gives

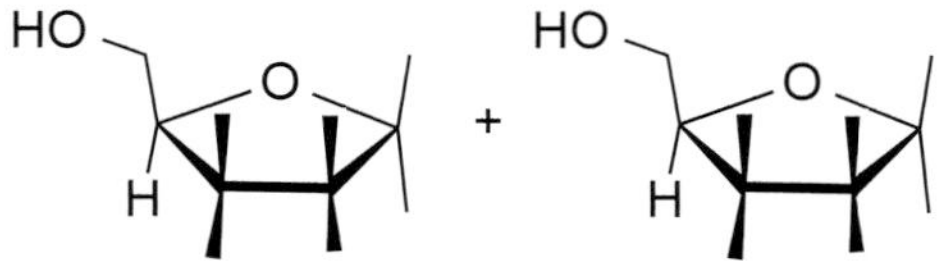

α-anomer + β-anomer

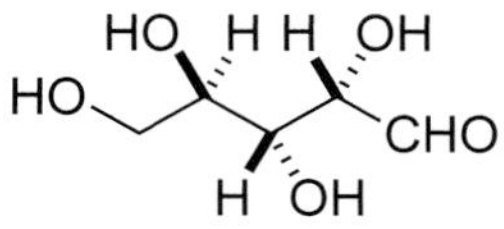

_____

is _____ gives

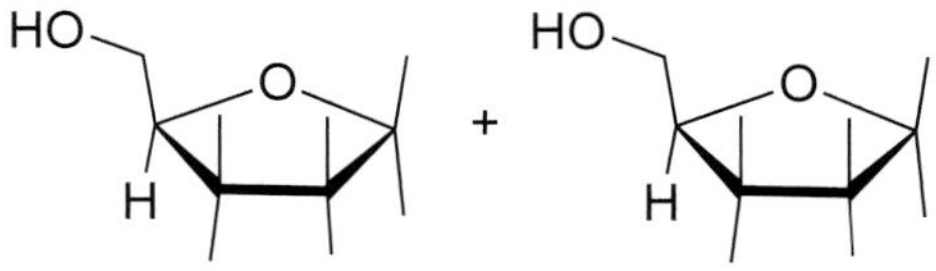

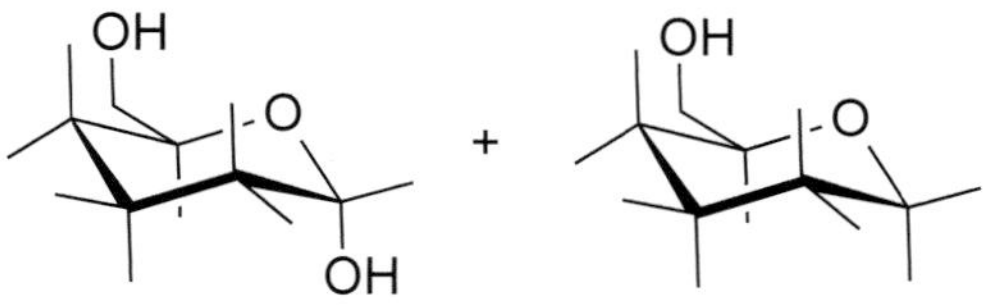

α-anomer + β-anomer

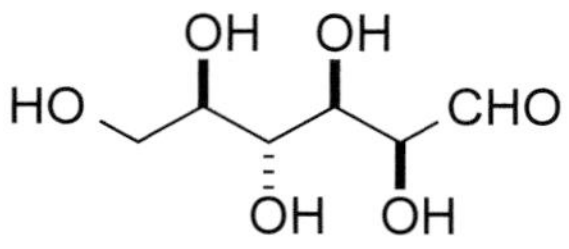

_____

is _____ gives

α-anomer + β-anomer

_____

Draw pyranose forms of the following monosaccharides by completing the structures below. This question is also easy to visualize with models but hard without. The boxes are provided for drawing alternative conformations. Check answers by assigning *R*- and *S*-configurations.

CHO
H——OH
H——OH
H——OH
H——OH
CH₂OH

α-anomer

β-anomer

CHO
H——OH
HO——H
H——OH
H——OH
CH₂OH

α-anomer

β-anomer

Complete the following diagram for glucose by filling in H and OH labels to indicate the correct stereochemistries.

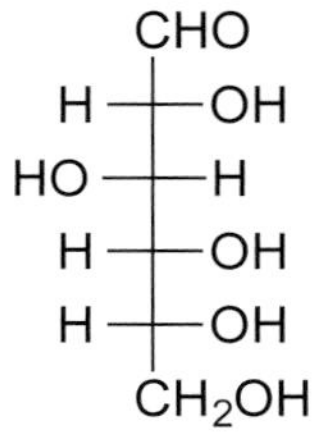

CHO
H———OH
HO———H
H———OH
H———OH
CH₂OH

glucose

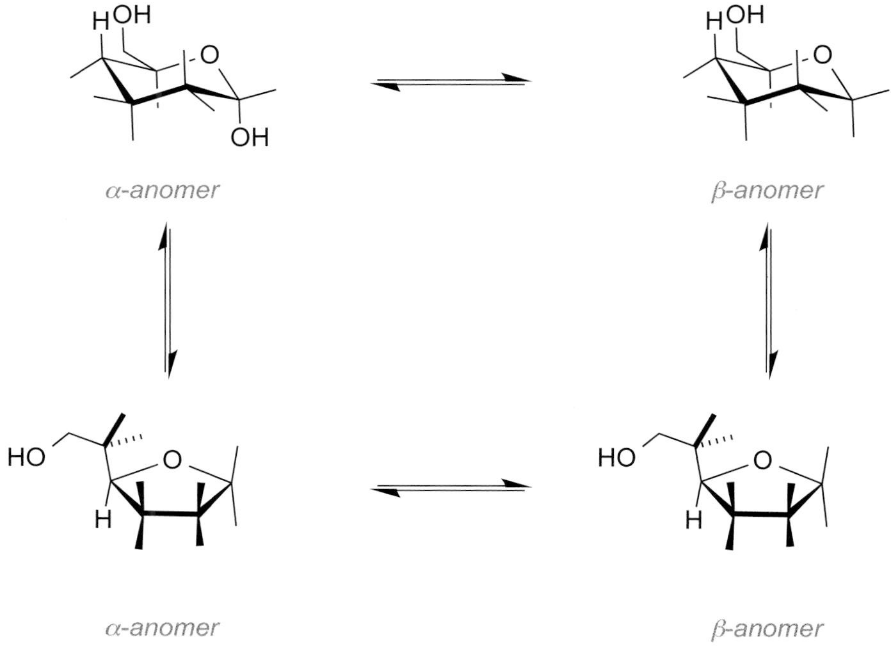

α-anomer

β-anomer

α-anomer

β-anomer

box for reasoning, write answers above

E Homologation Of Sugars By One Carbon (Reaction With HCN)

Monosaccharides, like other aldehydes, react with cyanide to form cyanohydrins. These cyanohydrins can be partially reduced to *imines / amines* then hydrolyzed to form homologated *aldoses / ketoses* as a mixture of epimers. Fill in the gaps in the following diagram.

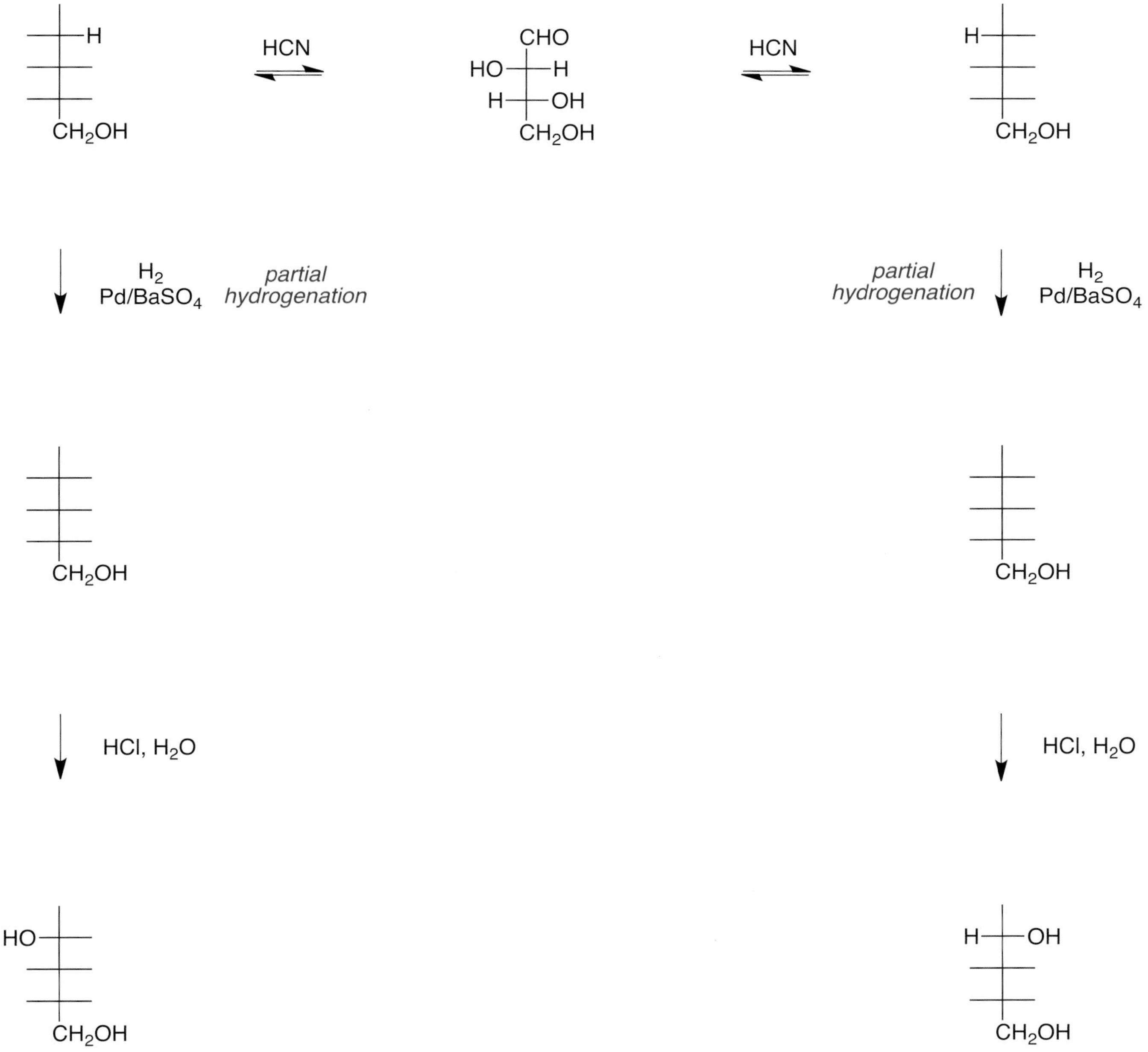

```
      ─┼─H                              CHO                         H─┼─
       ┼          HCN              HO─┼─H         HCN                 ┼
       ┼         ⇌                  H─┼─OH       ⇌                    ┼
      ─┼─                           ─┼─                              ─┼─
     CH₂OH                         CH₂OH                            CH₂OH
```

| H₂   *partial* | | *partial*   H₂ |
| Pd/BaSO₄   *hydrogenation* | | *hydrogenation*   Pd/BaSO₄ |

```
       ┼                                                            ┼
       ┼                                                            ┼
       ┼                                                            ┼
      ─┼─                                                          ─┼─
     CH₂OH                                                        CH₂OH
```

HCl, H₂O   HCl, H₂O

```
   HO─┼─                                                       H─┼─OH
      ┼                                                          ┼
      ┼                                                          ┼
     ─┼─                                                        ─┼─
    CH₂OH                                                      CH₂OH
```

A mixture of *enantiomers / epimers* which may then be separated.

If the starting material was one enantiomer, then the individual, completely separated monosaccharides produced in this sequence *would be / would not be* optically pure.

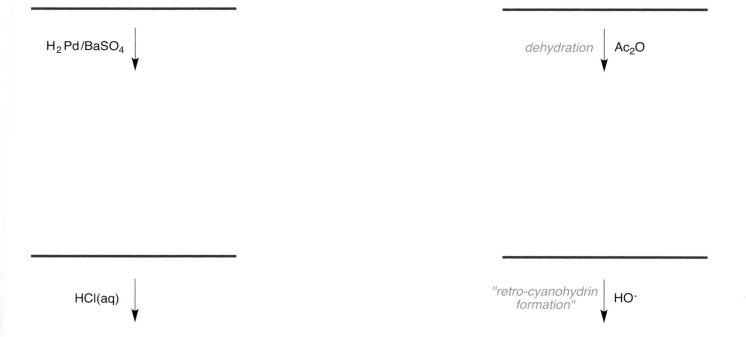

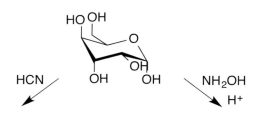

F Conversion Of Aldoses To Lower Homologs

Aldehydes react with hydroxylamines to form oximes. Oximes can be dehydrated, and the cyanohydrin product can collapse back to aldehydes with one less carbon. Predict the final products of these reactions; addition of one carbon is represented on the *left / right* and subtraction on the *left / right*.

HCN

HO OH

O

OH

OH   OH

NH$_2$OH
H$^+$

_____

H$_2$ Pd/BaSO$_4$

dehydration   Ac$_2$O

_____

HCl(aq)

"retro-cyanohydrin formation"   HO$^-$

_____   _____

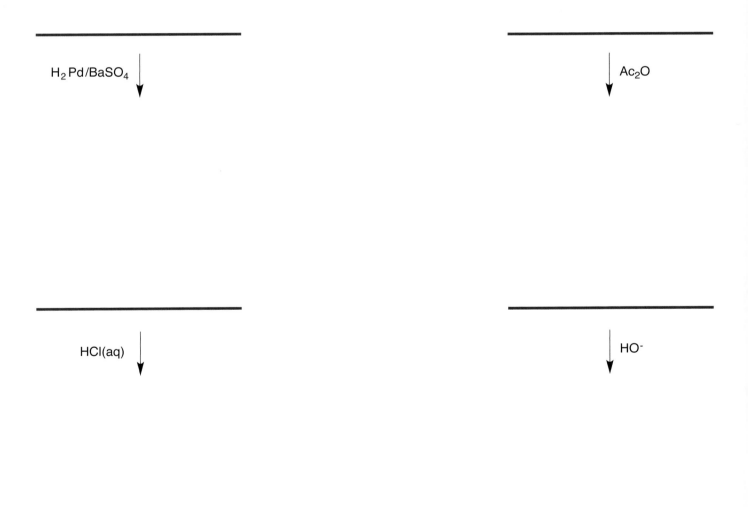

HCN

NH₂OH
H⁺

H₂Pd/BaSO₄

Ac₂O

HCl(aq)

HO⁻

Fill in the gaps in the following sequence.

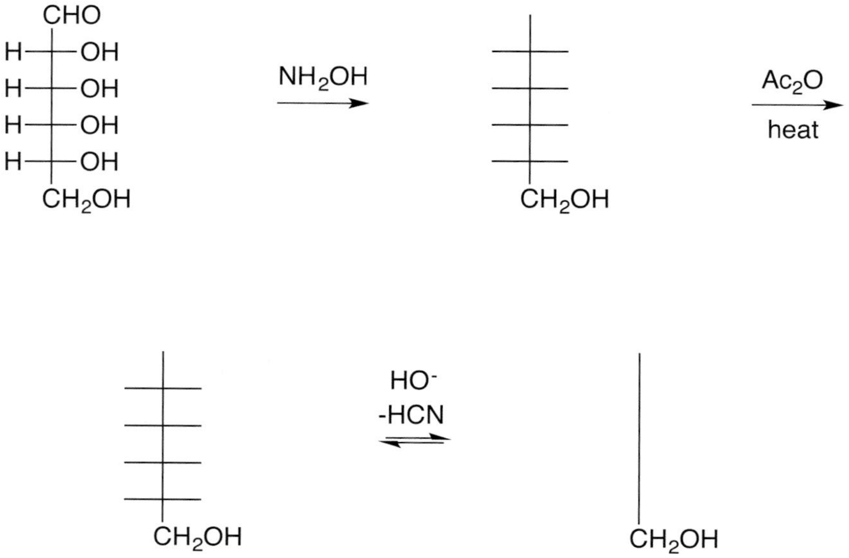
CHO
H—OH
H—OH
H—OH
H—OH
CH2OH
NH2OH
CH2OH
Ac2O
heat
CH2OH
HO-
-HCN
CH2OH

G Other Reactions Of Sugars

Aldoses are *oxidized / reduced* to the corresponding acids via treatment with Ag_2O, giving a *silver mirror*. Sugars that can precipitate silver from Ag_2O are called *reducing / oxidizing* sugars.

Like other hemiacetals, treatment with alcohols under anhydrous acid conditions will convert them to acetals. Cyclized forms are favored, and a mixture of anomers will be produced.

Draw the products of the following reactions.

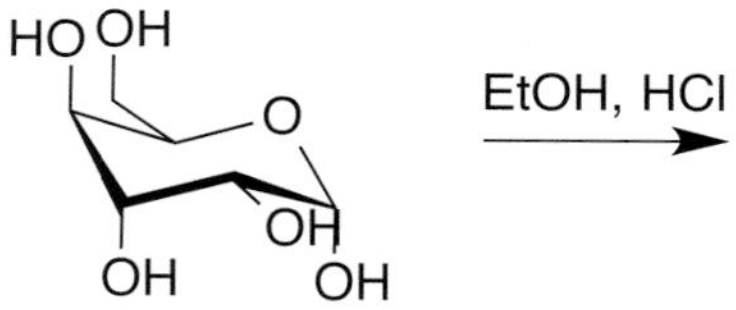
HO OH
O
OH
OH
OH
EtOH, HCl

α-anomer

β-anomer

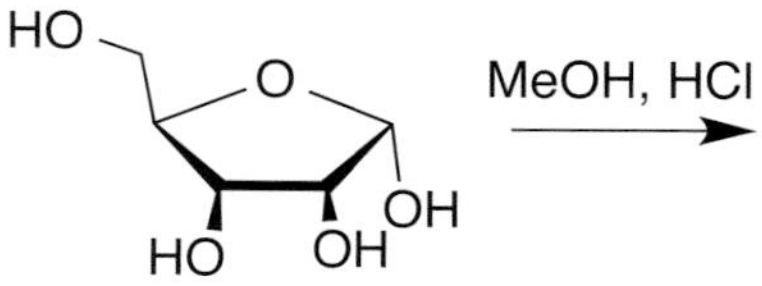
HO
O
HO
OH
OH
MeOH, HCl

α-anomer

β-anomer

H Relative Stabilities Of Anomers

Pyranosides are more stable as α-anomers because of overlap of the *axial / equatorial* non-bonded lone pair on the endocyclic oxygen with the σ*-orbital of the C-O bond; this is *the anomeric effect*. Draw orbitals on 2-hydroxytetrahydropyran to represent this process, and a diagram to illustrate how they mix to give a stabilized system.

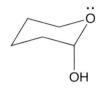

α-anomer
σ-to-σ* *interactions* <u>possible</u> / <u>*impossible*</u>

β-anomer
σ-to-σ* *interactions* <u>possible</u> / <u>*impossible*</u>

I Di- And Oligosaccharides

Connections between monosaccharides to form these polymers are made using *acetal or ketal / ester / amide* functional groups. These connections are then named according to the number of the carbon that uses the anomeric carbon (C^1) then a number of the carbon on which the oxygen at the second ring is attached. For example, two glucose units connected by a β-1,4-linkage is *cellobiose* but connection via a α-1,4-linkage is maltose. Draw these molecules.

cellobiose

maltose

Use words to characterize the anomeric linkages in the following molecules. For sucrose call the furanose ring 1 and the pyranose ring 2, so describe the linkage as something like $\alpha 1, \alpha 2$.

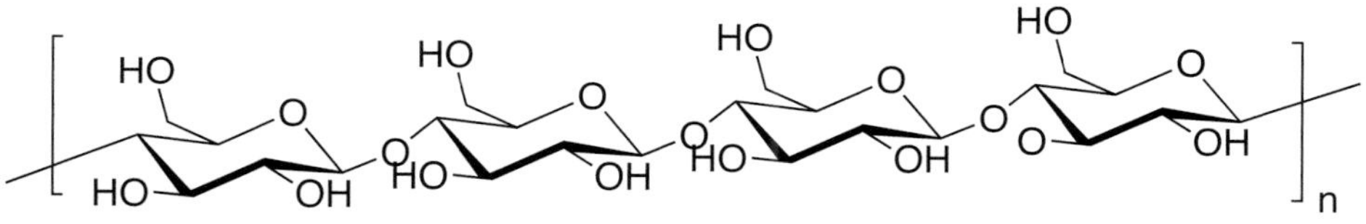

cellulose

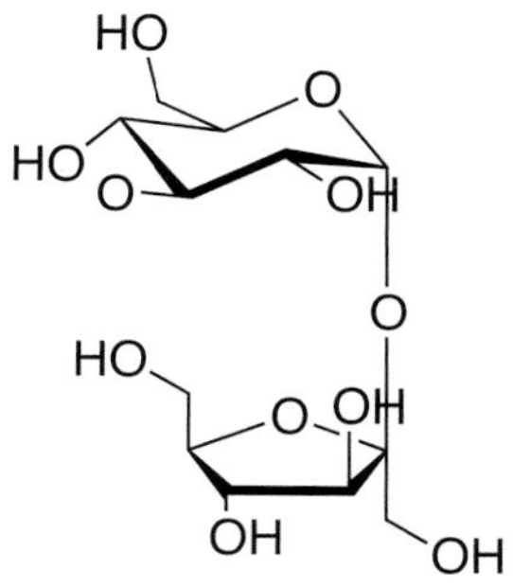

linkages are:

sucrose

linkage is:

Cellulose is a *mono- / di- / oligo- / poly*-saccharide, but sucrose is a *mono- / di- / oligo*-saccharide.

Oligosaccharides can feature two anomeric linkages to one sugar (branched), sugars with amino groups (amino sugars), and sugars linked to proteins and peptides (glycoproteins and peptides).

Plants make glucose from CO_2 and water in the process called _____ .

J The Most Important Carbohydrate Structures To Learn

It is unproductive to learn names and stereochemistries of all the monosaccharides. However, it is valuable to know terms like *anomeric carbon*, *furanose* and *pyranose* forms, and that, in aqueous acid, α- and β-anomers can interconvert. Transposing stereochemical diagrams of carbohydrates is not trivial and takes practice. It is important to remember the most important monosaccharides:

D-(+)-glyceraldehyde	*D-ribose*	*D-glucose*
D-(-)-tartaric acid	*α-D-ribofuranose*	*α-D-glucopyranose*
β-D-2-deoxyribofuranose	*β-D-ribofuranose*	*β-D-glucopyranose*

RNA is based on *α-D-ribofuranose / β-D-ribofuranose / α-D-2-deoxyribofuranose / β-D-2-deoxyribofuranose*.

DNA is based on *α-D-ribofuranose / β-D-ribofuranose / α-D-2-deoxyribofuranose / β-D-2-deoxyribofuranose*.

6 Heterocycles In Biological Chemistry

from chapter(s) _____ in the recommended text

A Introduction

Focus

Cyclic compounds containing heteroatoms, *heterocycles*, are diverse, but some simple ring systems occur frequently in biochemistry and in biomedicinal chemistry. This section focuses on some of the most common ring systems, and on features that define their chemistry.

Reasons To Care

Chemistry in living organisms occurs predominantly in an aqueous environment. Compounds with ring-systems containing only carbon atoms play significant roles in this chemistry, but the extent of that involvement is restricted by their poor water solubilities and limited opportunities for intermolecular interactions. Conversely, many heterocycles are basic and polar affording them greater water solubilities, especially when protonated (Figure 1). Lone pairs of electrons on the heteroatoms in heterocycles may be hydrogen-bond acceptors, or protonated to form hydrogen bond donors.

folic acid

Figure 1. Some heterocycles in biochemistry.

pyridoxal phosphate   *riboflavin*   *nicotine*   *nicotinamide*

Concepts

aromaticity • acids and bases • electrophilic aromatic substitution

Objective

To introduce some common heterocycles, and understand how heteroatoms in a ring can influence aromaticity, basicity and reactivity.

B Nomenclature

Complete the following diagram by giving whatever is missing: name or structure.

pyrrole	*imidazole*	*pyrrazole*	*tetrazole*

pyridine	*1,3-pyrimidine*	*indole*	*thiophene*

1,2,3-triazole	*piperidine*	*pyrrolidine*	*aziridine*

oxirane	*oxetane*	*furan*	*benzofuran*

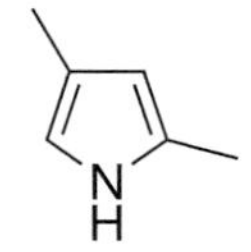

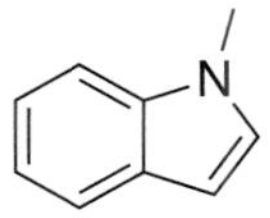

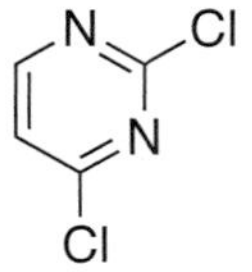

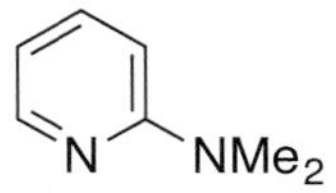

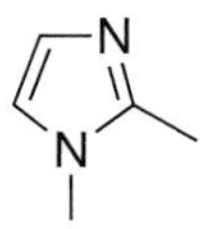

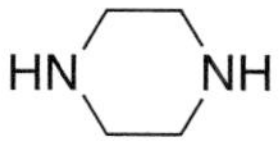

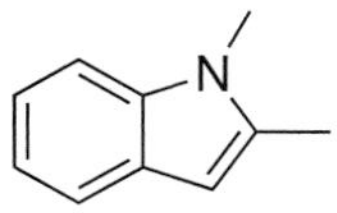

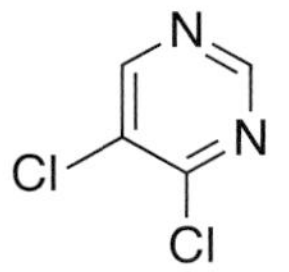

Name the heterocyclic core component colored in blue for each of the following pharmaceuticals.

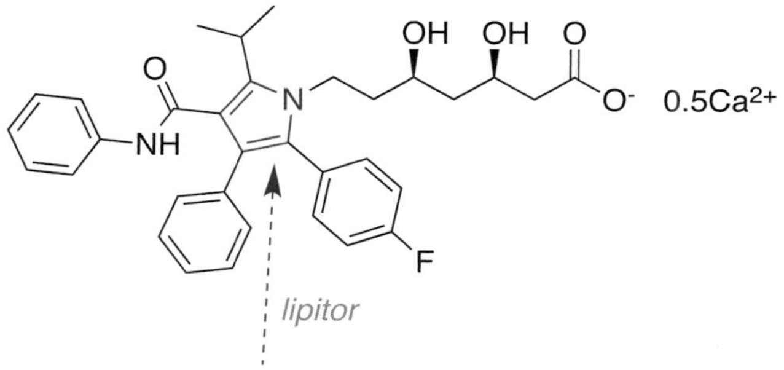

lipitor

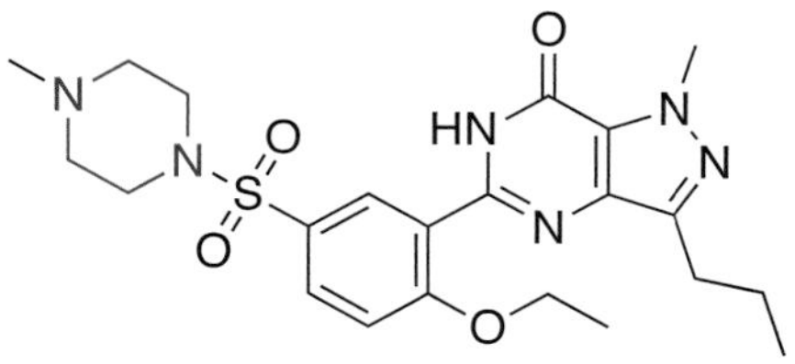

viagra

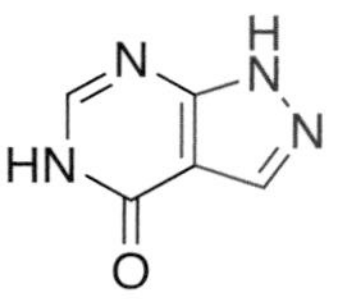

_____   _____

allopurinol 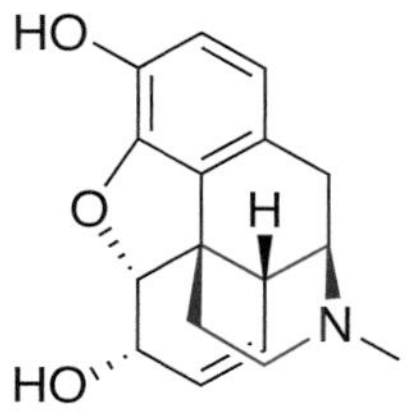   *morphine* 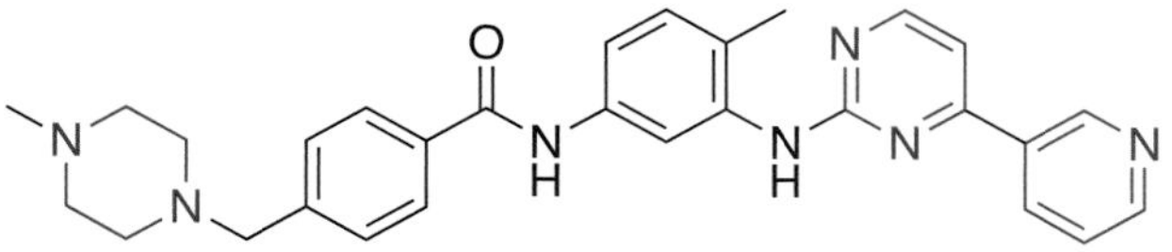   *imatinib*

and   *and*

_____   _____   _____

C Aromaticity And Basicity Of Heterocycles

Pyridines And Pyrimidines

In pyridine, the *N*-atom is *sp³ / sp² / sp* hybridized with *a lone pair / a proton* occupying one of the lobes, and there is/are *1 / 2 / 3* electron(s) in the *p*-orbital that is not hybridized; this heterocycle is therefore *aromatic / non-aromatic*.

Complete the following diagram to show the arrangement of *p*-orbitals, π-electrons and *N*-hybridization states in pyridine.

pyridine

In 1,3-pyrimidine, the *N*-atom is/are *sp³ / sp² / sp* hybridized with *a lone pair / a proton* occupying one of the lobes, and there is/are *1 / 2 / 3* electron(s) in the *p*-orbital that is not hybridized.

1,3-Pyrimidine is *aromatic / non-aromatic*.

Complete the following diagram to show the arrangement of *p*-orbitals, π-electrons and *N*-hybridization states in 1,3-pyrimidine.

1,3-pyrimidine

In 1,4-pyrimidine, the *N*-atom is/are *sp³ / sp² / sp* hybridized with *a lone pair / a proton* occupying one of the lobes, and there is/are *1 / 2 / 3* electron(s) in the *p*-orbital that is not hybridized.

1,4-Pyrimidine is *aromatic / non-aromatic*.

Draw the arrangement of *p*-orbitals, π-electrons and *N*-hybridization states in 1,4-pyrimidine.

1,4-pyrimidine

Pyrrole

In pyrrole, the *N*-atom must be *sp³ / sp² / sp* hybridized with *0 / 2 e⁻* occupying one of the lobes, and there is/are *1 / 2 / 3* electron(s) in the *p*-orbital that is not hybridized.

The pyrrole nitrogen *can / cannot* be sp³-hybridized and simultaneously give a flat conjugated aromatic system; this heterocycle is therefore *aromatic / non-aromatic*.

Draw the arrangement of *p*-orbitals, π-electrons and *N*-hybridization of pyrrole.

pyrrole

Imidazole

In imidazole there are two *different N*-atoms, that *can / cannot* interconvert via tautomerism.

The nitrogen atoms in imidazole *are / are not* both sp² hybridized, and *one / both* contributes 2e⁻ to the aromatic system, consequently this heterocycle *is / is not* basic.

Draw the arrangement of *p*-orbitals, π-electrons and *N*-hybridization of imidazole.

imidazole

The drive to attain aromaticity *does / does not* influence the hybridization state and therefore the basicities of *N*-atoms in heterocycles like pyridine, pyrimidine, pyrrole, and imidazole.

Pyrazole

Pyrazole has two *different N*-atoms, that *can / cannot* interconvert via tautomerism.

Pyrazole nitrogen atoms *are / are not* both sp² hybridized, and *one / both* contributes 2e to the aromatic system.

Pyrazole *is / is not* easily protonated relative to pyrrole.

Draw the arrangement of *p*-orbitals, π-electrons and *N*-hybridization of pyrazole.

pyrazole

In nitrogen heterocycles like pyrrole and imidazole it is possible for a *N*-atom to be sp³ hybridized. The *N*-atom preferentially hybridizes to the sp² state to gain *aromatic stabilization / to become basic*.

1,3,4-Oxadiazole

In 1,3,4-oxadiazole, the *N*-atoms must be *sp³ / sp² / sp* hybridized and each contributes *0 / 1 / 2 e⁻* to the aromatic system.

The 1,3,4-oxadiazole oxygen is *sp³ / sp² / sp* hybridized and contributes *0 / 1 / 2 e⁻* to the aromatic system; this heterocycle is therefore *aromatic / non-aromatic*.

Draw the arrangement of lone pairs and *p*-electrons, hence the *O,N*-hybridization of 1,3,4-oxadiazole.

1,3,4-oxadiazole

When a proton adds to a lone pair *in a sp²-hybridized orbital* in an aromatic heterocycle it *does / does not* remove electrons from the $4n + 2$ delocalized system.

That lone pair is therefore a relatively *good / bad* base because the aromatic stabilization *is / is not* lost.

D Common Heterocycles In Nature

For each of the heterocycles below that is aromatic, show how many πe^- each of the nitrogen atoms contribute to the aromatic system (leave blank if not aromatic). To solve this problem, it is necessary to consider the tautomeric form of each heterocycle that closest resembles an aromatic state.

N³:

N²:

N¹:

cytosine

N²:

N¹:

thymine

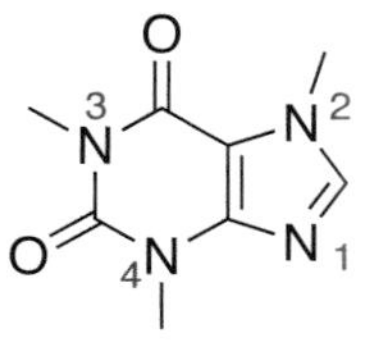

caffeine

N⁴:
N³:
N²:
N¹:

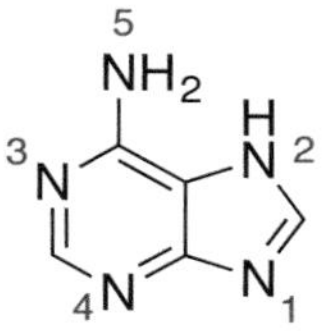

adenine

N⁵:
N⁴:
N³:
N²:
N¹:

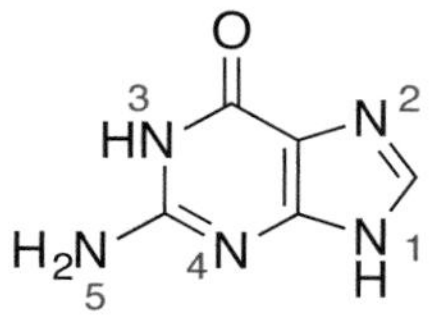

guanine

N⁵:
N⁴:
N³:
N²:
N¹:

Draw a rectangle around any of these heterocycles that are *not* found in RNA.

Porphyrin ring systems involve *4 / 2 / 0* pyridine-like nitrogen atoms, *4 / 2 / 0* pyrrole-like nitrogen atoms, and _____ π-electrons; they *are / are not* aromatic.

In the presence of base it may be easily deprotonated *1 / 2 / 3* times to create a ligand that is ideally suited to complex with transition metals in their M(2+) oxidation states.

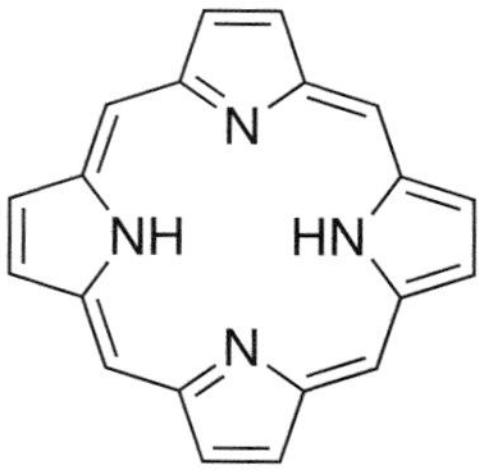

porphyrin

Drawing porphyrins takes practice! Draw the complexes of porphyrin with Fe^{2+} and with Mg^{2+} as neatly as possible, and indicate their overall charges. Porphyrin must lose two protons to form these complexes.

Fe^{2+} complex   overall charge 0 / 1 / 2 / 3 / 4   *Mg^{2+} complex   overall charge 0 / 1 / 2 / 3 / 4*

Iron complexes like this are found in *cholesterol / hemoglobin / chlorophyll / bilirubin*, while the magnesium complexes feature in *cholesterol / hemoglobin / chlorophyll / bilirubin* (circle all that apply).

Complexes like those are (circle all that apply): *strongly UV absorbing / fluorescent / toxic even in small doses / capable of redox chemistry*.

E Aromatic Characteristics Of Protonated Heterocycles

Indicate numbers of π-electrons and therefore the aromaticities of the following systems.

aromatic / not aromatic because it has _____ πe⁻.

aromatic / not aromatic because it has _____ πe⁻.

aromatic / not aromatic because it has _____ πe⁻.

aromatic / not aromatic because it has _____ πe⁻.

aromatic / not aromatic because it has _____ πe⁻.

aromatic / not aromatic because it has _____ πe⁻.

aromatic / not aromatic because it has _____ πe⁻.

aromatic / not aromatic because it has _____ πe⁻.

aromatic / not aromatic because it has _____ πe⁻.

aromatic / not aromatic because it has _____ πe⁻.

In the last examples, the *N*-atom is, in fact, *not* where indole protonates. Can you suggest another atom to which a proton might add?

Circle all the basic atoms in the following heterocycles and, to review, write their names underneath.

_____   _____   _____   _____   _____   *oxazole*

F Electrophilic Attack On Pyrrole And Indole Compared

Pyrrole

The *N*-nucleophilicity of pyrrole is *low / high* in S_N2 reactions for the same reasons that account for the basicity of that atom.   Electrophiles tend to add to the carbon atoms of pyrrole in electrophilic aromatic substitution reactions.

Show all the resonance structures for the intermediate that would arise by adding Br^+ to pyrrole (fill in bonds and curly arrows):

in the 2-position

complete diagrams and show arrows

in the 3 position

complete diagrams and show arrows

Electrophilic attack on pyrrole is favored at the *2-position / 3-position* because the transition state preceding the first intermediate is more stabilized; this is a *kinetic / thermodynamic* argument.

The fundamental chemical postulate that indicates transition state energies are more closely related to the entity closest to them in terms of energy is *The Curtin-Hammett principle / Hammond's postulate*. This relates the kinetics of the process to the thermodynamics.

Pyrroles could undergo electrophilic aromatic substitution at either the position marked *a* or the one marked *b*. In fact, one of these is preferred because it has three resonance structures to delocalize the charge while the other has only two.

Deduce the preferred regiochemistry of electrophilic attack on pyrrole, and show the contributing resonance structures and the product.

$\longleftrightarrow$ $\longleftrightarrow$

_____   _____   _____

choose correct regiochemistry, show resonance structures, and electron flow that relates them using curly arrows

$\xrightarrow{-H^+}$

_____   _____

Pyrrole is *more / less* electron rich than benzene, hence it reacts *faster / slower* with electrophiles.

Draw structures on the line below to rank the following aromatic compounds in order of reactivity towards electrophiles: benzene, furan, thiophene, pyrrole.

_____→

least reactive   *most reactive*

Indole

Show all the resonance structures for the intermediate that would arise by adding Br⁺ to indole (fill in bonds and curly arrows):

in the 2-position

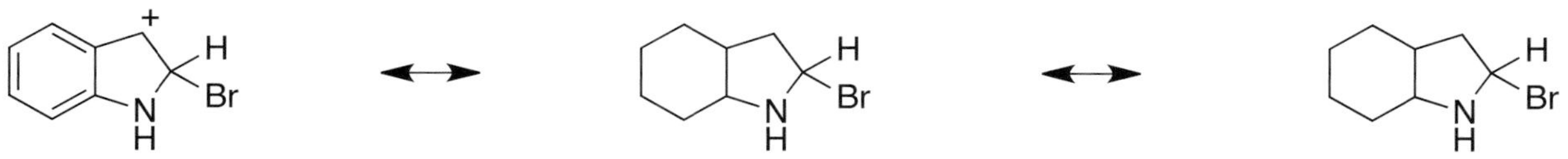

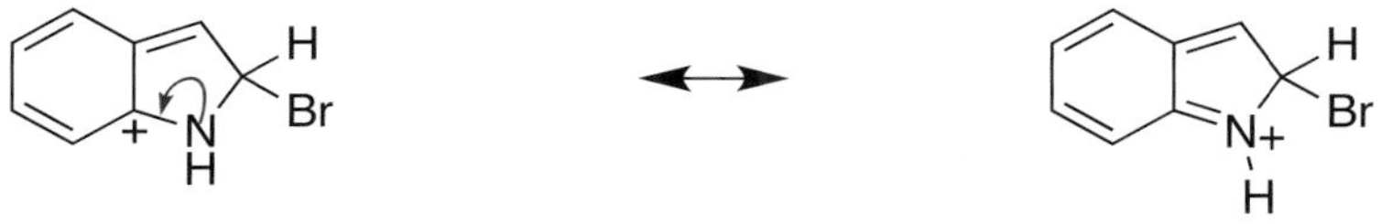

donation of the N-lone pair does / does not disrupt aromaticity of the benzene ring

---

in the 3 position

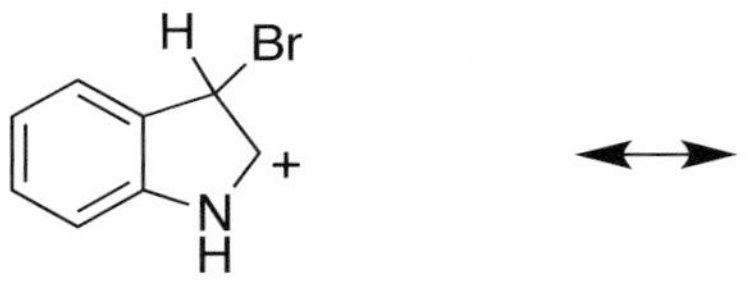

donation of the N-lone pair does / does not disrupt aromaticity of the benzene ring

From the reasoning above, indoles preferentially add electrophiles at the *2- / 3*-position because

_____

_____

_____

_____ .

7   Nucleosides And Nucleotides

from chapter(s) _____ in the recommended text

A Introduction

Focus

This section deals with identification of the DNA and RNA building blocks, how they base pair, and the mode of action of some nucleoside-based drugs and prodrugs.

not phosphate

X and Y variable

nucleoside

nucleotide

Reasons To Care

DNA encodes the proteins, and some critical fragments of RNA, on which all forms of life are based. Pairing of the heterocyclic bases in DNA and RNA is based upon a simple set of principles. The predominant role of nucleosides and nucleotides in the body is via interactions with DNA or RNA replicated enzymes such as polymerases.

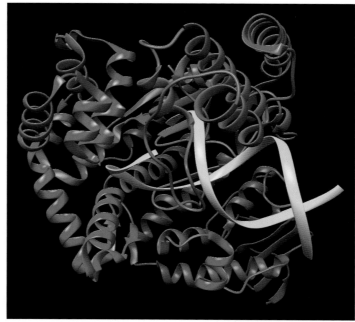

Figure 1. Interaction of Taq polymerase (red) with a modified DNA double strand (yellow).

A significant fraction of all pharmaceuticals are nucleosides, and the mode of action of these is mostly related to their interaction with DNA or RNA replicated enzymes. Some general and straightforward characteristics of nucleoside drug design are described.

Concepts

carbohydrates • heterocycles in Nature • elimination reactions • S_N1 in the context of protecting groups

Objective

This section is to describe DNA, RNA, how nucleosides may be phosphorylated, and how this impacts nucleoside drug design.

B Nucleosides

Draw the purine and pyrimidine *bases* (not the carbohydrate parts) associated with deoxynucleic acid (DNA), and with RNA (ribonucleic acid).

pyrimidine	*thymine* *DNA / RNA / both*	*cytosine* *DNA / RNA / both*	*uracil* *DNA / RNA / both*

purine	*adenine* *DNA / RNA / both*	*guanine* *DNA / RNA / both*

The sugar fragment of RNA is derived from *glucose / ribose / sucrose* in a *furanose / pyranose* form.

When the heteroatom at the anomeric position is *cis*-oriented to the CH_2OH group then that is a *β- / α-* anomer.

Bases in DNA and RNA are *β- / α*-anomers.

Draw the β- and α-anomers of ribofuranose, number the carbons from the anomeric position (C^1), and draw a generic structure for a *2-deoxy*ribofuranose of DNA using "B" to represent the base part, and the same for RNA.

α-D-ribofuranose	*β-D-ribofuranose*	*generic RNA*	*generic DNA*

C Nucleotides

Nucleoside refers to the carbohydrate and heterocyclic base component *with / without* a phosphate attached.

Nucleotides are nucleosides except they have the '-O or 3'-O incorporated into a *phosphate / carboxylic* esters.

Draw phospho- mono-, di- and triesters representing the alkyl groups attached as "R".

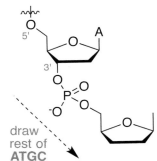

O
||
HO–P–OH
  |
  OH

phosphoric
acid

————————   ————————   ————————
phosphomonoester   phosphodiester   phosphotriester

Confusingly, **A**, **T**, **U**, **C**, and **G** symbols can be used to represent just the base in nucleosides and nucleotides, or whole nucleobase units. Units of DNA are connected by phospho *mono- / di- / tri*-esters.

RNA bases are connected by phospho *mono- / di- / tri*-esters.

Complete the following diagram to show a DNA fragment of the sequence.

CGTA has *the same / a different* structure to **ATGC**.

When reading DNA sequences, start at the *3'- / '-* ends and list towards the *3'- / '-* end.

Primes in these numbers mean they refer to *the sugar part / the heterocyclic base*.

The phosphorus atoms in RNA and DNA *are / are not* chiral in their dibasic state.

draw
rest of
ATGC

RNA is *more / less* stable than DNA because it has a 2'-*OH* that can cyclize onto the phosphorus giving a 2',3'-cyclic phosphate and displacing the '-O of the next residue.
Complete the following diagram to illustrate this cyclization; push electrons from the 2-OH, and show the two products (no intermediates).

The reaction shown above cannot happen with DNA because it has no *2'-OH / 3'-OH*.

In all organisms, excluding some viruses, genetic information is stored as deoxynucleic acid (DNA) sequences. That DNA information is *transcribed / translated* into RNA (ribonucleic acid) when genes are switched on, then *transcribed / translated* into proteins.

Complete the following (the number of *H*-bond donors and acceptors refers only to the parts highlighted).

A / T / G / C / U	*A / T / G / C / U*	*A / T / G / C / U*	*A / T / G / C / U*
# H-bond donors: 0 / 1 / 2 / 3	# H-bond donors: 0 / 1 / 2 / 3	# H-bond donors: 0 / 1 / 2 / 3	# H-bond donors: 0 / 1 / 2 / 3
# H-bond acc's: 0 / 1 / 2 / 3	# H-bond acc's: 0 / 1 / 2 / 3	# H-bond acc's: 0 / 1 / 2 / 3	# H-bond acc's: 0 / 1 / 2 / 3

refers to H-bond acceptors and donors, as indicated in structure

Due to geometric constraints in base-pairing, T and U can only use one of their H-bond acceptors.
Based on the hypothesis that bases with two correctly oriented H-bond donors and one H-bond acceptor should pair with others that have two correctly oriented H-bond acceptors and one H-bond donor:

G should *H*-bond most effectively with *A / T / C / U* in DNA

G should *H*-bond most effectively with *A / T / C / U* in RNA

A should *H*-bond most effectively with *G / T / C* in DNA

A should *H*-bond most effectively with *G / U / T / C* in RNA

C should *H*-bond most effectively with *A / T / G / U* in DNA

C should *H*-bond most effectively with *A / T / G / U* in RNA

T should *H*-bond most effectively with *A / T / G / U* in DNA

Complete the following illustration of the *H*-bonding arrangement in double stranded DNA or RNA. To achieve this, orient the structure such that the bonds to the sugar residues point towards the bottom right.

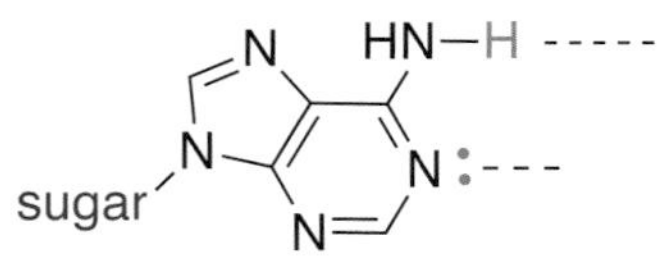

A H-bonded to U

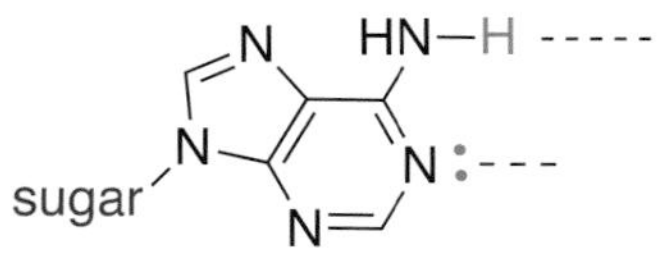

A H-bonded to T

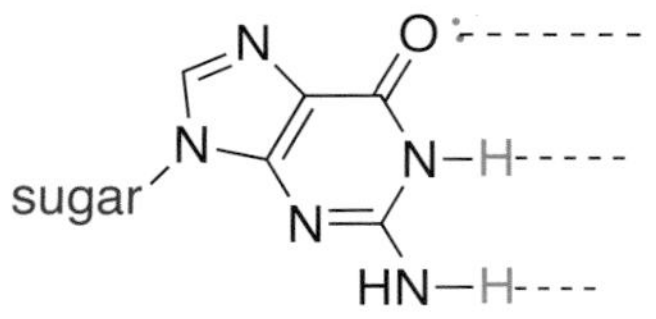

G H-bonded to C

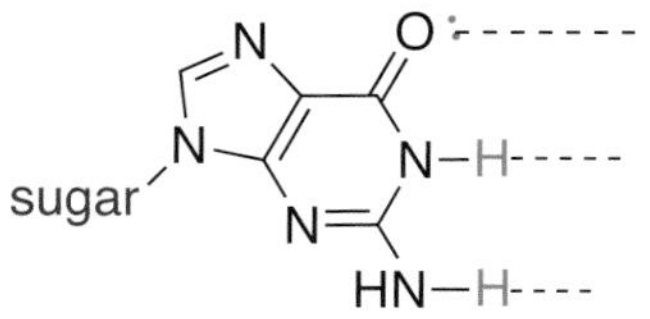

G H-bonded to A
does / does not match well

Draw the H-bonds between the DNA bases on the diagram below, and identify each base by writing A, T, G, or C beside them.

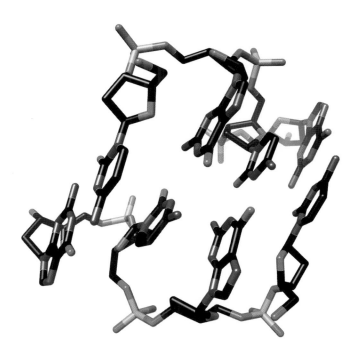

H-bonding between A and T is *stronger / weaker* than between G and C because there are *less / more* inter-residue H-bonds.

The diagram below is a representation of a crystal structure of a double stranded DNA. A phosphodiester linkage, various **T**, **A**, **G**, **C** nucleobases (perhaps more than once) and a ribose fragment (**R**) are highlighted in purple boxes. Label each box with one of those indications.

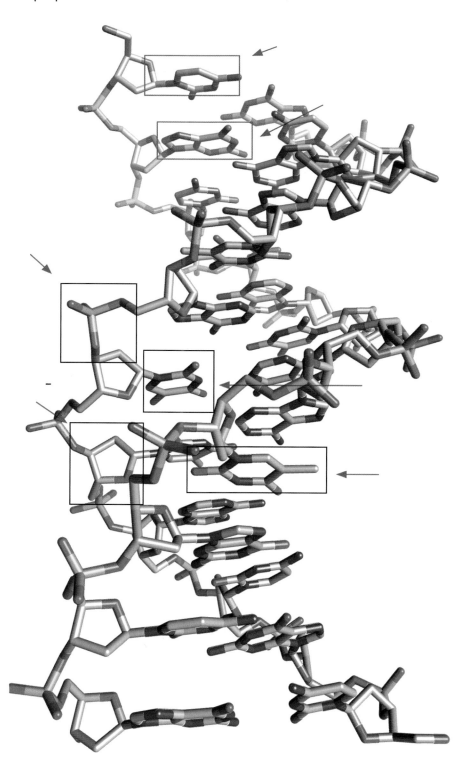

In double stranded DNA the *riboses / phosphodiesters / nucleobases* are on the perimeter, and the *riboses / phosphodiesters / nucleobases* form the core.

Deamination in living organisms converts **C** into *U / T* bases.

DNA tends to exist in a *left / right* handed helical arrangement using the *H*-bonds outlined above.

DNA handedness is normally *the same as / opposite to* helices in proteins.

RNA has *more / less* regularly ordered secondary structures than DNA.

Bases of *RNA / DNA* can be distinguished by the prefix "d" as in **dA, dT, dC,** and **dG**, relative to **A, U, C,** and **G** used for *RNA / DNA*.

Mono-, di-, and tri-phosphates are abbreviated to "MP", "DP", "TP" suffixes. Phosphates referred to by these abbreviations are on the '-O unless something specifically indicates otherwise. Complete the structures of the following nucleotides.

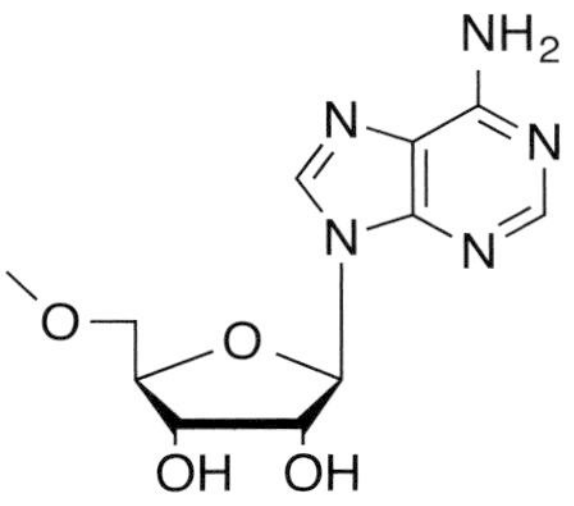

AMP

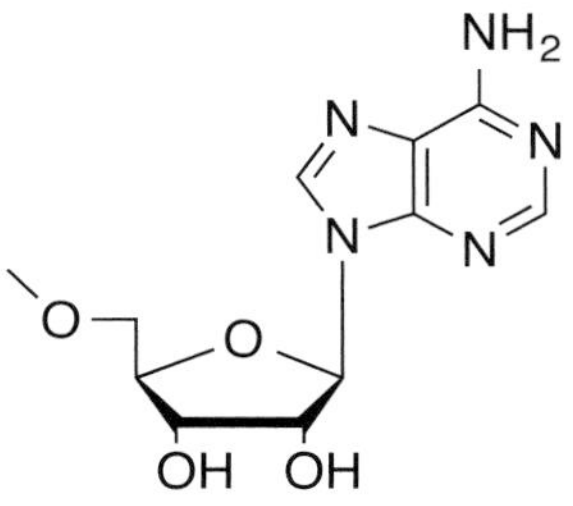

ADP

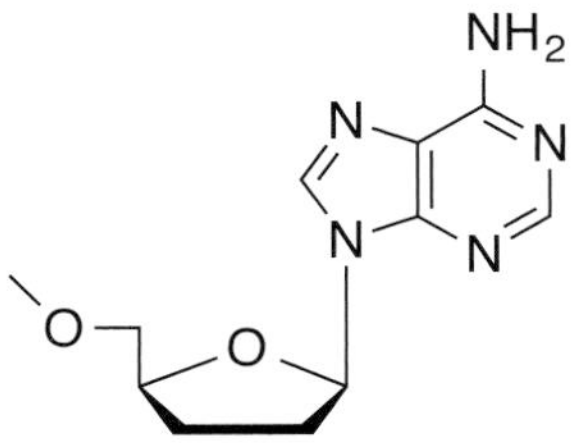

dAMP

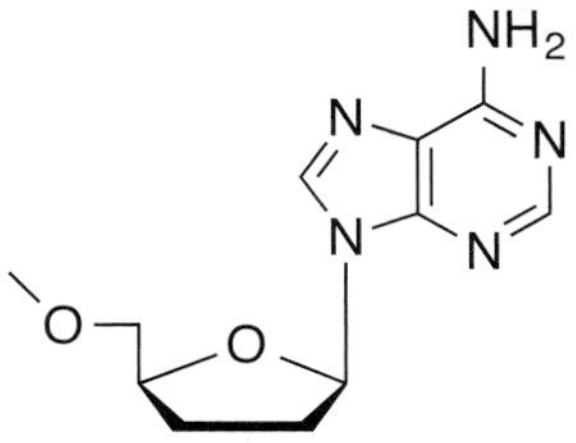

dATP

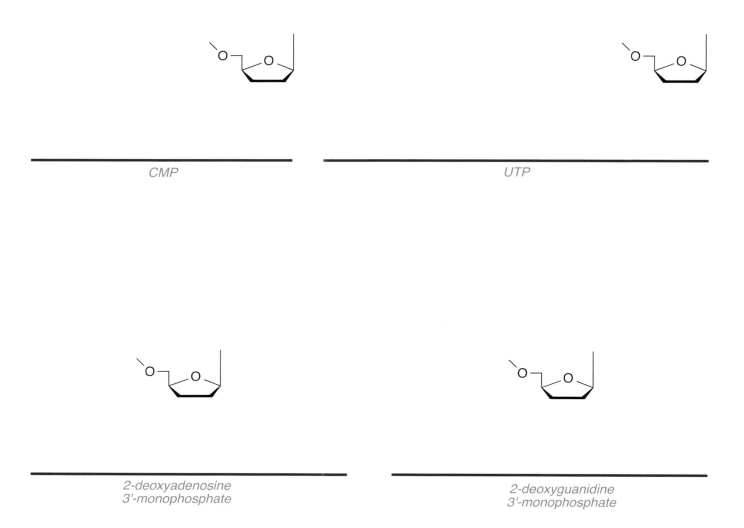

CMP

UTP

2-deoxyadenosine
3'-monophosphate

2-deoxyguanidine
3'-monophosphate

DNA synthesis is mediated by enzymes called *polymerases / isomerases*.

These enzymes build a second *parallel / antiparallel* strand of DNA to complement the first by selecting the complementary triphosphate (dATP, dGTP, dCTP or dTTP) to pair with the next base in the sequence, and add it to the *' - / 3'- end* of the growing strand.

A *mono- / di- / tri-* phosphate is lost whenever a base is added by a polymerase.

Genes are turned on by interacting with *promoter / switcher* proteins bind to *promoting / switching* regions of DNA sequences to initiate synthesis of a complementary strand of *messenger / transfer* RNA.

Syntheses of mRNA stops at particular three-base sequences of DNA called *stop codons / condoms*.

Exon / intron DNA encodes for proteins, and regions that do not are called *exons / introns*.

Non-encoding regions in the transcribed mRNA are cut out in the process of RNA *exorcism / splicing*.

In the ribosome, *messenger / transfer* RNA reads three base codons on the *messenger / transfer* RNA and converts this sequence information into proteins.

D Nucleoside Drugs

Viruses are particularly vulnerable to nucleoside drugs because these are somehow incorporated into replicating viral *DNA / proteins* thereby *arresting / enhancing* replication in a similar way to incorporation of dsDNA in Sanger sequencing (next section).

Zidovudine	*Lamivudine*	*Acyclovir*	*Penciclovir*
treatment of HIV		*treatment of herpes*	

However, the substrates for DNA replicating enzymes are *nucleosides / nucleotide triphosphates*.

This implies the nucleosides shown above enter cells and are converted to triphosphates by *kinase / esterase* enzymes as illustrated below.

*cell permeability
likely /unlikely*

*cell permeability
likely /unlikely*

*cell permeability
likely /unlikely*

The fact that the above process does not occur for all nucleosides limits development of new antivirals. The first step, formation of *mono- / tri*-phosphates is the difficult one in many cases.

Cell membranes are partially composed of lipids (fats) with phosphate head groups hence they tend to be impermeable to *negatively / positively* ionized species.

Nucleotide monophosphates *do / do not* tend to permeate easily into cells, so these *do / do not* make effective anti-viral drugs.

*Sofosbuvir
treatment of hepatitis C*

Nucleotide Prodrugs

A solution to the problem outlined above is to design nucleoside derivatives that are *neutral / negatively* **charged**, *cell permeable / unable to cross cell membranes* and which form nucleoside monophosphates inside cells.

A(n) *prodrug / antidrug* is one introduced in a protected form, then converted to the active form inside the body.

One such drug is Sofosbuvir, illustrative of a class of drugs called *ProTides / AntiTides*.

Complete the following sequence to rationalize how drugs like Sofosbuvir are converted to their active monophosphate forms in the body.

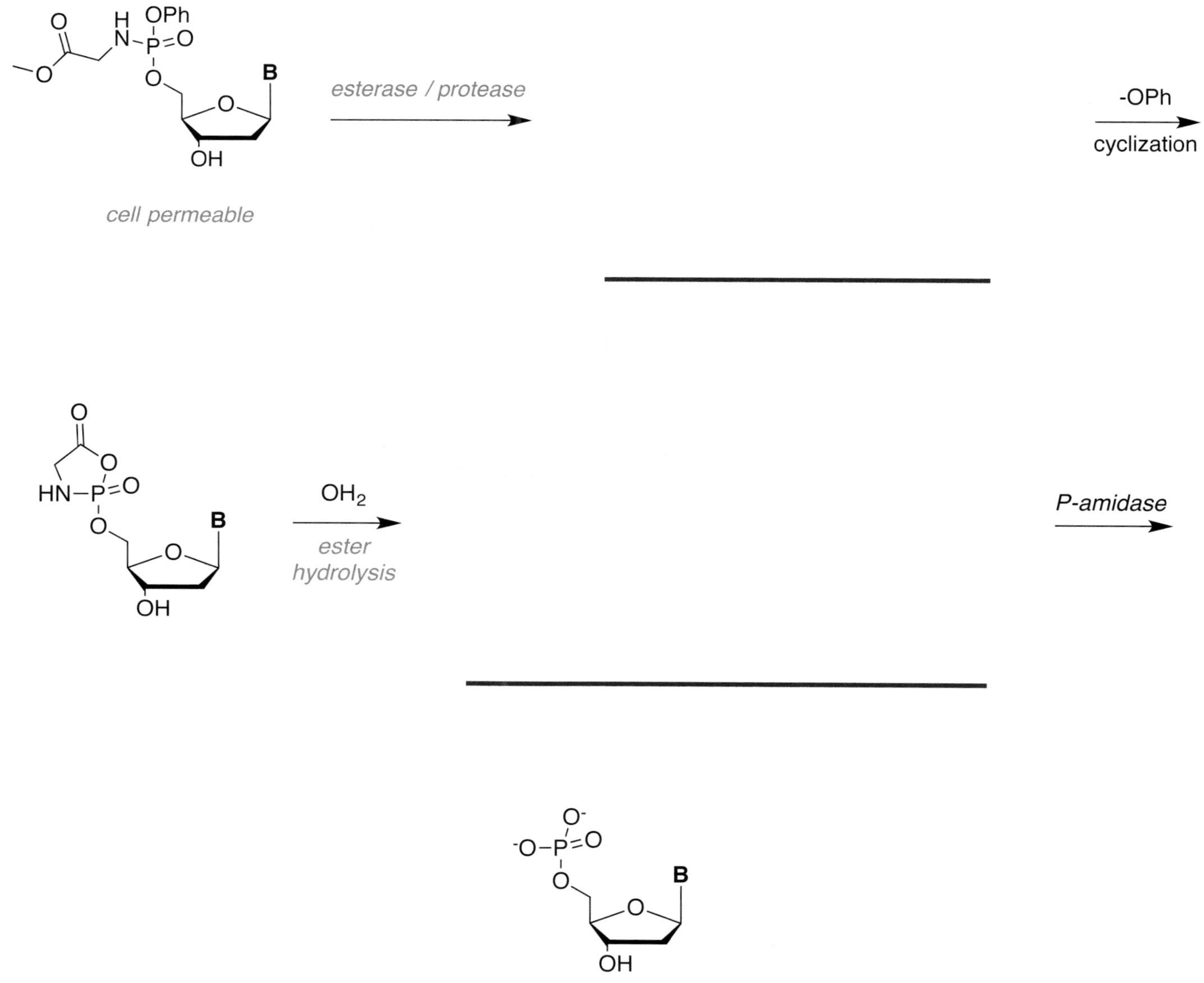

esterase / protease

cell permeable

-OPh
cyclization

OH₂
ester
hydrolysis

P-amidase

8 DNA Synthesis And Sequencing

from chapter(s) _____ in the recommended text

A Introduction

Focus
This section deals with how DNA is synthesized and sequenced.

Reasons To Care
DNA encodes the proteins, and some critical fragments of RNA, on which all forms of life are based. The first step in being able to sequence DNA on a large scale was chemical syntheses of primers in polymerase-mediated reactions. This facilitated high throughput sequencing of DNA, first by methods like Sanger's, then via next generation methods like sequencing by synthesis.

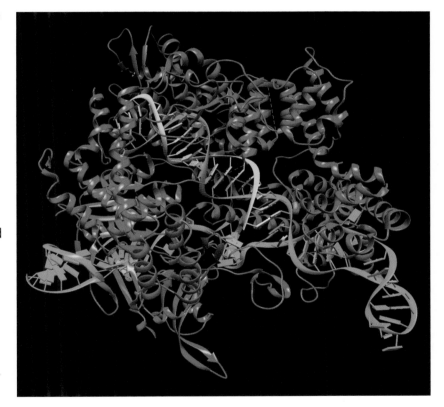

Figure 1. The Cas9 endonuclease complexed with single guide RNA (green) and target DNA (yellow).

Now it is possible to sequence genomic DNA using methods that have become so efficient that it is feasible to correlate genetic differences in individuals with their proclivity to contract certain diseases. Now the forefront is manipulating genomic DNA using the CRISPR system featuring the endonuclease Cas9 (Figure 1). Together, these efforts have caused a paradigm shift in biomedicinal chemistry.

Concepts
carbohydrates • heterocycles in Nature • H-bonding • elimination reactions • S_N1 in the context of protecting groups

Objective
This section is to describe DNA, RNA, and select features of DNA-synthesis, sequencing methods, and nucleotide drug design.

B Chemical Synthesis Of DNA

Protecting Groups

DNA sequences of 100 bases, or even longer can be made so efficiently via automated syntheses that even chemists tend to buy DNA strands from commercial suppliers.

One of the most widespread methods for DNA synthesis involves protection of the '-O with a trityl (CPh_3) group and $P - O$ bonds with O-cyanoethyl.

Draw a mechanism for cleavage of a trityl ether with acid by completing the scheme below.

$$\text{Ph} \diagdown \overset{O_{\diagdown R}}{\underset{\diagup}{\diagup}} \quad \xrightarrow{H^+} \quad \qquad \longrightarrow \qquad + \quad C^+Ph_3$$

quenched in reaction medium

This is a S_N1 / S_N2 reaction, "seen through the eyes of the protecting group".

If two of the phenyl groups in the trityl were replaced with 4-methoxybenzene, (to give dimethoxytrityl, DMT) the reaction above would be *easier / harder* because the cation formed would be *more / less* stabilized by resonance.

Draw a mechanism for removal of a cyanoethyl group from a phosphodiester with a base.

$$R^{-O}\diagdown \underset{\overset{\|}{O}\,\,\overset{\|}{O}}{\overset{}{P}}\diagdown^{O}\diagdown \overset{H}{\diagup}\diagdown_{\displaystyle \equiv N} \quad \xrightarrow{NH_3} \qquad \longrightarrow \qquad + \quad \diagup\!\!\diagdown_{\equiv N}$$

carbanion

This is an *E1cb / E2* reaction, also "seen through the eyes of the leaving group".

Circle the cyanoethyl group and put a square around the dimethoxytrityl group in the following protected nucleoside.

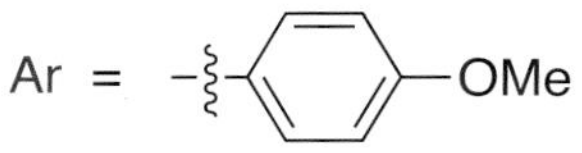

Ar = —OMe

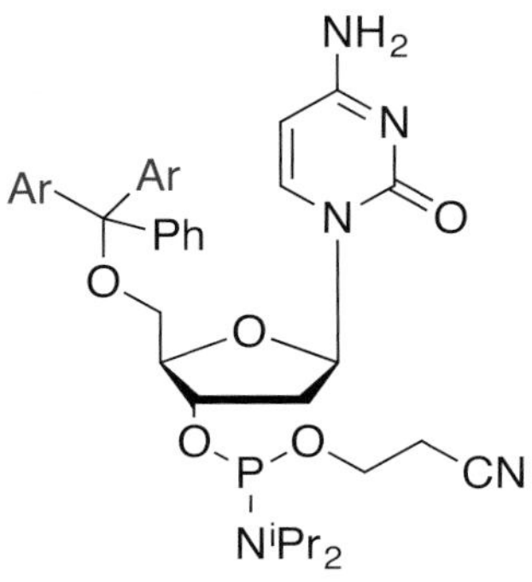

Exocyclic amine groups in the bases **G**, **A**, and **C** must be protected to withstand the conditions of DNA synthesis. Draw the following protected bases in the same style as **T** below (*ie* just show the word "sugar" and draw the base):

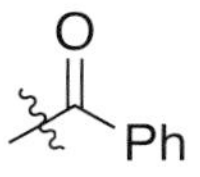

benzoyl
Bz

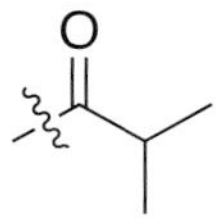

iso-butyryl
CO*i*Bu

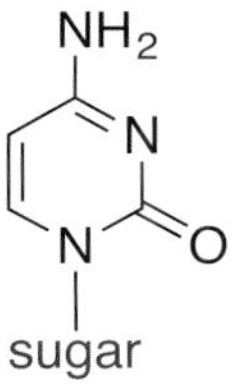

no protection
required

_____

N-Bz **C**

_____

N-Bz **A**

_____

N-iso-butyryl **G**

The Phosphoramidite Method

The first step in the *phosphoramidite method* is to 3'-anchor the first base to a support, typically a glass bead. Show the product of this acylation reaction, then that after removal of the 'DMT.

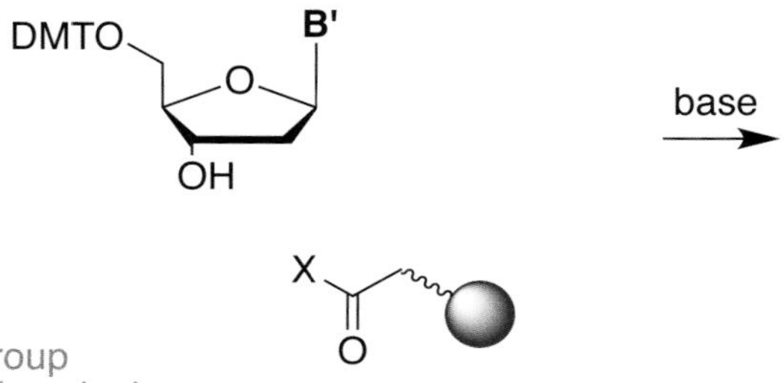

X = leaving group
B' = protected nucleobase

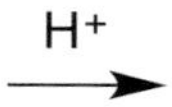

base

⟶

H+

⟶

The key coupling step in the phosphoramidite method involves activation of the next phosphoramidite base to be coupled via protonation at $P - NR_2$; complete the following mechanistic outline of that process.

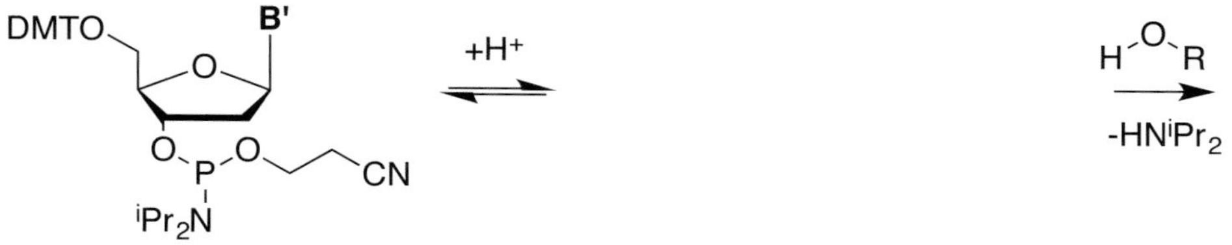

+H+

⇌

$-HN^iPr_2$

⟶

The acid used must be mild enough to promote the reaction without removing the DMT group. *Tetrazole / pyridine / pyrrole* is a preferred acid for this step.

Coupling, as shown above, is the first step in each cycle of DNA syntheses, and the last is DMT removal. Between these comes *oxidation / reduction* of the *P*-atom in the phosphoramidite.

Complete the following structures to show that.

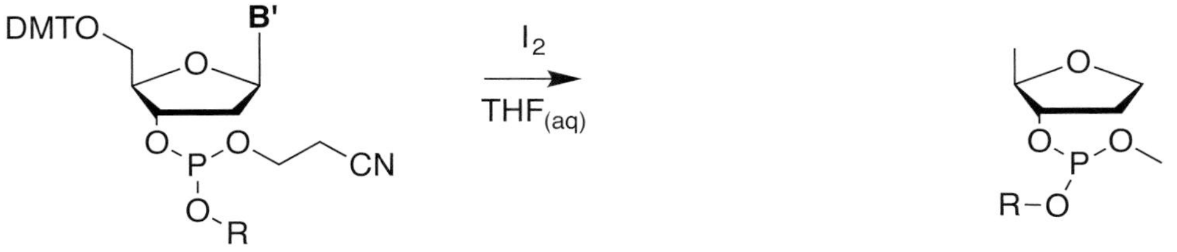

phosphotriester

The oxidation state of the starting phosphoramidite is *0 / 1 / 2 / 3 / 4 / / 6*, and that of the phosphodiester product is *0 / 1 / 2 / 3 / 4 / / 6*.

After repetitive couplings of phosphoramidite, oxidation, then DMT removal, DNA is cleaved from the support by treatment with ammonia; this *also removes / does not remove* the *iso*-butyryl, benzoyl, and cyanoethyl protecting groups.

Complete the following diagram to show the product of this reaction (recall **B'** stands for *protected* base).

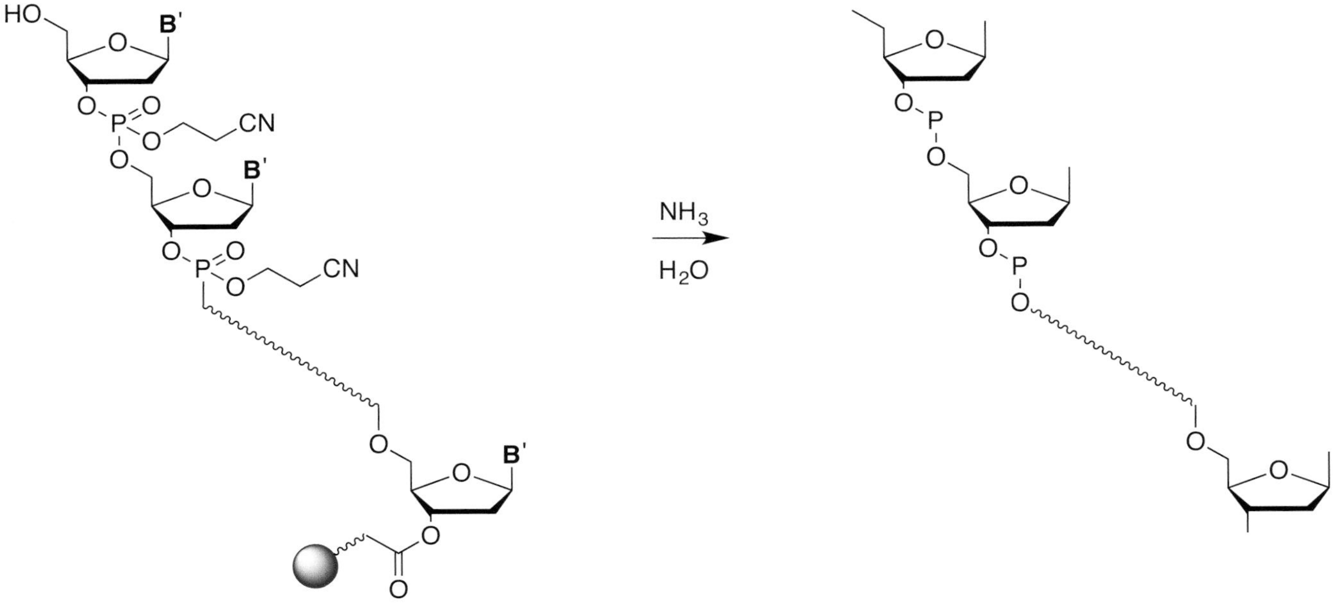

Indicate the reagents for each step in the phosphoramidite synthesis of DNA below, and show the structure of tetrazole.

c DNA Sequencing

Sanger's Method

Polymerase enzymes recognize double strand (ds) DNA in which the -terminus extends beyond the 3' terminus of the short strand. In this case the short strand is called a *lead / primer / initiator / template* and the long strand is called the *lead / primer / initiator / template*.

Circle the dNTP that the polymerase incorporates in the short strand opposite a **T** residue, and draw a rectangle around the one it adds when a **G** is encountered.

dNTP

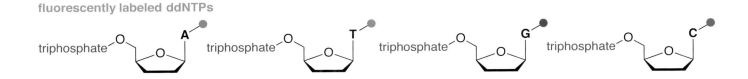

Imagine a polymerase that is not perfectly selective and sometimes incorporates differentially fluorescently-labeled 2',3'-didexoynucleotide triphosphates (**ddNTPs**, as shown below) *even if the complementary dNTP is present.*

fluorescently labeled ddNTPs

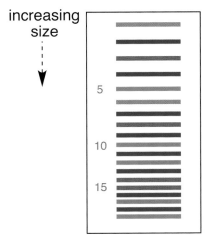

increasing size

If the polymerase is supplied all the **dNTPs** *and* carefully determined amounts of the labeled-**ddNTP** then it may occasionally incorporate a **ddNTP** instead of a **dNTP**, *eg dCTP* opposite *A / T. G / C* and the synthesis *can still / cannot* progress beyond that point.

In that experiment, when the polymerase replicates the primed DNA, each terminated complementary strand produced contains *only one / more than one / all the fluors*.

If the terminated DNA strands are then separated according to size, *ie* to the number of nucleobases incorporated, then the order of incorporation *can / cannot* be read, and the sequence of the complement *can / cannot* be deduced.

Deduce the sequence of 19 bases incorporated as revealed by the gel to the left that separates according to size.

5'-_____-3'

Deduce the sequence of the template DNA after the primer.

5'-_____-3'

Sequencing By Synthesis (SBS)

Genomic sequencing is now performed via several different *next generation* methods, of which sequencing by synthesis (SBS) is one.

Envisage a polymerase, a primed DNA template (to be sequenced), and *only* the four derivatives shown below mixed (the colored circles represent fluorescent dyes attached to the bases via a cleavable linker).

fluorescently labeled, blocked, dNTPs

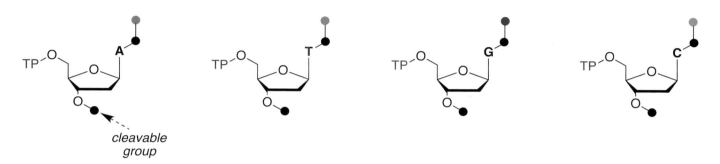

cleavable group

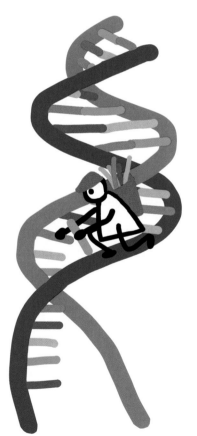

Further synthesis *would / would not* occur after addition of one base, just as in the Sanger method.

The identity of that base and its complement *could / could not* be deduced from fluorescence.

If the cleavable group were cleaved, the fluor would be lost, and further synthesis *would / would not* be possible because the 3'-OH was also liberated.

Incorporation, fluorescence read-out, and cleavage could be repeated until the signal disappeared into the noise for the read-out steps. If n bases could be sequenced via this route, and in Sanger sequencing, say, n could be sequenced, then the most efficient approach would be *Sanger / SBS*.

Imagine the same very long DNA template molecules (*eg* genes), somehow anchored to a solid surface, in such a way that groups of these molecules, *or even single molecules*, had constant locations that could be remembered and uniquely addressed. These could then be treated with different primers that would anneal to *the same / different* parts of the DNA template.

If polymerase and the four fluorescently-labeled, blocked dNTPs were added, then SBS could be performed to give *the same / different* sequences on all the primed templates. Consequently, y different parts of the DNA could be sequenced at the same time.

The efficiency of Sanger sequencing n (see above) is greater than the efficiency of the SBS method, *ie* y x $n / n^2 / y^2$ if y is <. However, y can be >> because a huge number of spatially addressable DNA templates can be supported. Consequently, SBS can be made to be much *more / less* efficient than Sanger sequencing.

Reduction Of Azides By Phosphines And Azidomethyl Protection In SBS

3'-Protection of the fluorescently labeled-ddNTPs described above has to be compatible with the polymerase selectivity, and it is important that dsDNA *dissociates / remains annealed* when this group is removed, hence the conditions required must be *harsh / gentle*. One protection strategy is based on reduction of azides with phosphines, *ie* the *Staudinger / N₂ displacement* reaction.

Complete the following mechanism, including curly arrows if they are not shown.

At the beginning of this reaction, in triphenyl phosphine, the *P*-atom is in the *+3 / +4 / + / +6*, but at the end it is *+3 / +4 / + / +6*, *ie* it has been *oxidized / reduced*.

It follows that the azide in this reaction has been *oxidized / reduced*.

126

Draw the products of the following reactions.

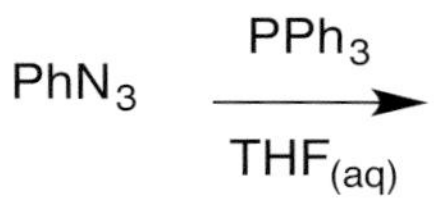

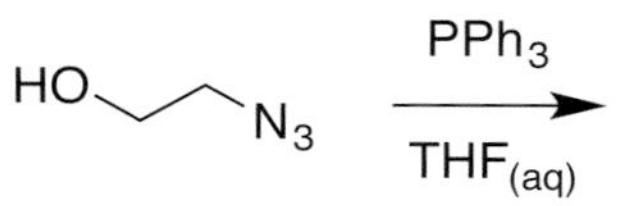

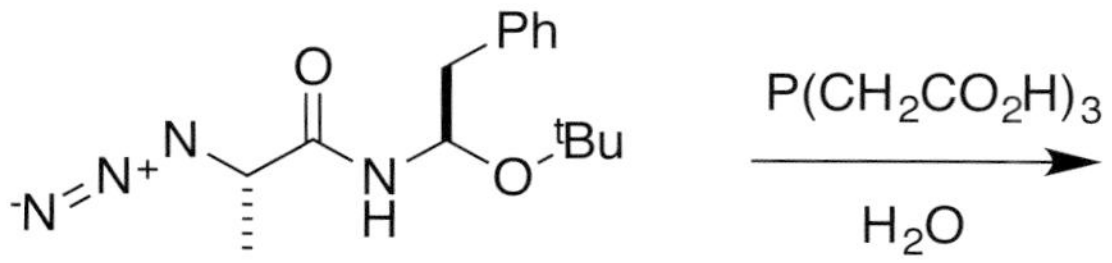

PhN$_3$ $\xrightarrow[\text{THF}_{(aq)}]{\text{PPh}_3}$

HO$\diagup\diagdown$N$_3$ $\xrightarrow[\text{THF}_{(aq)}]{\text{PPh}_3}$

-N≡N⁺=N... (structure with Ph, O, tBu) $\xrightarrow[\text{H}_2\text{O}]{\text{P(CH}_2\text{CO}_2\text{H)}_3}$

Draw the intermediate in the following reaction, and superimpose curly arrows on it to express electron flow that implies the final product can form.

(sugar structure with R, O, B, N$_3$) $\xrightarrow[\text{H}_2\text{O}]{\text{P(CH}_2\text{CO}_2\text{H)}_3}$

$\xrightarrow[\substack{-\text{H}_2\text{CO}\\-\text{NH}_3}]{\text{H}_2\text{O}}$ (sugar structure with R, O, B, O-H)

aminal

The alcohol protecting group in the last reaction, *azidoethyl / azidomethyl,* is one frequently used in sequencing by synthesis approaches.

Part 2:
Towards Understanding Esterases And Proteases

9   Ester Hydrolysis And Transesterification

from chapter(s) _____ in the recommended text

A Introduction

Focus

Mechanistically, acid-mediated hydrolysis of esters is like acid-mediated formation of hydrates from aldehydes and ketones, except that esters can lose alcohols, as illustrated below. Thus hydration of esters mirror hydration of aldehydes or ketones, except they are at one oxidation state above.

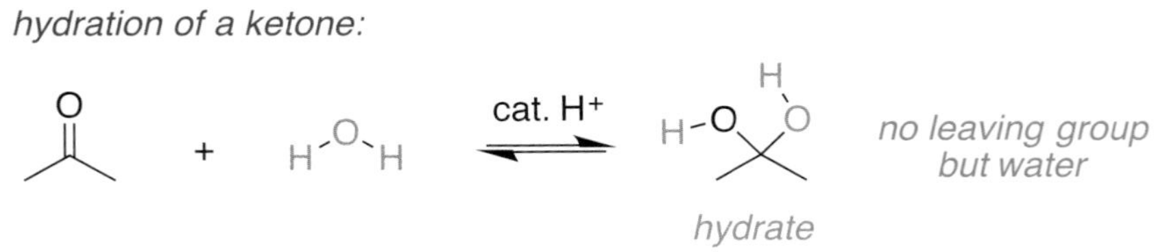

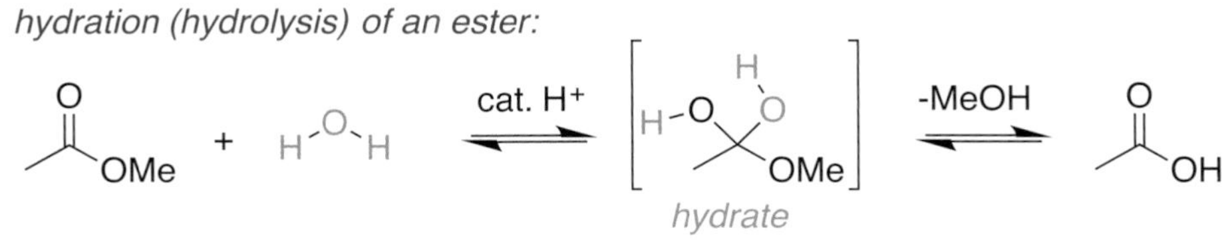

hydration of a ketone:

hydrate

no leaving group but water

hydration (hydrolysis) of an ester:

hydrate

This section is about ester hydrolyses, and closely related transesterification reactions.

Reasons To Care

Esterases, enzymes that catalyze ester hydrolysis, have evolved mechanisms to fine-tune substrate selectivities for key molecules in transmission of signals through the nervous system, and for digestion of lipids. Even though the details of these mechanisms are complex and intriguing, the underlying chemical process is the same.

Concepts

acids and bases • curly arrows for electron flow • esterases

Objective

To show the connections between hydration of ketones and aldehydes and hydrolyses of esters.

B Reactivity

Esters are *more / less* reactive than acid chlorides in acylation of nucleophiles.

Under neutral conditions, neutral nucleophiles, which tend to be *more / less* nucleophilic than similar anionic ones, *do / do not* tend to react with esters.

Conditions that are acidic enough to protonate the carbonyl group of esters cause it to be *more / less* reactive hence *more / less* likely to react with some neutral nucleophiles.

Consider whether an ester carbonyl is more or less likely than an amine to be protonated. The following step is *likely / unlikely*.

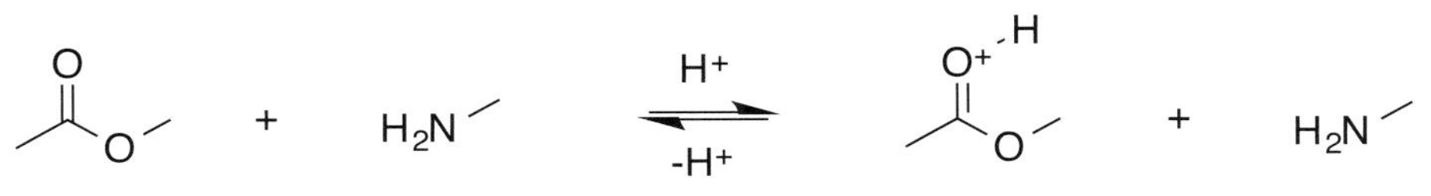

Reactions of esters with amines therefore *are / are not* likely to proceed under acidic conditions.

C Acid-mediated Hydrolysis

A Common Mechanism

Fill in the products or intermediates in the following reaction mechanism.

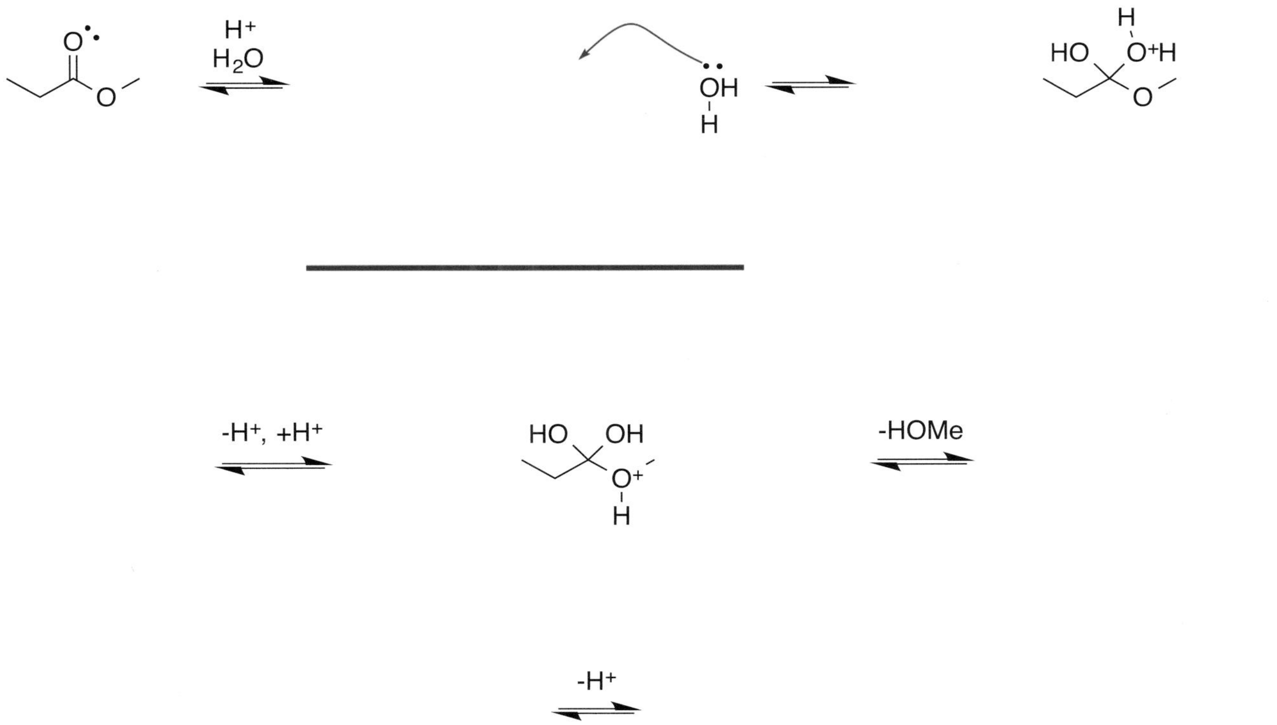

Esters react with water under acidic conditions to give *carboxylic acids / alcohols / amides*; these reactions are acylation of *protons / water*.

Reaction Scope

Give both products of the following reactions.

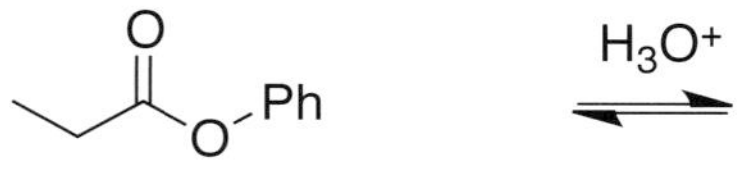

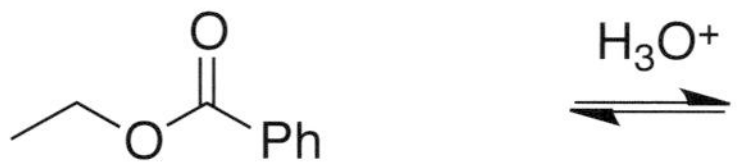

$$\xrightarrow{H_3O^+}$$ +

———————————————————————

$$\xrightarrow{H_3O^+}$$ +

———————————————————————

$$\xrightarrow{H_3O^+}$$ +

———————————————————————

$$\xrightarrow{H_3O^+}$$ +

———————————————————————

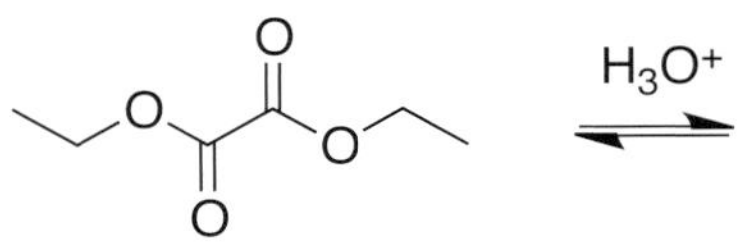

H_3O^+

H_3O^+

These reactions are *reversible / irreversible*, so carboxylic acids can react with alcohols under acid conditions to give esters. Excess reagents are used to force the reactions in the desired direction (*eg* water or alcohol as the solvent).

Predict the products of the following reactions when one of the starting materials is used in excess.

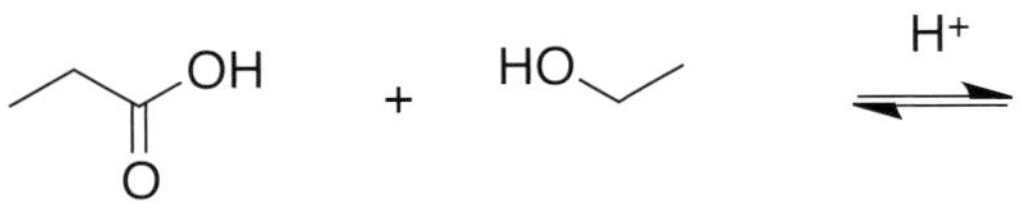

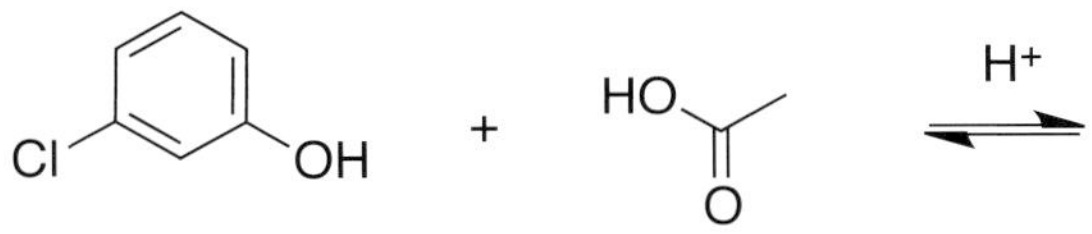

H^+

H^+

Phthalic acid + HO— (methanol), excess, H⁺ ⇌ _____

(Z)-but-2-ene-1,4-diol + AcOH, excess, H⁺ ⇌ _____

4-hydroxybutanoic acid, H⁺ ⇌ _____

6-hydroxyhexanoic acid, H⁺ ⇌ _____

Show the alcohols and carboxylic acids that would be used to make the following esters.

⟹

_____

⟹

_____

Explain why the last product is thermodynamically favored over the other possibilities: _____

_____ .

Hydrolysis Of *tert*-Butyl Esters Occurs Via A Different Mechanism

Hydrolysis of *tert*-butyl esters is special, because protonation of the carbonyl group can lead to formation of a(n) *unstable / stable* carbocation and the carboxylic acid is formed *with / without* attack of water on the carbonyl group.

Complete the following mechanism to show this.

⇌   ⇌   +

_____   _____

Carbocations generated in the reaction above can react in various ways; show the S_N1 nucleophilic substitution and E1 elimination reaction products.

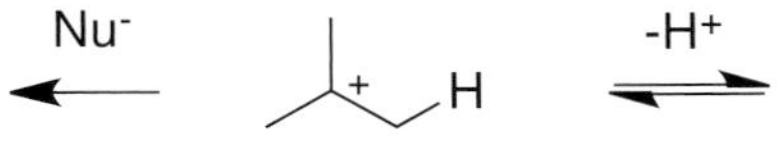

$$Nu^- \longleftarrow \quad \text{(isobutyl cation)} \quad H \overset{-H^+}{\rightleftharpoons}$$

_____   _____

Predict the acylation products of the following reactions (TFA is *trifluoroacetic acid*).

MeCOO^{t}Bu $\overset{H^+}{\longrightarrow}$

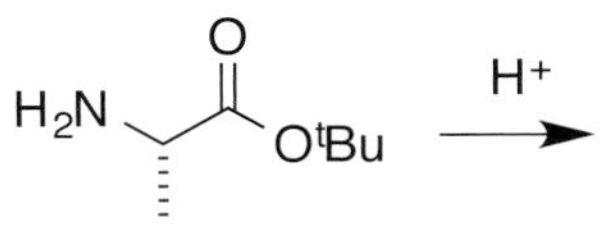

H_2N—(alanine structure)—O^{t}Bu $\overset{H^+}{\longrightarrow}$

_____   _____
                                              alanine

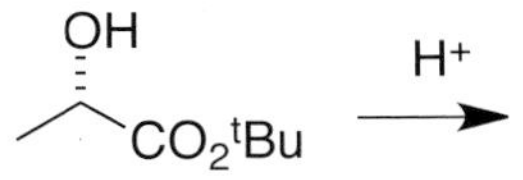

(lactic acid tert-butyl ester structure) OH / CO$_2^t$Bu $\overset{H^+}{\longrightarrow}$

tert-butyl glycine $\overset{TFA}{\longrightarrow}$

_____   _____
       lactic acid   *glycine*

H_2N—(valine structure)—O^{t}Bu $\overset{H^+}{\longrightarrow}$

H_2N—(leucine structure)—O^{t}Bu $\overset{H^+}{\longrightarrow}$

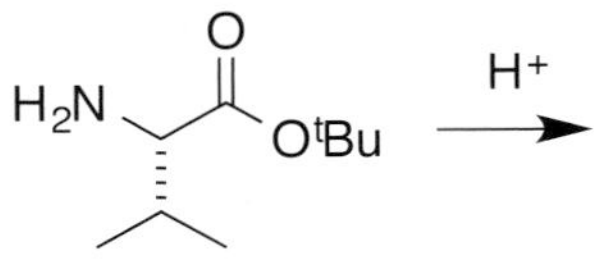

_____   _____
        valine 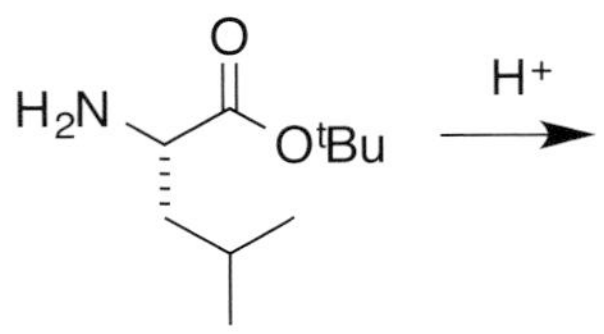   *leucine*

The type of mechanism illustrated above may be applicable to any ester (not exclusively ^tBu) that can dissociate to form a stable *carbanion / carbocation*.

Rank the following esters in order of ease of acid-catalyzed hydrolysis *via a mechanism that generates benzylic carbocations* (1 is easiest, 6 is least).

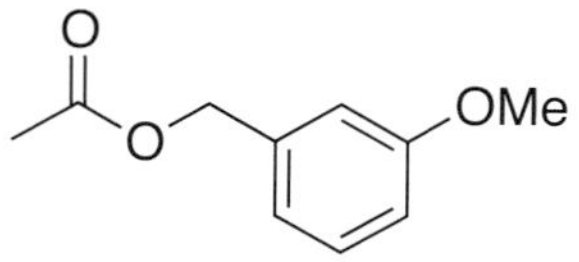

1 / 2 / 3 / 4 / 5 / 6

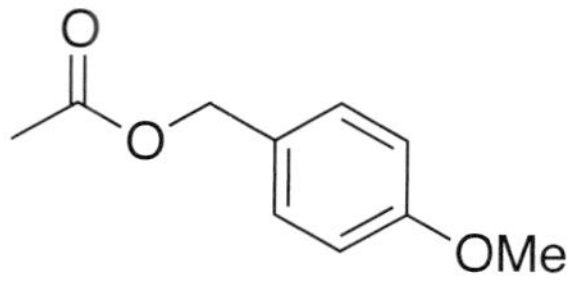

1 / 2 / 3 / 4 / 5 / 6

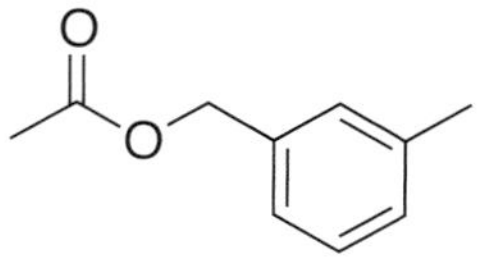

1 / 2 / 3 / 4 / 5 / 6

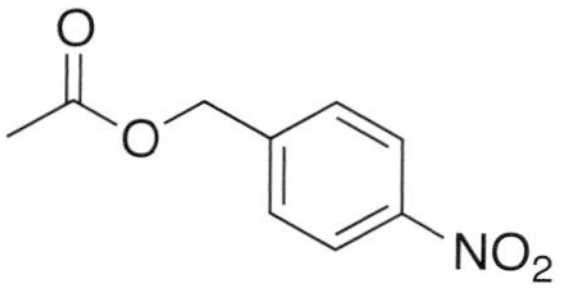

1 / 2 / 3 / 4 / 5 / 6

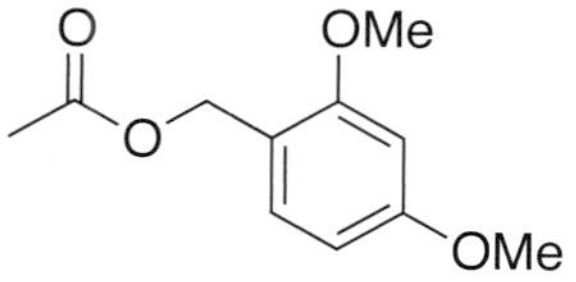

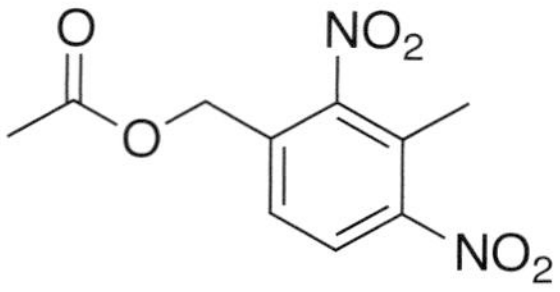

1 / 2 / 3 / 4 / 5 / 6

1 / 2 / 3 / 4 / 5 / 6

D Base-mediated Hydrolysis

A Common Mechanism

Esters hydrolyze to acids under *basic* conditions, but the mechanism is different; the carbonyl group is not protonated first, and there is no need to invoke proton transfer steps involving the nucleophile reagent. Use curly arrows in the following mechanistic pathway to show the electron flow.

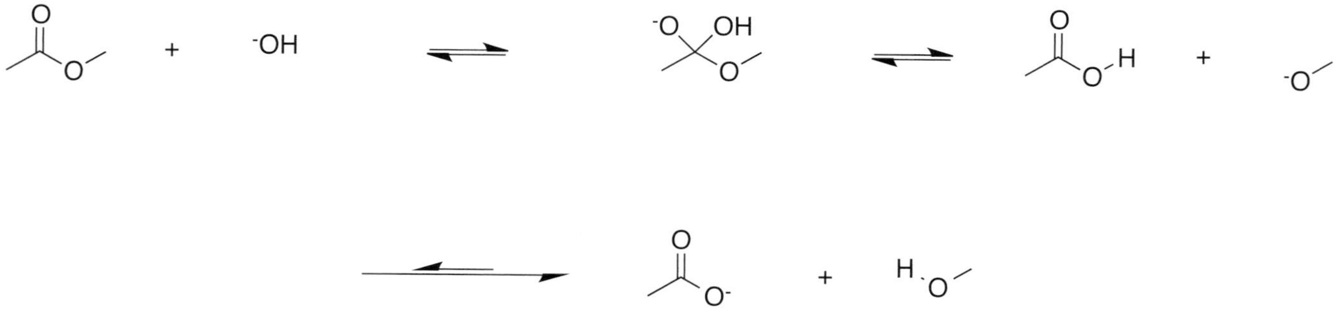

Technically, the last step is reversible like all the others, but the equilibrium constant vastly favors formation of carboxylate salt and alcohol.

Base-mediated ester hydrolyses are effectively *reversible / irreversible*, but *acid-mediated* ester hydrolyses are *reversible / irreversible*.

A common mistake is to show protons under basic conditions. Push arrows for the following mechanism and circle the error.

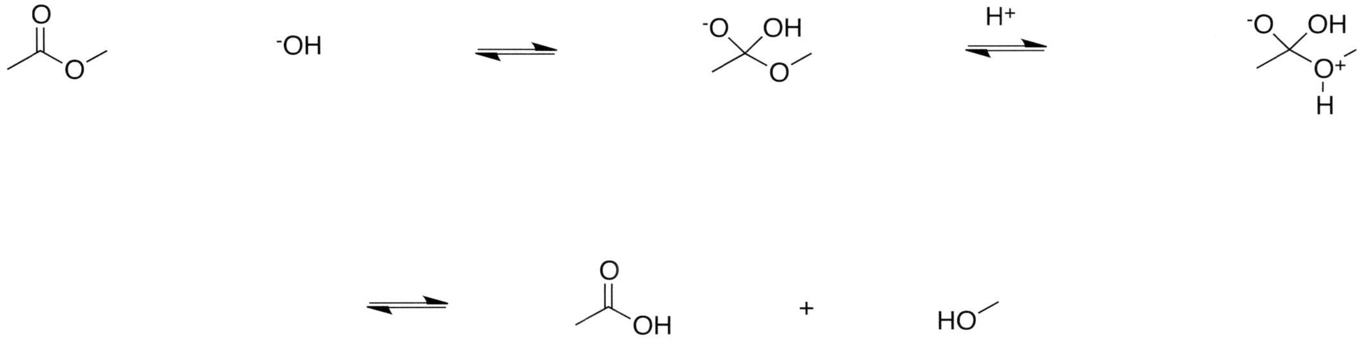

Hydroxide is a good base and a poor nucleophile so the following reaction is *likely / unlikely*.

Similarly, this one is *likely / unlikely*.

Similarly, this one is *likely / unlikely*.

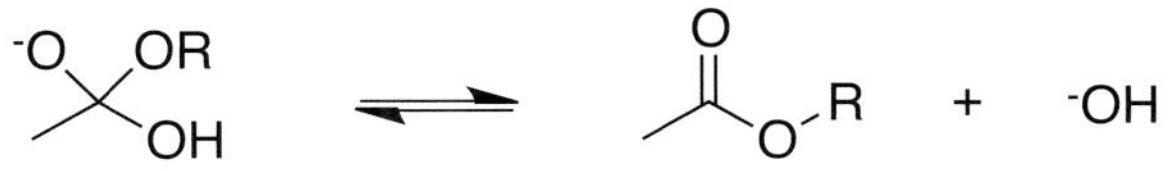

Complete the following mechanism for base-mediated ester hydrolysis by showing arrows, missing intermediates, and products after an acidic work-up.

O
‖
Et   OPh   ⁻OH ⇌   ⇌   +

_____   _____

Deduce the ester starting material and products in the following base-mediated ester hydrolysis.

HO⁻ ⇌   ⁻O   OBn   (i) -OBn
            ⤬   ───────────→   +   HOBn
                 OH   (ii) -H⁺/+H⁺

_____   _____

Show ^{18}O in the product of the following base-mediated ester hydrolysis by shading it.

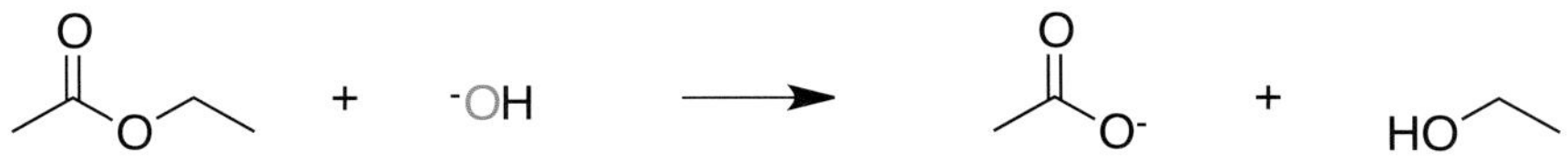

Observation of the heavy oxygen in the carboxylate *would / would not* be consistent with the following mechanism that features S$_N$2 displacement (shade the hydroxyl-O to indicate where it goes).

Observation of the heavy oxygen in the carboxylate *would / would not* be consistent with the following mechanism that features S$_N$1 dissociation (shade the hydroxyl-O to indicate where it goes).

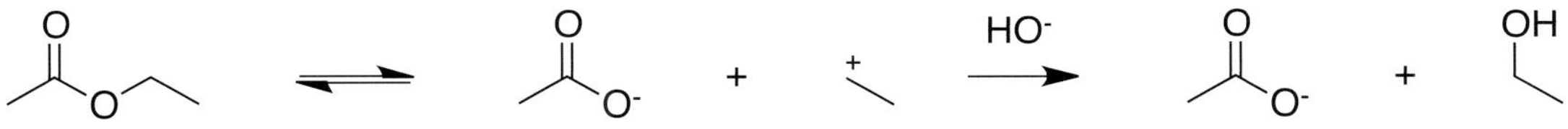

Reactions involving isotopes like ^{18}O *can / cannot* be used to exclude certain mechanistic possibilities. Hydrolysis of a glycerol triester (fats) gives a triol and three carboxylates, like this:

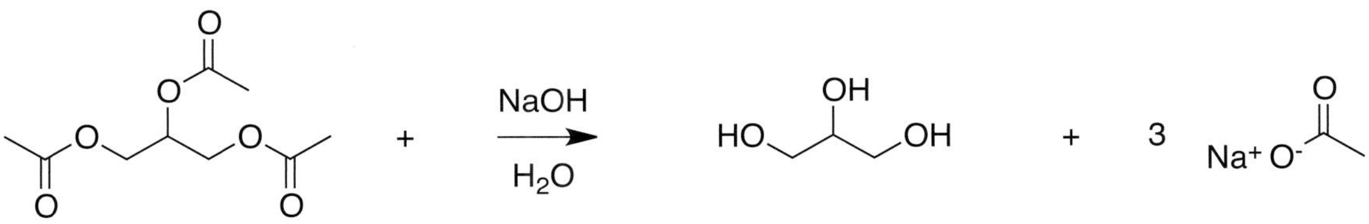

If those carboxylates have long alkyl chains they are referred to as *soaps / acids / nitriles*. Hydrolysis to give fatty acids (or their carboxylates) under basic conditions is called "saponification."

Predict the products formed from *saponification* of the following fats and oils (glycerol triesters).

OAc
—OCOnPr $\xrightarrow[\text{H}_2\text{O}]{\text{NaOH}}$
OCOnBu

_____

$\xrightarrow[\text{H}_2\text{O}]{\text{NaOH}}$

_____

Soaps in aqueous solutions form *micelles*. Describe what micelles are:

_____

_____

Draw a micelle formed from a collection of long-chain fatty acids represented like tadpoles with negatively charged heads.

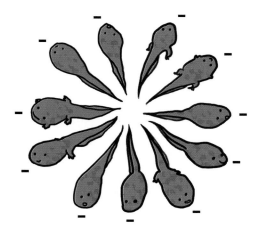

_____

cartoon of a micelle

E Transesterification Reactions

Mechanism Under Acidic Conditions

Under acidic conditions, esters can undergo *transesterification* with alcohols through a process similar to acid-catalyzed hydrolysis.

Transesterification is a process wherein an ester is transformed into *an amide / a nitrile / another ester*.

Fill in the products/intermediates and arrows in the following mechanism.

Examples Of Transesterifications

Transesterification reactions swap an alcohol for the *alkoxide / carbonyl* of an ester.

Predict the products of the following transesterification reactions where, in the intermolecular reactions, excess alcohol is used.

(structure) + EtOH $\xrightarrow{\text{H}^+}$

(lactone structure) $\xrightleftharpoons[\text{cat. H}_2\text{O}]{\text{H}^+}$

check by assigning (R)- or (S)-configurations

(propionate OMe structure) $\xrightleftharpoons{\underset{}{\overset{\text{EtOH}}{\text{H}^+}}}$

(o-toluate OEt structure) $\xrightleftharpoons{\underset{}{\overset{\text{MeOH}}{\text{H}^+}}}$

$\xrightleftharpoons[\text{MeOH}]{\underset{}{\overset{\text{Et}^{17}\text{OH}}{\text{H}^+}}}$ (acetate ^{17}OEt structure)

(pentenol structure) OH $\xrightleftharpoons[\text{AcOH}]{\underset{}{\overset{\text{AcOMe}}{\text{H}^+}}}$

Mechanism Under Basic Conditions

Under basic conditions, transesterification occurs by reaction of the ester carbonyl with *alcohols / alkoxides*.

Provide curly arrows to indicate the electron flow on the mechanism below.

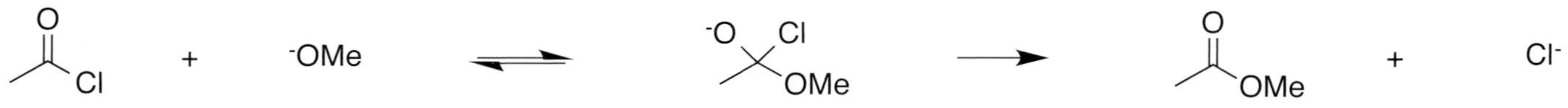

Draw a similar diagram for addition of ethoxide to methyl acetate, and carefully indicate if each step is *reversible* or *irreversible*.

show arrows

Examples Of Base-Mediated Transesterifications

Predict the products of the following reactions performed in a large excess of alcohol solvents.

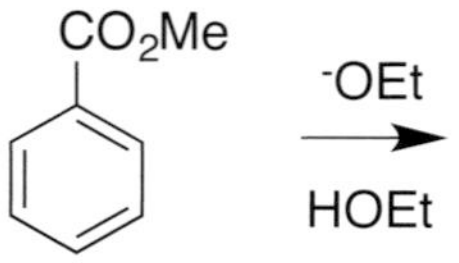

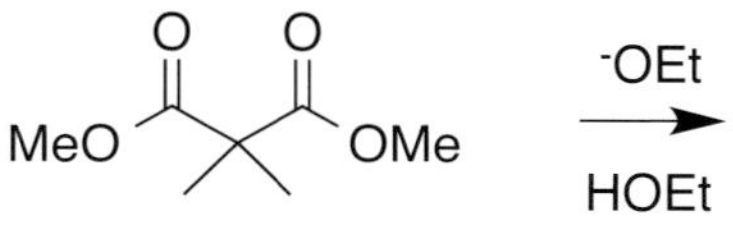

$$HCOOBn \xrightarrow[HOMe]{^-OMe}$$

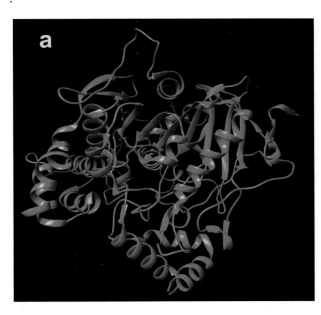

Base-mediated hydrolyses of hindered esters are slow because the reaction involves rate-limiting formation of a *more / less* hindered sp^3 / sp^2 / sp-hybridized intermediate; indicate which of the reactions above will be slow. *Acid-mediated* hydrolysis of the same ester *would / would not* be similarly affected.

F   Some Ester Hydrolyses In Biochemistry

In The Central Nervous System

Enzymes that hydrolyze ester bonds in biochemistry are called *proteases / esterases / polymerases*.

Identify the enzyme ACHE (**a**) by considering the reaction it catalyzes, **b** (Figure 1).

ACHE stands for: _____. Check your answer on the web, hence answer the following questions

.

a

b

$$\xrightarrow{ACHE}$$

acetyl choline

Figure 1. **a** ACHE structure. **b** Reaction mediated by ACHE.

In neurotransmission, presynaptic neurons liberate acetylcholine which migrates across the synaptic cleft and binds *acetylcholine receptors / pig liver esterase / TrkA* on the postsynaptic neurons.

ACHE hydrolyzes bound acetylcholine giving acetic acid and *cholesterol / choline / chlorophyll*.

Acetylcholine is only released into the synaptic cleft for the next neural impulse if its concentration in the synaptic cleft is low. Consequently, if it is not cleared by *ACHE / pig liver esterase*, accumulation of acetylcholine can result in *paralysis / pneumonia*.

Well known inhibitors of ACHE include *aspirin / Tylenol / mustard gases / nerve gases*.

In The Digestive System

Search lipases on the web.

Lipids contain *long alkyl chains / lysine residues / amides*; they feature in *alkaloids / triglyceride* fats.

Esterases, including lipases, are *substrates / catalysts*.

Hydrolyses and transesterification reactions featured in this section are accelerated under acidic or basic conditions. Esterases act under *basic / neutral / acidic* conditions by placing water atoms near hydrogen-bond acceptors to make them better *nucleophiles / electrophiles* and carbonyls of ester substrates near hydrogen bond donors making the carbonyls better *nucleophiles / electrophiles*.

Enzymes in general, have highly specialized active site cavities; because of this, lipases, for instance, *can / cannot* hydrolyze one ester in the presence of another as shown in Figure 2b, because one ester only fits well in the active site.

Lipases play a role in *metabolism of triglycerides / removing sugars* from the body.

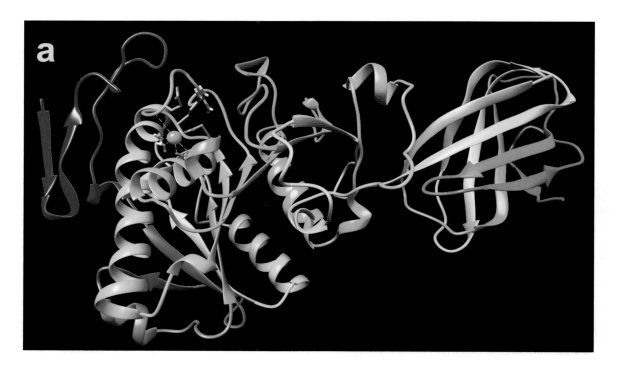

R¹, R², R³ long alkyl chain

Figure 2. a Structure of a lipase. **b** Hydrolysis of triglyceride.

Some esterases retain their activities in alcohol solvents and may mediate *amide bond formation / amide bond hydrolyses / transesterifications*.

Examples of such enzymes include the *proteases / lipases*.

10 Hydrolysis And Dehydration Of Amides

from chapter(s) _____ in the recommended text

A Introduction

Focus
This section is primarily about adding water to amides to hydrolyze them into amines and acids.

Reasons To Care
Proteases cleave amide bonds in peptides and proteins. They play critical roles in many different biological pathways, and preventing their action with *protease inhibitors* is a common strategy in biomedicinal chemistry. Mechanisms by which proteases selectively catalyze cleavage of certain amide bonds are detailed and complex, but the fundamental chemical mechanism for amide hydrolysis is similar throughout.

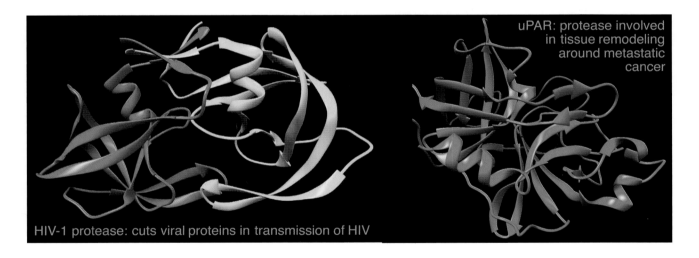

Concepts
acids and bases • curly arrows to depict electron flow • protonation of amides in hydrolysis • proteases

Objective
This section covers the chemical mechanisms for hydrolysis of amides and nitriles, and how amide hydrolysis relates to proteases.

B Reactivity Of Amides

Amides are *more / less* reactive than acid chlorides in acylation reactions because chloride is a better leaving group than NH_3 or NH_2^- (or substituted derivatives of these).

Similarly, amides are *more / less* reactive than esters in some acylation reactions because alkoxides are better leaving groups than amide anions, NH_2^- or NR_2^-.

Amides tend to be flat with *sp / sp^2 / sp^3* hybridized nitrogen atoms, whereas the alkoxide oxygen of esters is *trigonal / pyramidal* and *sp / sp^2 / sp^3* hybridized; this indicates the nitrogen is *more / less* electron donating in an amide than the alkoxide oxygen of an ester.

For the amide and ester shown below, the energy barrier for rotation is greater for *a / e* than *a / e*.

A ^{1}H NMR spectrum of the amide above will show *1 / 2 / 3* NCH_3 resonances at ambient temperature and *1 / 2 / 3* at elevated temperatures.

Under acidic conditions, however, amides are *more / less* easily protonated than esters, leading to activation of the carbonyl.

Amide oxygen atoms are *more / less* basic than the *N*-atoms because resonance stabilization is only possible when the *O-* is protonated, not the *N-*.

Complete the following diagrams, with curly arrows, to show preferred sites of protonation of esters and amides, and how the cations formed are resonance stabilized.

c Hydrolysis Of Amides

Acid-catalyzed hydrolysis of amides involves protonation of the carbonyl group, addition of water to give a *trigonal planar / tetrahedral* intermediate, proton transfer, then loss of amine.

Draw the mechanism for acid-mediated hydrolysis of ethanamide.

Under these acidic conditions, the by-product of the reaction above is H_2O / NH_4^+ / NH_3, and the transformation is *irreversible / reversible* because _____
_____
_____

Uncatalyzed amide hydrolysis reaction cannot proceed under neutral conditions because _____
_____
_____.

Use accurate curly arrows to show the mechanism for acid-mediated hydrolysis of benzamide.

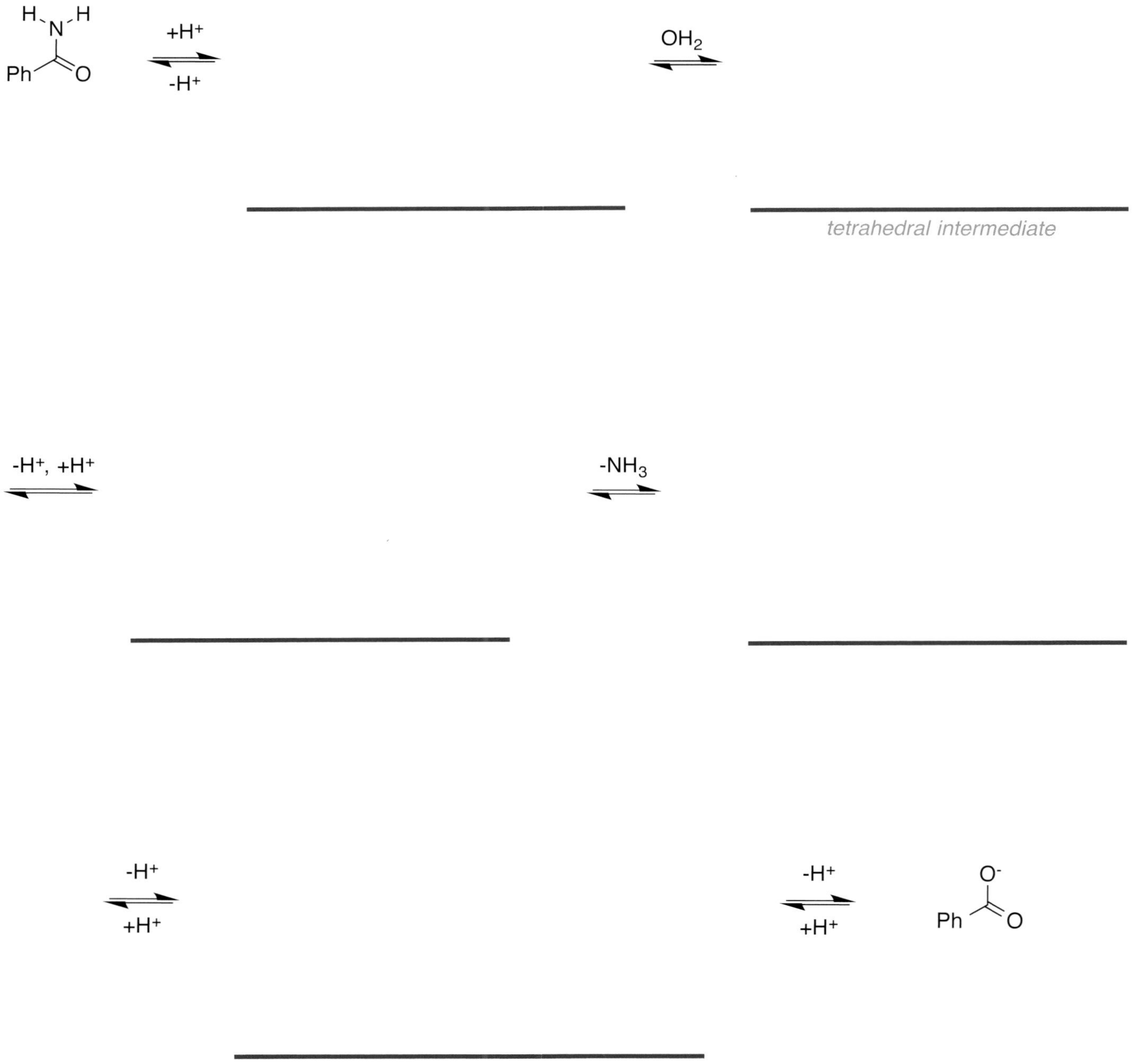

H—N—H

Ph—C=O   +H⁺
        ⇌
          -H⁺   OH₂
                                                ⇌

_____   _____
                                    tetrahedral intermediate

-H⁺, +H⁺   -NH₃
⇌   ⇌

_____   _____

        -H⁺   -H⁺   O⁻
        ⇌   ⇌ |
        +H⁺   +H⁺   Ph—C=O

_____

Draw the mechanism for hydrolysis of 2-methylbutanamide.

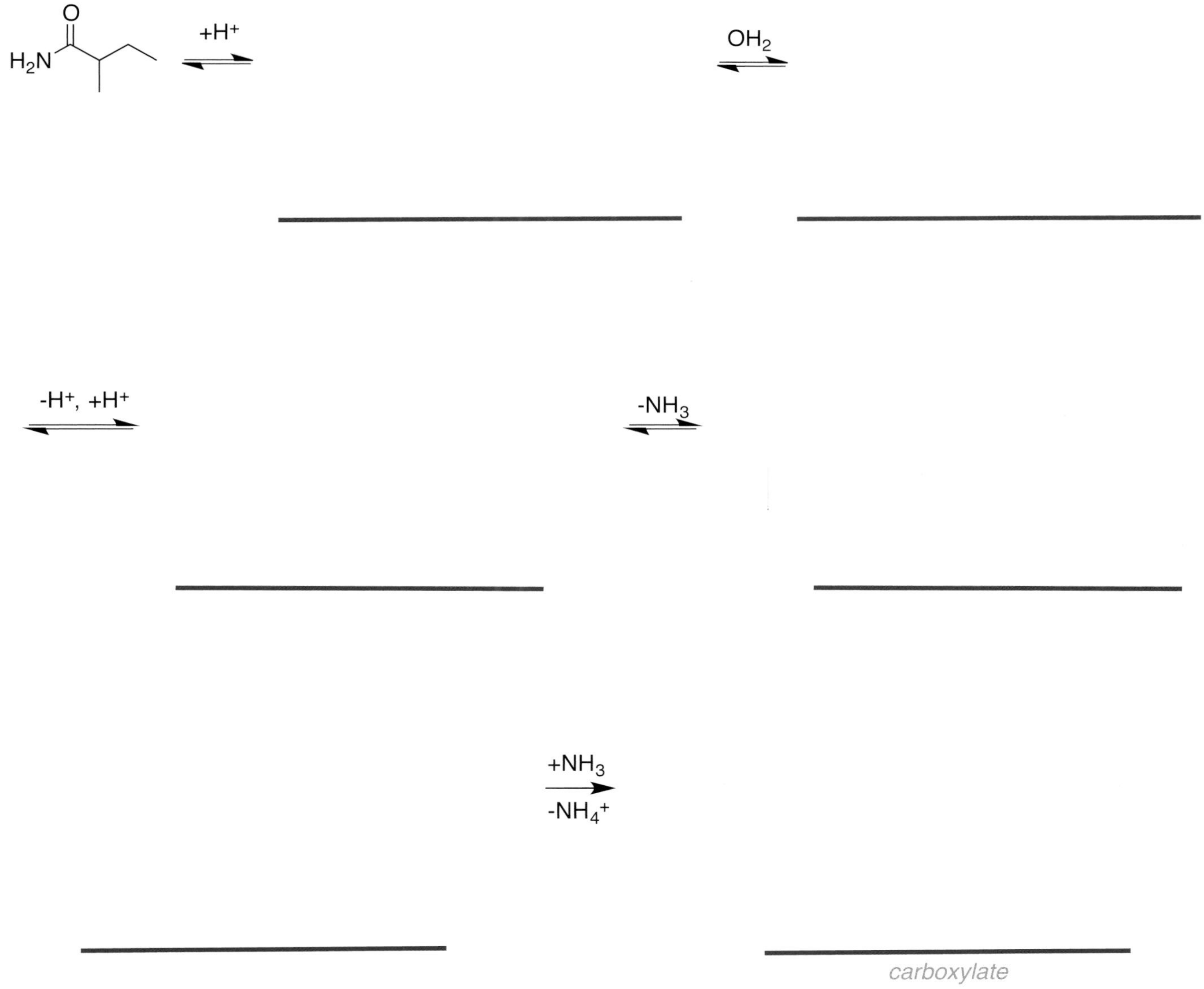

H₂N—C(=O)—CH(CH₃)—CH₂CH₃   +H⁺ ⇌   OH₂ ⇌

_____   _____

-H⁺, +H⁺ ⇌   -NH₃ ⇌

_____   _____

+NH₃
─────→
-NH₄⁺

_____

_____
carboxylate

Show the products of the following reactions.

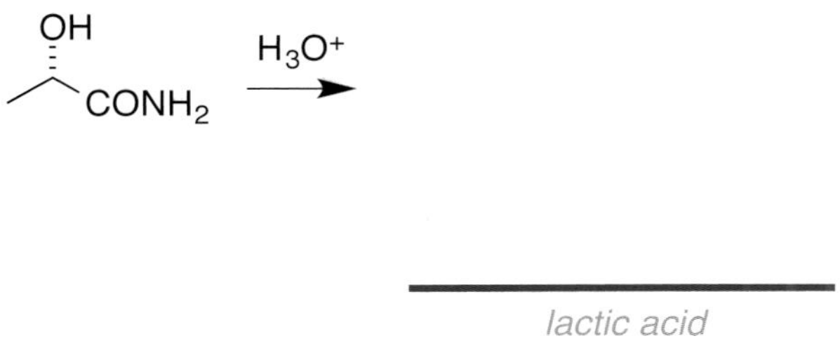

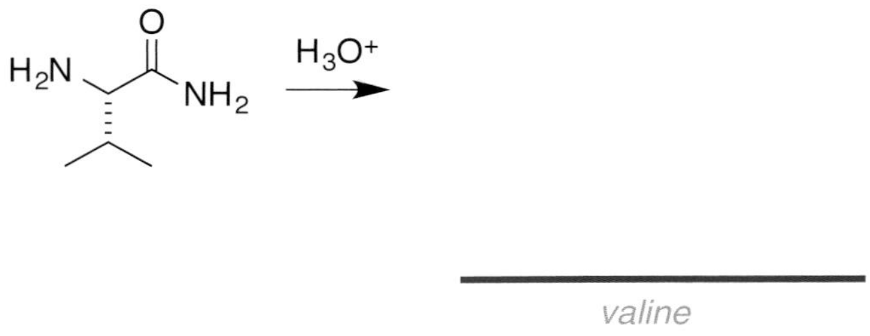

OH
|
CH₃—CH—CONH₂   H₃O⁺ →

H₂N—CH(CH(CH₃)₂)—C(=O)—NH₂   H₃O⁺ →

_____   _____
lactic acid   *valine*

152

D Proteases

Function

Enzymes that mediate hydrolysis of esters are called *proteases / nucleases / esterases* while amide hydrolysis is promoted by *proteases / nucleases / esterases*.

Proteases cleave amide bonds at pH *<<7 / ~7 / >>7* hence in living organisms they cleave peptides or proteins into fragments.

Catalytic / stoichiometric cleavage of amide bonds by proteases in near-neutral aqueous media is possible because these *enzymes / transcription factors / growth hormones* encapsulate their substrates, placing them in environments where amide carbonyls can be activated via *heating / hydrogen bonding* and nucleophiles can be activated by basic atoms in the cavity.

Proteases *do / do not* cleave every available amide bond in all proteins and peptides.

Instead, protease *active / building*-sites recognize shapes of the peptide or protein substrates, and the amino acid side-chain residues (like $R^1 - R^3$ in Figure 1 below) around the particular amide that is cleaved.

Figure 1a shows the structure of a protease called caspase 1. If caspase 1 selectively cleaves a peptide at the site indicated in Figure 1b, draw the hydrolysis products that would be produced.

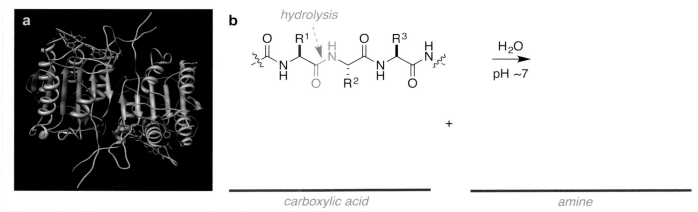

Figure 1. **a** Structure of caspase 1. **b** A generic substrate for proteases.

Too much caspase 1 is implicated in neuronal cell death because this enzyme *assembles / degrades* proteins that are important for cell survival.

Complete the diagram below by showing curly arrows that depict the key step in collapse of a tetrahedral intermediate in a peptide hydrolysis to amine and carboxylic acid products.

Catalysis

Catalysis is primarily a *kinetic / thermodynamic* phenomenon.

Clearly show the *activation energy barrier*, and *intermediate* on the profile below for amide hydrolysis.

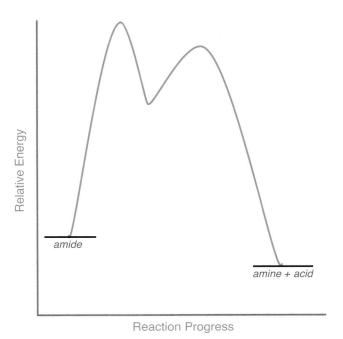

A protease could accelerate amide hydrolysis by *destabilizing the substrate / stabilizing the substrate* and/or *destabilizing the intermediate / stabilizing the intermediate*.

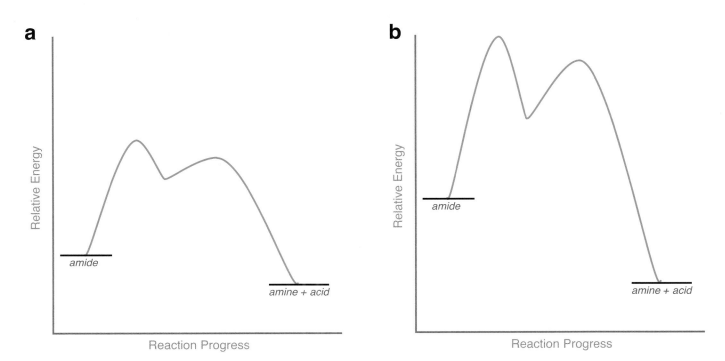

These two ways of catalyzing amide hydrolysis are represented above. A protease that encapsulates a substrate and stabilizes the tetrahedral intermediates is represented by *a / b* (compare with diagram at top of page). That *is / is not* the way most proteases catalyze amide hydrolysis.

Protease Inhibitors

The genome of the HIV-1 virus expresses *9 / 19 / 199* proteins (search the web) and disruption of the function of any of these is likely to suppress propagation.

Nearly all *proteins / enzymes* are *proteins / enzymes* but not all *proteins / enzymes* are *proteins / enzymes*.

An enzyme expressed in the HIV-1 genome, HIV-1 protease, cuts other proteins into smaller, active fragments. HIV-1 protease is inhibited by the AIDS medicine Crixivan.

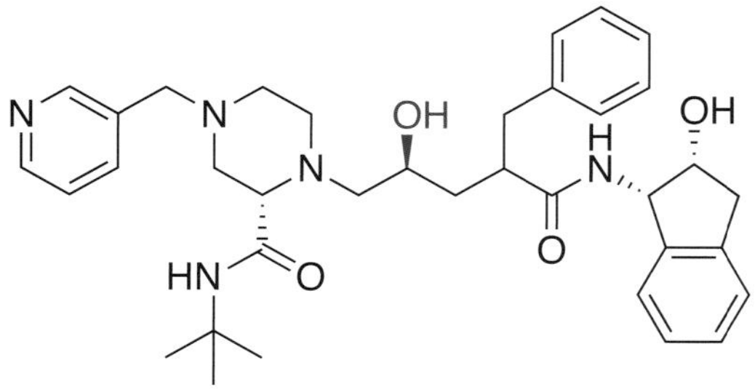

crixivan

Crixivan docks in the *active- / excavation-* site of HIV-1 protease with a *high / low* affinity thus preventing binding of the natural protein substrates.

Crixivan can act in this way because the *amide / alcohol* functionality shown in blue was designed to *make the molecule hydrophobic / mimic the tetrahedral intermediate in amide hydrolysis*.

Thermolysin is a protease that hydrolyzes certain peptides in a particular bacteria. Circle the functionality that acts as a transition-state analog in the thermolysin inhibitor **1**.

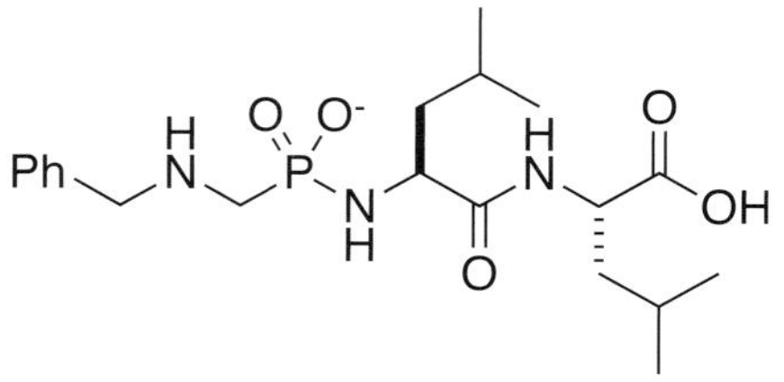

1
thermolysin inhibitor

Detection Of Protease Substrate Selectivity

Amino coumarin dyes, like many other fluors, are fluorescent because of resonance-delocalized chromophores.

Circle the amino coumarin derivative that is most fluorescent in the following reaction.

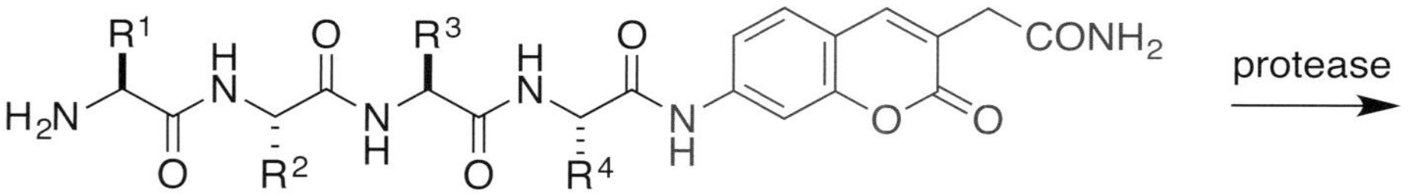

2

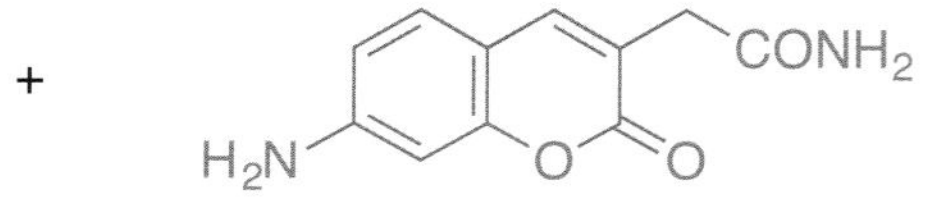

$\xrightarrow{\text{protease}}$

+

Selectivities of proteases may be determined if many substrates **2** with different amino acid side-chains $R^1 - R^4$ were exposed to the protease in reactions that could be conveniently monitored via *X-ray crystallography / fluorescence / ^{31}P NMR*.

E Hydrolysis Of Nitriles Involves Amide Intermediates

Nitriles can be hydrolyzed to amides, and amides can be hydrolyzed to *carboxylic acids / alcohols*, hence hydrolysis of nitriles to amides is *complete / partial*.

Acid-mediated hydrolysis of nitriles to amides features *N*-protonation, attack of water at the nitrile carbon, then loss of a proton. *Tautomerization / resonance* of the product leads to formation of the amide.

Draw these steps for acid-mediated hydrolysis of the following nitriles to *amides* (use curly arrows).

Draw a mechanism for acid-mediated hydrolysis of 3-chlorobenzonitrile *to the carboxylic acid* using clear curly arrows.

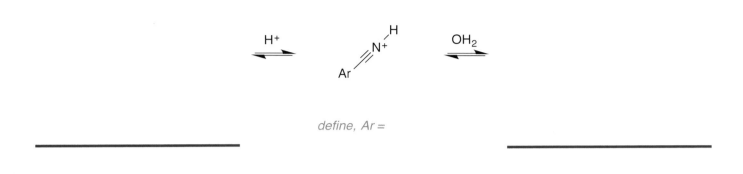

define, Ar =

-H+, +H+   OH₂   -H+, +H+

-NH₃

+NH₃
-NH₄⁺   +NH₃
                    -NH₄⁺

carboxylic acid   *carboxylate*

Complete the following "cartoon" to show where atoms of water add to the following substrates:

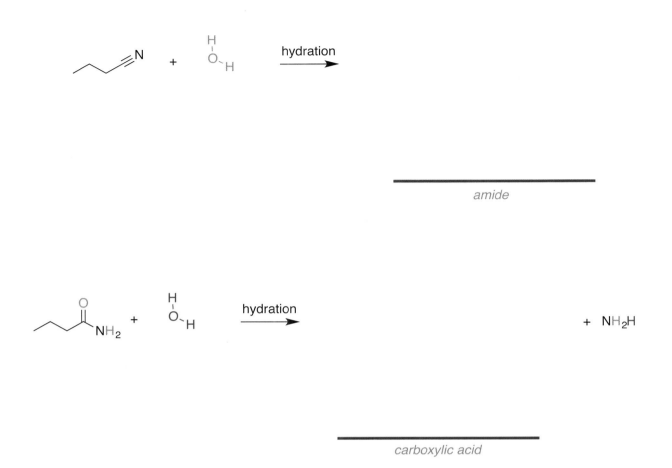

amide

carboxylic acid

F Dehydration Of Amides

Phosphorus pentoxide is a dehydrating agent because it can react with water to form phosphoric acid. Write a balanced equation for this.

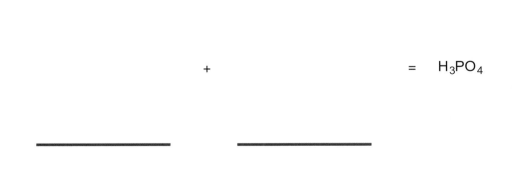

158

Dehydration of amides to nitriles involves loss of water to a *dehydrating reagent*. Predict the nitriles formed via the dehydration of the following amides.

Indicate amides that could be used to make the following nitriles and isonitriles.

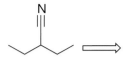

N≡C⁻

⁻C≡N⁺—Ph

Part 3:
Towards Understanding Peptides And Proteins

11 Reactivities Of Acylating Agents

from chapter(s) _____ in the recommended text

A Introduction

Focus

This section covers concepts to rationalize why some acylating agents are more reactive than others, and the generally applicable mechanisms for acylation under basic (or neutral) and acidic conditions.

Reasons To Care

Acylation reactions are one of the most common transformations in biological chemistry (Figure 1). For instance, in protein synthesis tRNA carries activated amino acids to *acylate* growing chains of amino acids. Acetyl-CoA conveys acetyl groups to the citric acid cycle in metabolism, and to fats via fatty acid syntheses, via *acylation* reactions.

Figure 1. Two cellular acylating agents.

These "naughty secrets" make acylation reactions hard to understand:

- they can proceed under acidic, neutral, or basic conditions;

- mechanisms of acylations under acidic, and neutral or basic conditions tend to be different;

- acid halides, acid anhydrides, esters, amides, and *modified* carboxylic acids will all undergo acylation reactions, but their reactivities are extremely different;

- reactivities of nucleophiles in acylation reactions also differ; consequently,

- only some combinations of conditions, acylating agents, and nucleophiles lead to acylation products.

Concepts

electron flow • acids and bases • ester hydrolyses and transesterifications (both acylation processes)

Objective

Acylation reactions in the laboratory include syntheses of peptides and their derivatives. Biochemical acylations usually do not involve pH extremes but enzyme active sites often contain acidic and basic centers in enclosed environments. This part of the *Inquisition* outlines concepts that enable understanding reactivities in acylation reactions.

B Acylation Reactions

Acylation reactions involve transfer of *RO / RCO / R* groups. Only one of the following processes is *not* an acylation reaction; circle that one.

C pH Dependent Mechanisms

Just as for reactions of aldehydes and ketones, acylation mechanisms usually depend on the acidity (pH) of the reaction mixture.

Acylations Under Basic Conditions

Good nucleophiles in acylation reactions are ones that *readily / reluctantly* receive acyl groups.

In the following acylation equilibrium, the leaving group Y is *displaced / not displaced* by good nucleophiles Nu⁻.

Basicity of a nucleophile *does / does not* give a rough guide to its nucleophilicity in acylation reactions.

Strong bases tend to be *good / bad* nucleophiles (eg *Cl⁻ / OMe⁻*) whereas *weak* bases are mostly *good / bad* nucleophiles (eg *Cl⁻ / OMe⁻*).

examples of weak bases Y⁻: Cl⁻, NO_3^-, _____ (add some more)

strong bases Nu⁻: Me_2N^-, HO⁻, _____ (add some)

The group that is expelled from the pivotal *tetrahedral intermediate* (Y⁻ or Nu⁻ in the example above) tends to be the *most / least* able to support negative charge in the anionic form.

Nucleophilic substitution at acyl groups under *neutral* or under *basic* conditions usually involves addition of the nucleophile to a carbonyl group, then loss of a leaving group from the *tetrahedral / trigonal* intermediate.

Show this mechanism in generic terms with curly arrows depicting the reaction flow for the acid chloride below.

Chemistry in living organisms involves aqueous environments and complex mixtures of nucleophiles. Biological acylating agents have to be *highly / moderately* reactive so that chemoselective reactions are possible in this environment.

In a chemistry lab, however, *more / less* reactive acylating agents like acid chlorides can be used.
Illustrate the pathway above for attack of OH⁻ on ethanoyl chloride (draw in arrows).

⁻OH → ⁻Cl⁻ →

ethanoyl chloride *tetrahedral intermediate* *ethanoic acid*

Illustrate this process for attack of methoxide on benzoyl chloride (draw in arrows).

⁻OMe → ⁻Cl⁻ →

benzoyl chloride *tetrahedral intermediate* *methyl benzoate*

Acylations Under Acidic Conditions

Acidic conditions are used in nucleophilic acylations to increase the reactivity of the carbonyl group by protonation on the C=O, and/or to protonate a leaving group to enable it to depart more easily.

Protonation of the carbonyl group *increases / decreases* its reactivity towards nucleophiles. Show this for a generic, non-basic, anionic nucleophile, by completing the diagram below (show curly arrows).

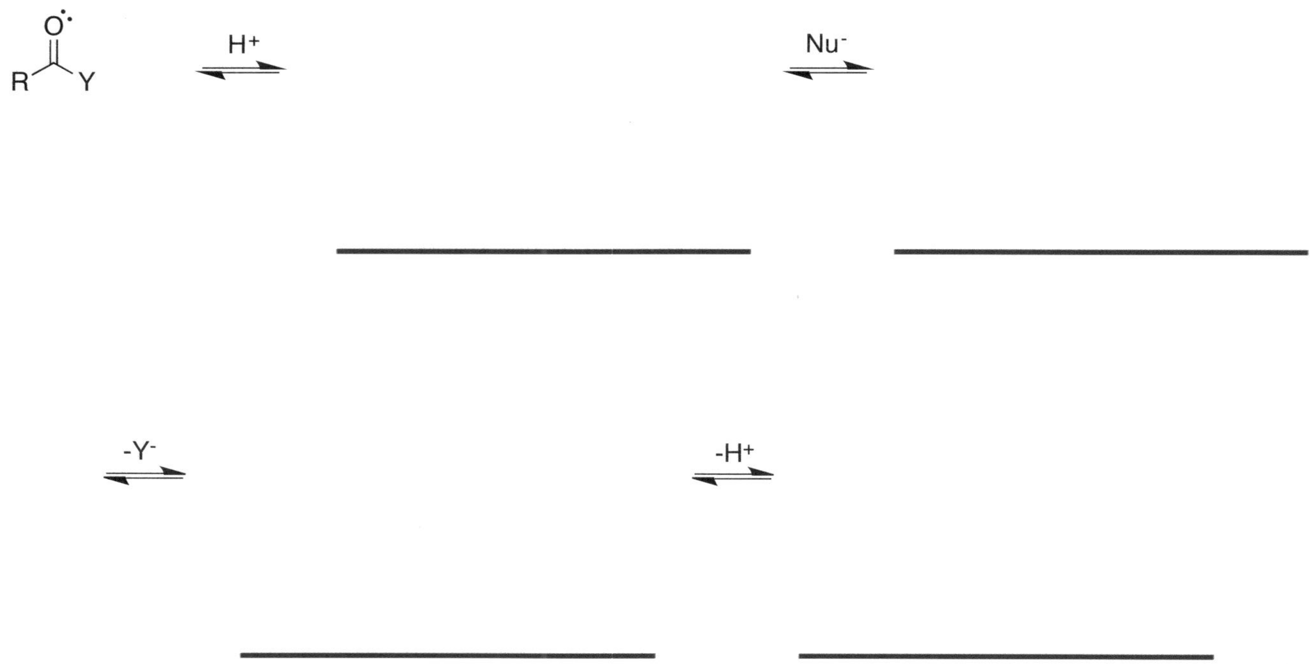

O
||
R   Y   H+ ⇌   Nu⁻ ⇌

_____   _____

-Y⁻ ⇌   -H+ ⇌

_____   _____

D Reactivities Of Acylating Agents

Chemical Intuition

Acylating agents with relatively unstable leaving groups tend to be relatively *reactive / unreactive*.

Acyl fragments attached to good leaving groups tend to be *reactive / unreactive* acylating agents.

Highly electronegative leaving groups *activate / deactivate* carbonyl carbons atoms they are attached to and this tends to give *reactive / unreactive* acylating agents.

Basic nucleophiles *can / cannot* be used under acidic conditions.

Deprotonation of an acylating agent renders it *more / less* reactive to nucleophiles.

Acids (protons and other Lewis acids) can complex carbonyl oxygen atoms making the associated carbonyl carbon *more / less* electrophilic.

Bulky leaving groups can sometimes *retard / accelerate* additions of nucleophiles to acylating agents (*cf* base-mediated hydrolysis of *tert*-butyl esters is *favorable / unfavorable*).

Small nucleophiles are acylated *faster / slower* than large ones, if all other factors are equal.

Molecular Orbital Description Of Acylation

Complete the following diagram by showing in part **a** the shapes of the carbonyl LUMO and the nucleophile HOMO, how they interact, and in **b** by filling in electrons into the bonding orbitals.

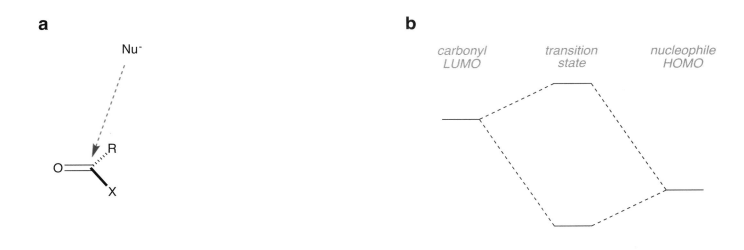

Factors that decrease the HOMO-LUMO gap *increase / decrease* the probability of combination.

Electron withdrawing groups (EWGs) attached to the carbonyl tend to *lower / raise* its LUMO energy.

Acyl groups connected to good leaving groups are *reactive / unreactive* to nucleophiles because they have relatively *low / high* energy LUMOs.

Good leaving groups tend to be *more / less* stable in the anionic form because they support negative charges well.

Delocalization of electrons into acyl substituents (as in carboxylates) *raises* the energy of the carbonyl LUMO and makes it *more / less* reactive to HOMOs of nucleophiles.

Reactive nucleophiles tend to have *low / high* energy HOMOs and this leads to *good / poor* orbital overlap with the LUMO of the acylating agent.

Acid chlorides, bromides, and fluorides are excellent acylating agents because the halogens *lower / raise* the LUMO of the carbonyl, and because halides are *poor / excellent* leaving groups.

Relative Reactivities Of Functional Groups In Acylation Reactions

Carbonyl Halides (Acid Halides) Are Hot
Show the product in the following reaction.

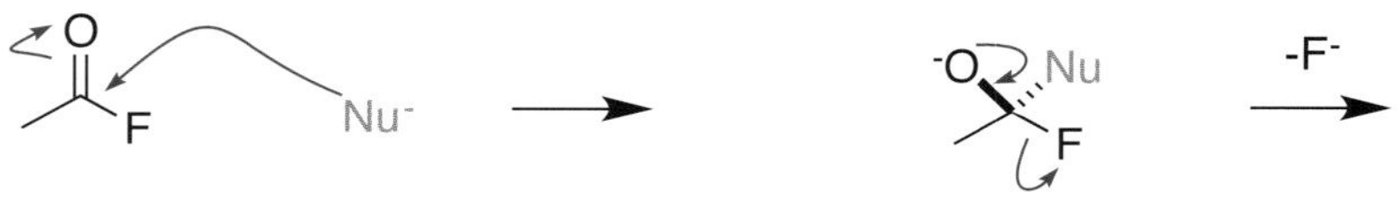

The description above shows the nucleophile is sufficiently reactive to add irreversibly under *basic / acid* conditions.

Check you understand the parallel between reactions of aldehydes and ketones, and of acylating agents, under acidic and basic conditions.

Complete the reaction below by showing the product.

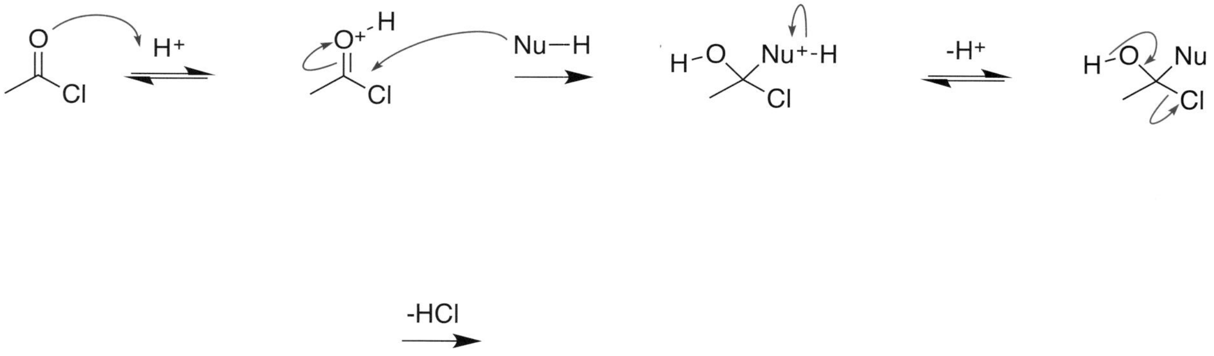

-HCl

The mechanism above could only be applicable under *basic / acid* conditions.

Carboxylic Acid Anhydrides Are Very Reactive

Carboxylic acid anhydrides are good acylating agents because carboxylates *lower / raise* the LUMO of the carbonyl, and they are *poor / excellent* leaving groups.

Complete the following reactions by showing the remaining curly arrows to depict electron flow, and the product.

under basic conditions .....

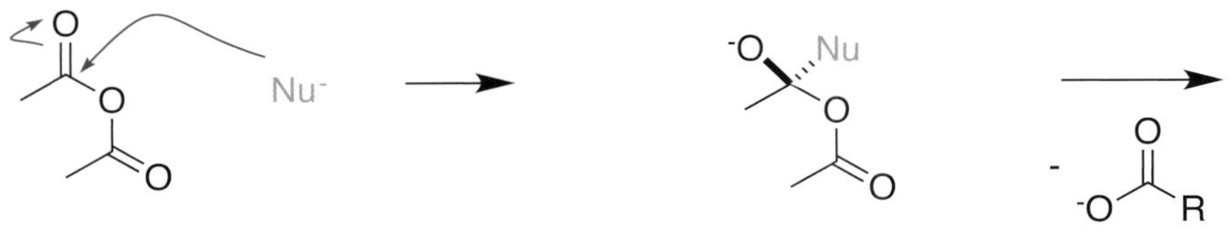

under acidic conditions .....

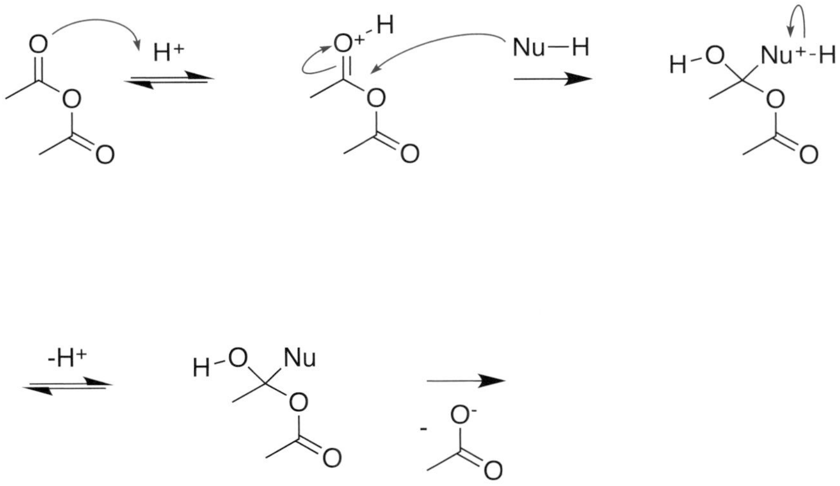

Carboxylic acid anhydrides in acylation reactions contain fragments from *1 / 2 / 3* carboxylic acid molecule(s).

In acylation reactions these fragments have different roles: one serves as *an electrophile / a nucleophile*, while the other serves as a *nucleophile / carboxylate leaving group*.

Esters Are Not Very Reactive

Esters are relatively poor acylating agents because delocalization of electrons from alkoxide into the carbonyl *lowers / raises* the LUMO of the carbonyl; alkoxides are *superior / inferior* leaving groups relative to halides and carboxylates.

Complete the following mechanisms showing omitted products and electron flow (throughout).

under basic conditions .....

under acidic conditions .....

Typical nucleophiles for the reaction above are water, *ie ester hydrolysis / ester reduction*, and alcohols in *hydrolysis / transesterification* reactions, but there are not so many others.

Amines *do / do not* tend to react with esters in this way.

Thioesters, Gentle Chemoselective Acylating Agents

Thioesters are *better / worse* acylating agents than esters because sulfur donates *more / less* electrons into the carbonyl group than oxygen in these compounds.

Complete the following reactions.

under basic conditions .....

tetrahedral intermediate

under acidic conditions .....

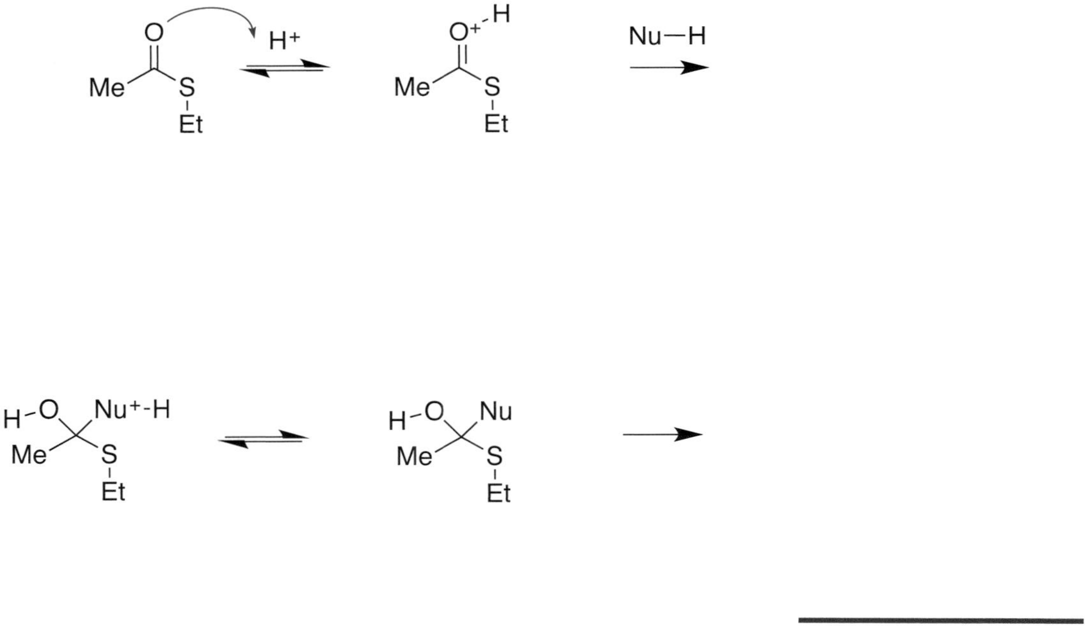

Amines *do / do not* tend to react with thioesters via the acid-catalyzed mechanism above.

Amides: Poor Acylating Agents

Amides are *better / worse* acylating agents than esters because amide anions (NR_2^-, where R = alkyl or *H*) are *good / poor* leaving groups.

The *N*-atom of an amide donates *more / less* electrons into the carbonyl group than oxygen of an ester.

Complete the following reactions.

under basic conditions .....

$$Me \overset{O}{\underset{NH_2}{\|}} \quad Nu^- \longrightarrow \qquad \qquad \overset{-NH_2^-}{\longrightarrow}$$

_____ _____

tetrahedral intermediate

under acidic conditions .....

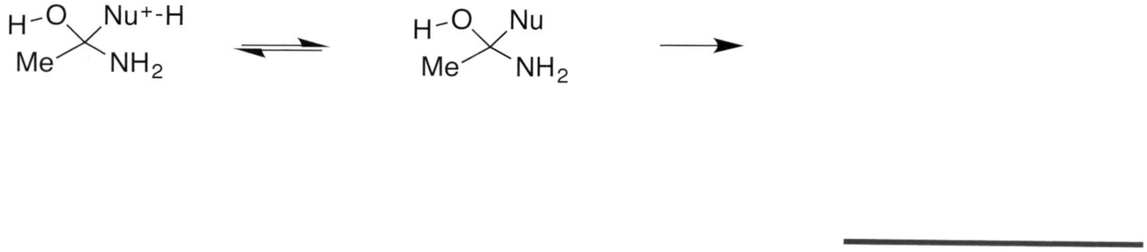

$$Me \overset{O}{\underset{NH_2}{\|}} \quad H^+ \rightleftharpoons \qquad \qquad \overset{Nu-H}{\longrightarrow}$$

_____

$$\underset{Me}{\overset{H-O}{\diagdown}} \overset{Nu^+-H}{\diagup} \underset{NH_2}{} \rightleftharpoons \underset{Me}{\overset{H-O}{\diagdown}} \overset{Nu}{\diagup} \underset{NH_2}{} \longrightarrow$$

_____

Carboxylic Acids Are Not Acylating Agents

Hydroxyl groups of carboxylic acids are poor leaving groups because:

(i)   carboxylic acids (pKa = *3 – / 10 - 13*) tend to exist as carboxylate forms that repel nucleophilic attack; and,

(ii) if a carboxylate was not deprotonated and a nucleophile did add to the carbonyl, then HO⁻ is not a particularly good leaving group.

Complete the following graphic that summarizes the potential of unmodified carboxylic acids as acylating agents.

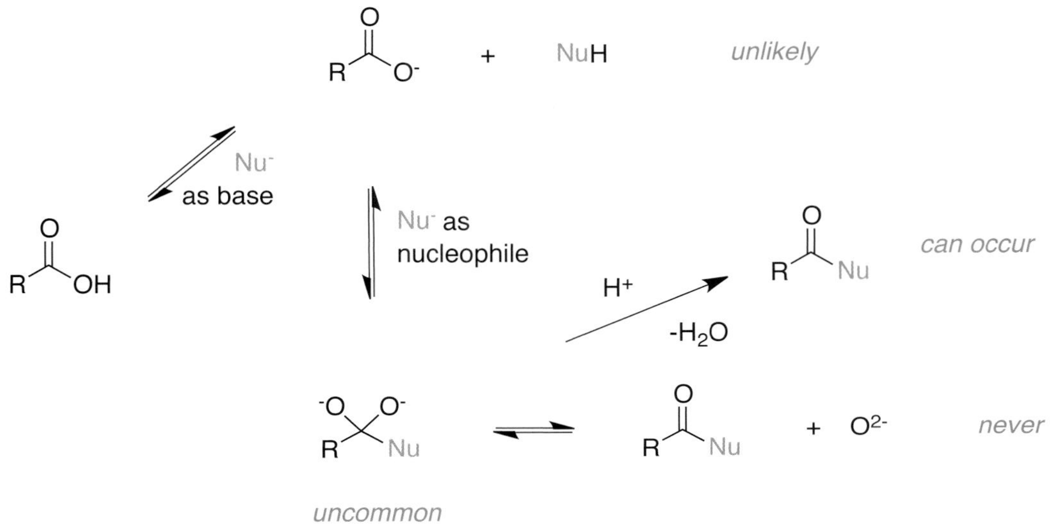

Peroxide dianion O^{2-} is *slightly / extremely* basic and a very *good / poor* leaving group.

Synopsis

Consider the compounds below and indicate if they are "excellent" (**E**), "sometimes suitable" (**SS**), or "inappropriate" (**I**) as acylating agents.

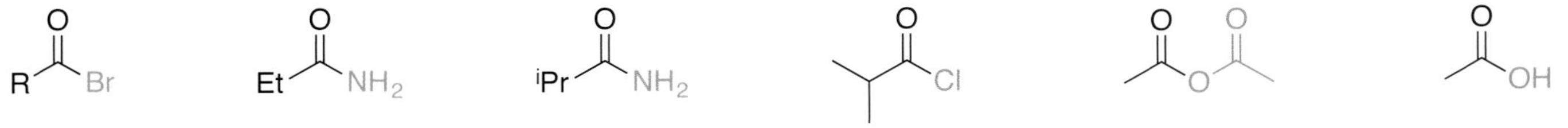

E / SS / I   E / SS / I   E / SS / I   E / SS / I   E / SS / I   E / SS / I

E / SS / I   E / SS / I   E / SS / I   E / SS / I   E / SS / I   E / SS / I

Compounds without a leaving group on the carbonyl *can / cannot* undergo acylation reactions. Circle two of the compounds above that fit that description.

Rank the following groups in terms of their ability to be displaced.

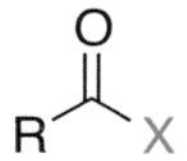

X =   OAc   OMe   O⁻ NH_2 Cl   OPh

_____

most reactive   _least reactive_

Rank the following nucleophiles in terms of their ability to add to be acylated.

Nu =   ⁻Me   ⁻OH   ⁻NH₂   ⁻Cl   NH₃   OH₂

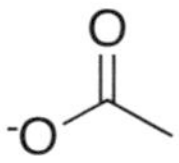

_____

most reactive   _least reactive_

Rank the following in terms of reactivities to nucleophiles by placing a 1 under the most reactive _etc._ If two compounds have functional groups of the same type, use other concepts to reason which is the more reactive.

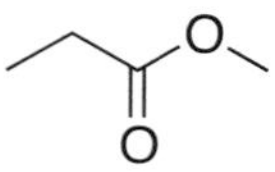

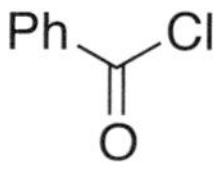

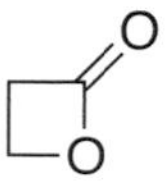

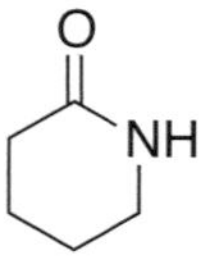

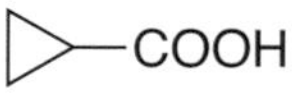

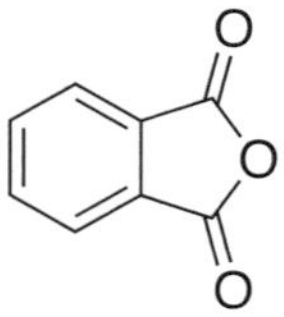

_____   _____   _____

_____   _____   _____

12 Acylations Via Acid Chlorides And Anhydrides

from chapter(s) _____ in the recommended text

A Introduction

Focus

Acid chlorides and anhydrides are superb acylating agents. Chloride ions are such good leaving groups in acyl chlorides that they can be displaced by carboxylates to give acid anhydrides; the reverse reaction does not occur indicating that acid chlorides are better acylating agents than anhydrides. This section covers their acylation reactions of water (hydrolysis), alcohols (esterification), and amines.

acylating agent   *nucleophile*

Reasons To Care

Acylation is a fundamental process in biochemistry and cell biology, for instance, in the transfer of amino acids residues in protein syntheses. Amine acylation reactions are central to chemical syntheses of peptides, and unnatural analogs.

aspartame

Concepts Involved

hydration • curly arrows • acids and bases • ester hydrolyses

Objective

To reinforce understanding of reactions leading to formation of ester and amide bonds via acylation processes.

B Reactions Of Acyl Halides

Under Basic Conditions

Chloride is a relatively *stable / unstable* anion, hence it can be displaced by *many / a few* nucleophiles without activation by acid, and the reaction is essentially *irreversible / reversible*.

Complete the following diagram.

Draw curly arrows for the following acylation of acetate under basic or neutral conditions.

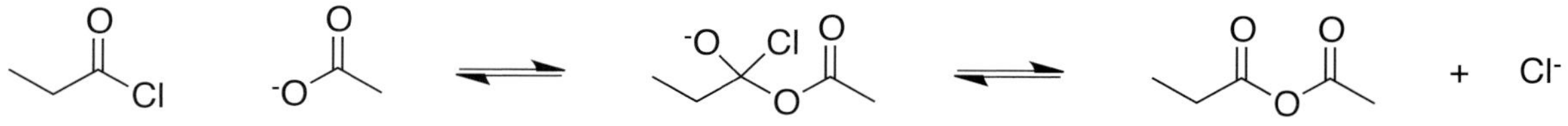

Under Acidic Conditions

Draw curly arrows for the following acylation of acetate nucleophile under acidic conditions and write "PT" above each equilibrium step involving *proton transfer*.

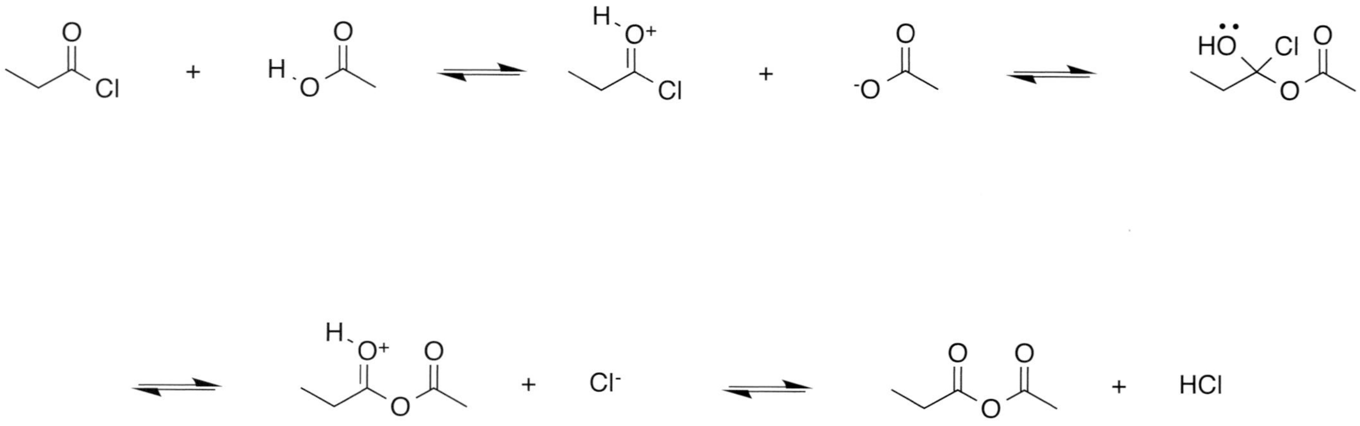

Syntheses Of Anhydrides Via Acylation Of Carboxylates

Show the products of the following reactions of acid chlorides with carboxylates.

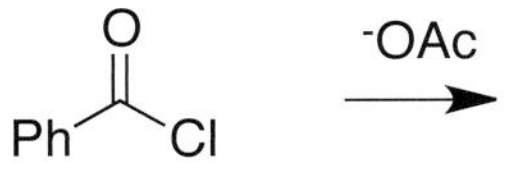

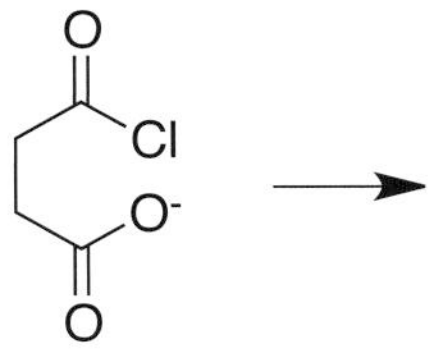

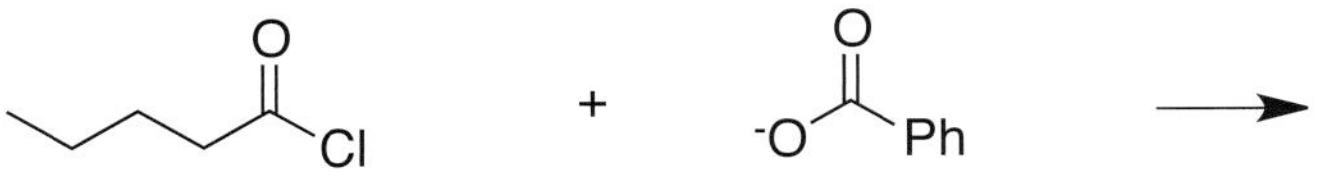

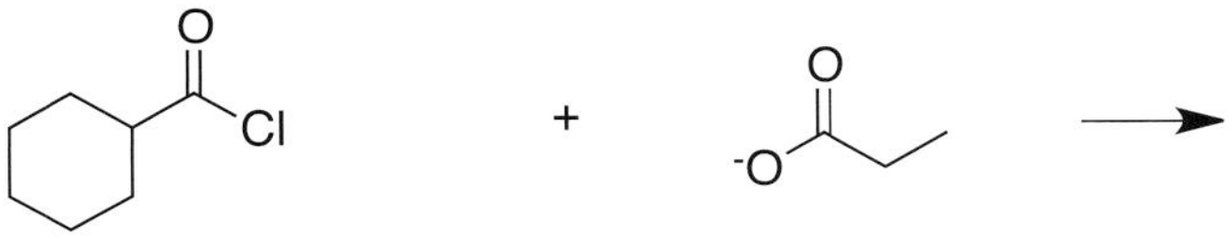

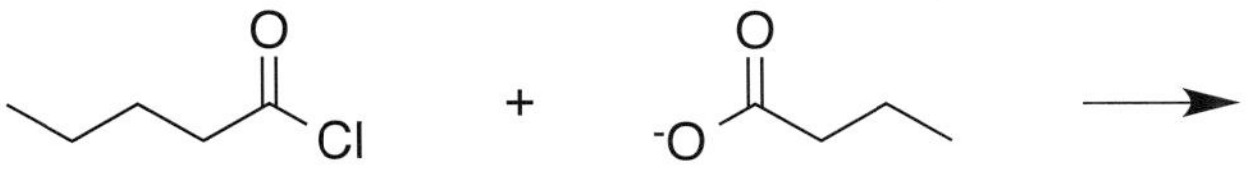

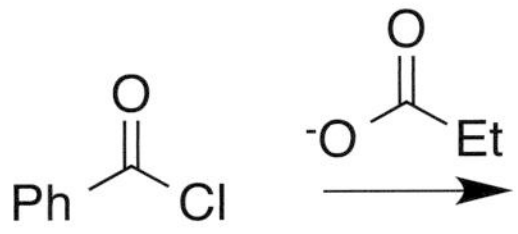

$^{t}BuCOCl \xrightarrow{^{-}OAc}$

Show how each of the following carboxylic acid anhydrides can be made from acid chlorides.

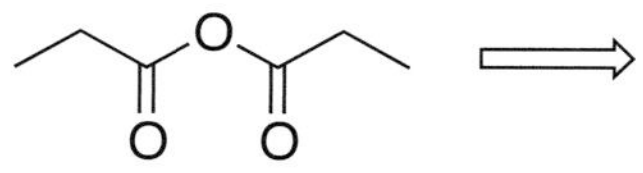

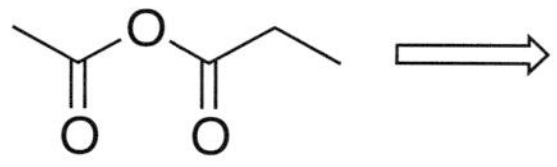

⟹

_____

⟹   +   or   +

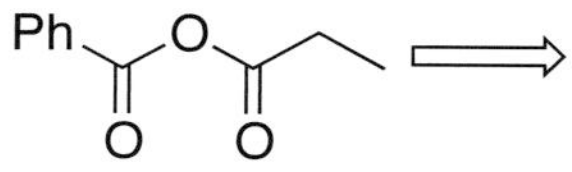

_____   _____

Ph ⟹   +   or   +

_____   _____

⟹

_____

⟹

_____

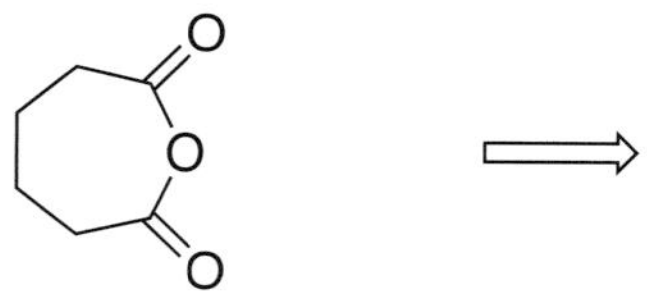

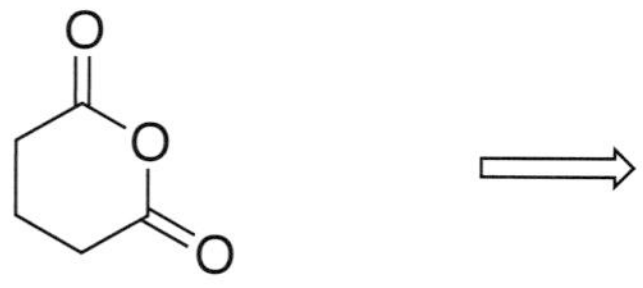

Hydrolysis Of Acid Chlorides To Form Carboxylic Acids

Water readily reacts with acid chlorides; under basic conditions the nucleophile is *water / hydroxide*, while under acidic conditions it is *water / hydroxide*; these reactions are *acylation / perspiration* of water.

Fill in the gaps in the following mechanism that shows a reaction under *acidic / basic* conditions.

Acylation Of Alcohols To Form Esters

Draw the products of the following reactions of acid chlorides with alcohols.

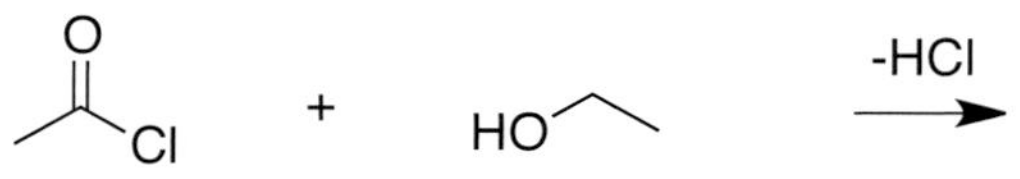

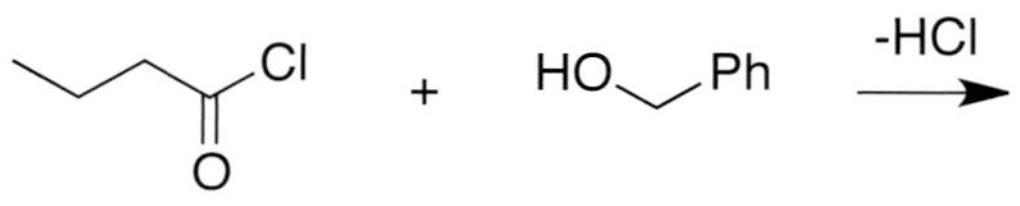

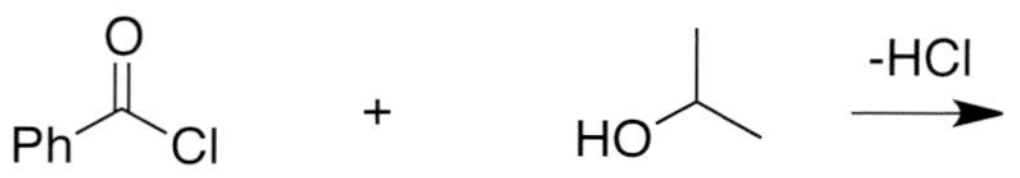

(acetyl chloride) + HO⌒ (propanol) →⁻HCl

_____

(butyryl chloride) + HO⌒Ph (benzyl alcohol) →⁻HCl

_____

Ph—C(=O)—Cl + HO—CH(CH₃)₂ →⁻HCl

_____

Indicate acid chloride and alcohol starting materials that could be used to make the following esters.

⟹

_____

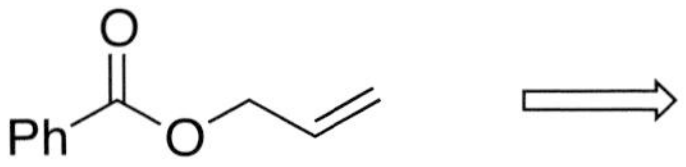

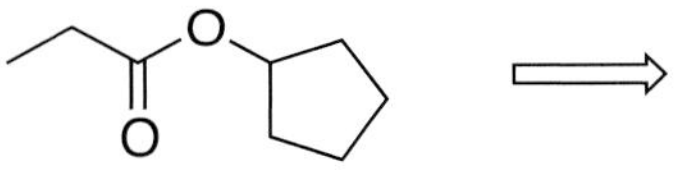

⟹

_____

⟹

_____

⟹

_____

EtCO$_2$Bn   ⟹

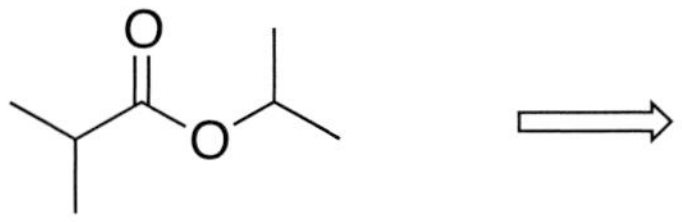

_____

⟹

_____

Acylation Of Amines To Give Amides

Acid chlorides react with ammonia, primary, and secondary amines via mechanisms similar to their reactions with water and alcohols. A base is often added to sequester protons evolved and prevent the solution becoming acidic.

Complete the following diagram including curly arrows.

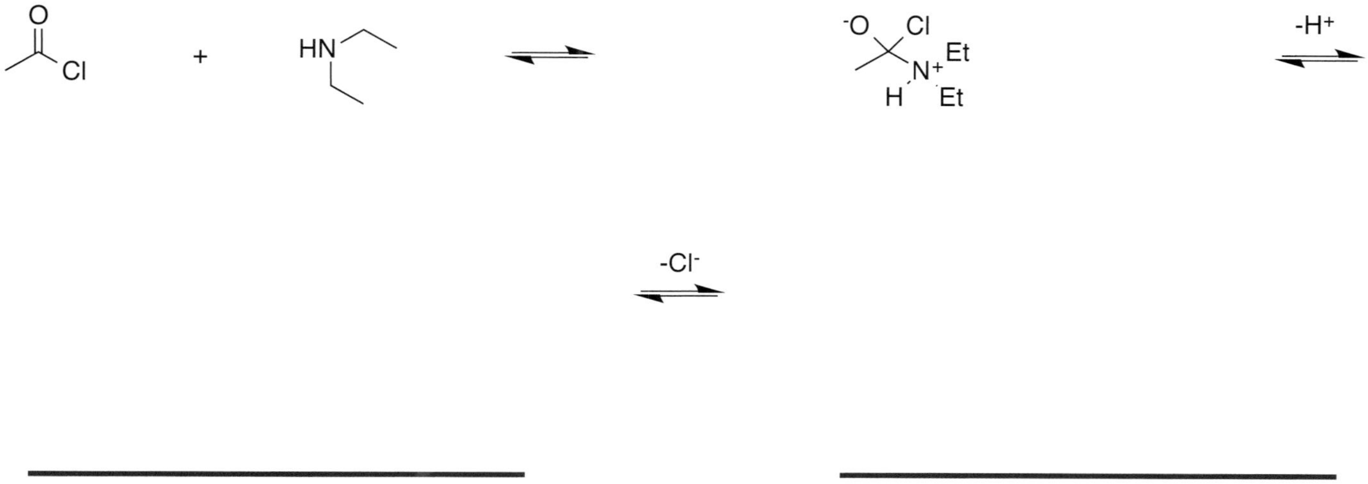

The mechanism above shows loss of a proton *before / after* chloride loss, while the one below shows it *before / at the same time / after*.

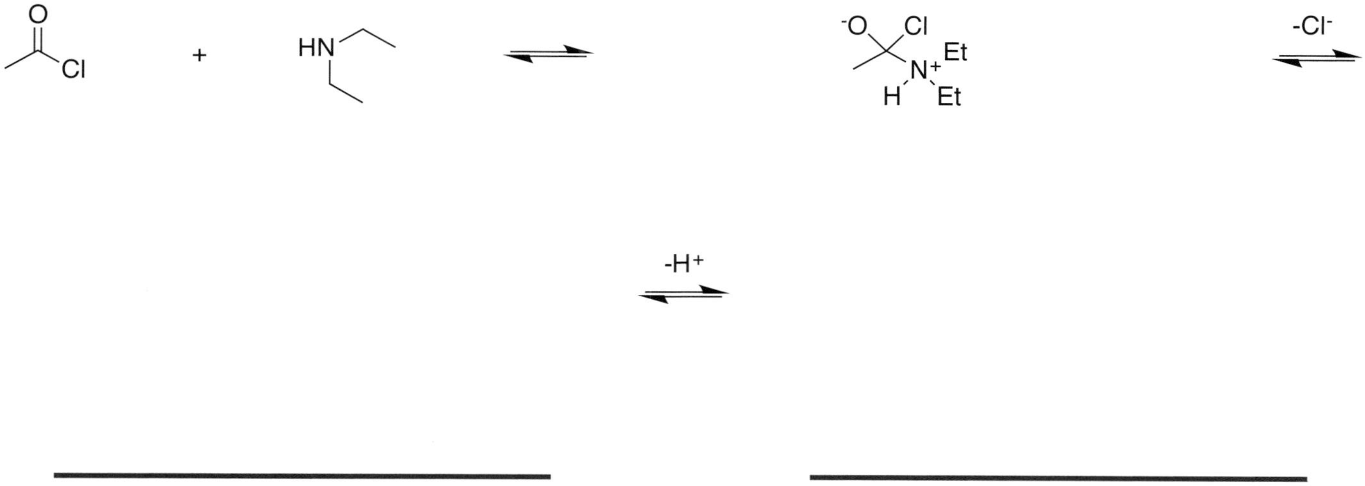

Both mechanisms shown above are acceptable.

Combination of acid chlorides with *tertiary* amines gives *stable / unstable* products that tend to collapse to the starting materials.

Most often combinations of tertiary amines with acid chlorides are unproductive, but sometimes it is. Draw 4-(dimethylamino)pyridine (DMAP), and the product formed when this is acylated on the pyridine-*N* (which is like a tertiary amine) by acetyl chloride.

_____

DMAP

_____

N-acetyl DMAP
good acylating agent for other nucleophiles

In general, when amines are added to acid halides under neutral conditions zwitterionic tetrahedral intermediates form. Complete the following equilibria showing that (draw arrows, and fill in starting material or product).

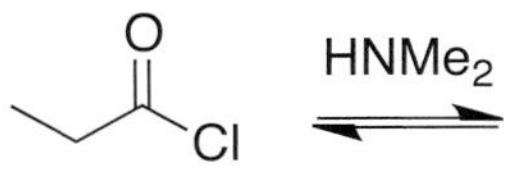

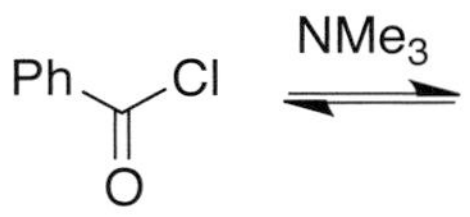

_____

_____

$+$

_____

which amine?

Show the products of the following reactions of acid chlorides with amines. Polymers might form in some cases; if this is a possibility, show the polymer *and* the intramolecular acylation product.

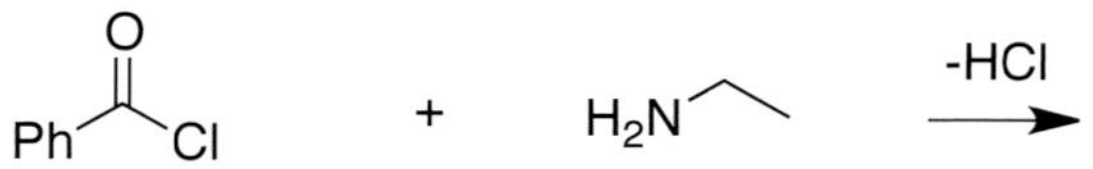

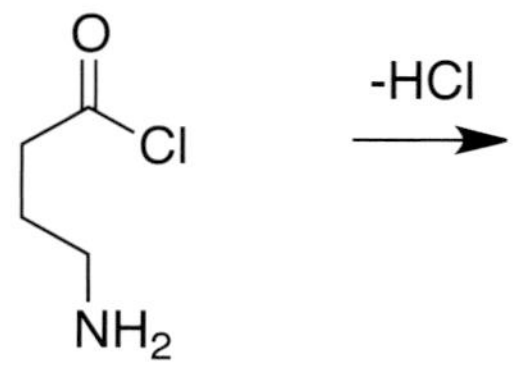

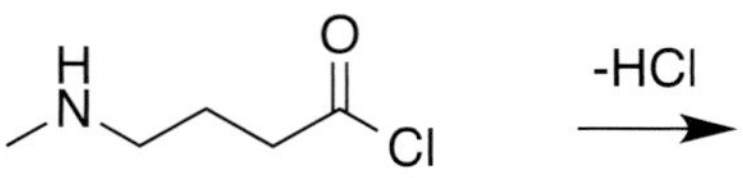

+ NH₃   -HCl →

_____

Ph   +   H₂N⌒   -HCl →

_____

-HCl →

_____

-HCl →

_____

Indicate acid chloride and amine starting materials from which the following amides can be made.

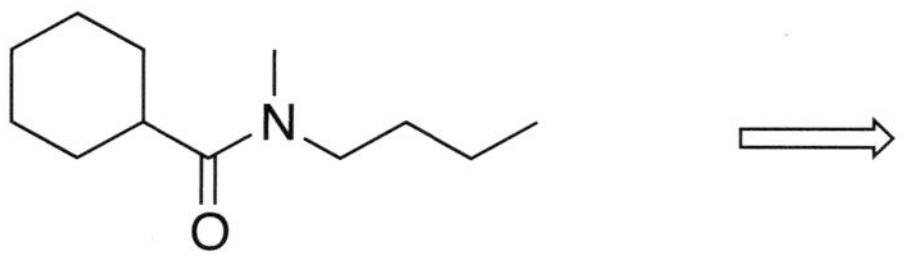

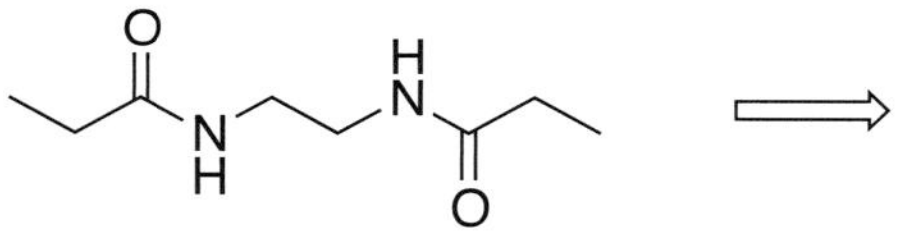

$\implies$

———————————————————————————

$\implies$

———————————————————————————

$\implies$

———————————————————————————

In general, carboxylic acid chlorides react with alcohols to give *amides / esters / nitriles / acids*, with water to give *amides / esters / nitriles / acids*, and with ammonia to give *amides / esters / nitriles / acids*.

C Acylation Reactions Of Carboxylic Acid Anhydrides

Acid anhydrides are *more / slightly less / much less* reactive than acid halides, and they undergo much the same reactions.

Nucleophiles could add to either carbonyl of symmetrical anhydrides, and the outcome would be *the same / different*.

In acylation reactions, one carbonyl of a symmetrical anhydride serves as *an electrophile / a nucleophile* and the remaining carboxylate forms a leaving group.

If an acid is expensive or hard to obtain, converting it to a symmetrical anhydride for use in acylation reactions would be *a good strategy / wasteful*.

Predict the products of the following reactions of amines with anhydrides.

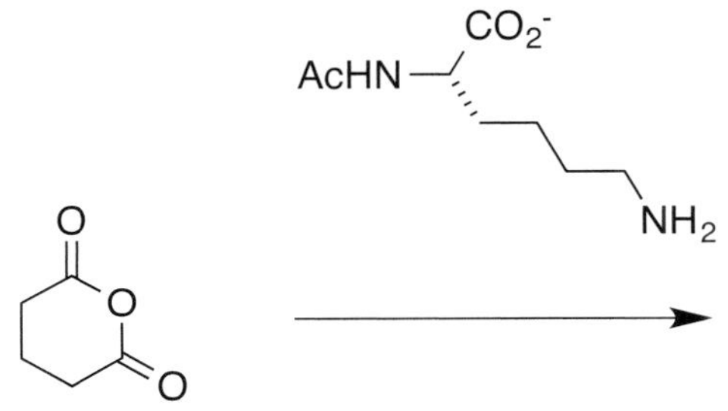

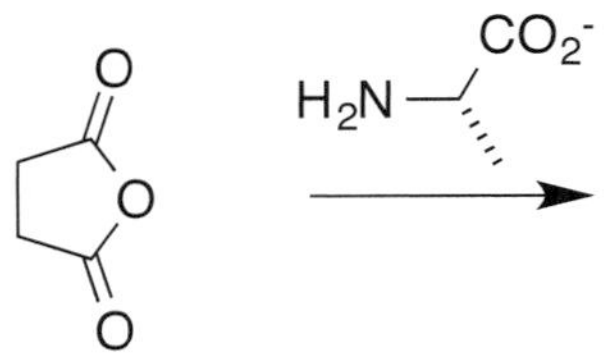

isatoic
anhydride

187

13 Activation Of Carboxylic Acids

from chapter(s) _____ in the recommended text

A Introduction

Focus

Carboxylic acids do not directly react with amines and several other important nucleophiles; they often must be converted to something that is more reactive first. Chemists often will refer to this process as "activation of a carboxylic acid". Consequently, *in vivo* and in the laboratory, carboxylic acids (or functional groups that are easily converted to carboxylic acids, *eg* esters) lie dormant in a chemical environment until they are activated *when needed*.

Approaches to activation of carboxylic acids are the focus of this section.

Reasons To Care

Carboxylic acids are ubiquitous in living systems and they are common starting materials for laboratory syntheses. Activation of carboxylic acids is required for many processes including ribosomal and chemical syntheses of peptides and proteins, and construction of fatty acids and polyketide natural products *in vivo*.

Concepts Involved

substitution at acyl groups • symmetrical, unsymmetrical, and mixed anhydrides

Objective

To gain an appreciation of some of the ways by which carboxylic acids can be made into more reactive functional groups to facilitate acylation reactions.

B Reactivity

Unmodified carboxylic acids are extremely *good / poor* acylating agents because:

(i)   hydroxide is a *mediocre / excellent* leaving group; and,

(ii) if the medium is neutral or basic then the acid exists *in the protonated form / as a carboxylate*.

It is for these reasons that carboxylic acids are frequently converted to acid halides or acid anhydrides; both these *are / are not* reactive to nucleophiles.

C Common Carboxylic Acids Derivatives

Many of the compounds named below are useful for understanding this section, and all are common chemicals.

Use Wikipedia to help you draw the following carboxylic acid derivatives. Indicate if they are closely related to esters (**A**), carboxylic acids (**B**), amides (**C**), acid chlorides (**D**), or carbon dioxide (**E**).

_____	_____	_____
thiourea *A / B / C / D / E*	*carbamic acid* *A / B / C / D / E*	*N,N'-dimethylurea* *A / B / C / D / E*
_____	_____	_____
ethyl chlorocarbonate *A / B / C / D / E*	*methyl carbamate* *A / B / C / D / E*	*oxalyl chloride* *A / B / C / D / E*
_____	_____	_____
phosgene *A / B / C / D / E*	*dimethyl carbonate* *A / B / C / D / E*	*urea* *A / B / C / D / E*
_____	_____	_____
dicyclohexylcarbodiimide (DCC) *A / B / C / D / E*	*thiophosgene* *A / B / C / D / E*	*N,N'-dicyclohexylurea* *A / B / C / D / E*

D Activation Of Carboxylic Acids By Conversion To Acid Chlorides

Thionyl Halides: Excellent Dehydrating Agents

Thionyl chloride $SOCl_2$, and thionyl bromide (formula: _____), are excellent dehydrating reagents because they form only gaseous products when they react with water. Predict what those gaseous products are in the following reactions (balance the equations).

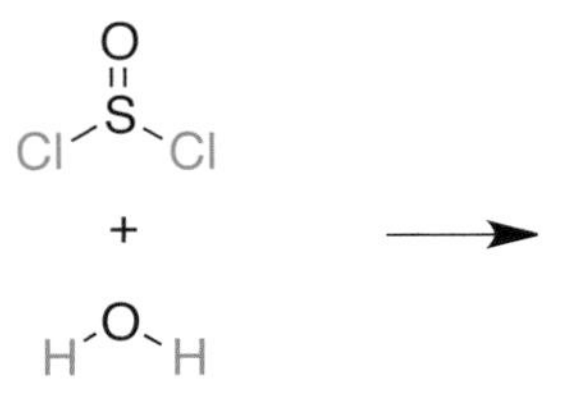

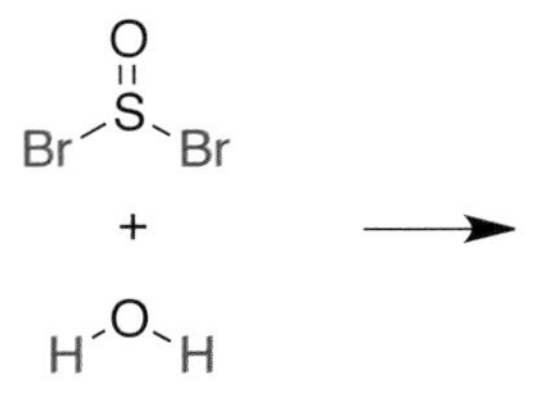

Thionyl Halide Plus Carboxylic Acid Gives Acid Halide, SO₂, And HX

Carboxylic acids *can* be reacted with thionyl chloride or -bromide giving *amides / acid halides / cyanides*.

Identify the acid halides formed from carboxylic acids and the following thionyl halides.

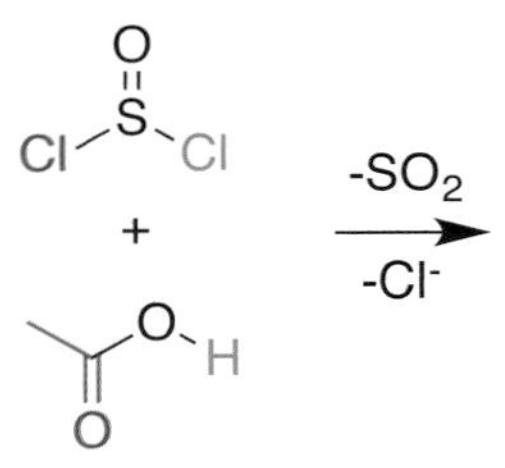

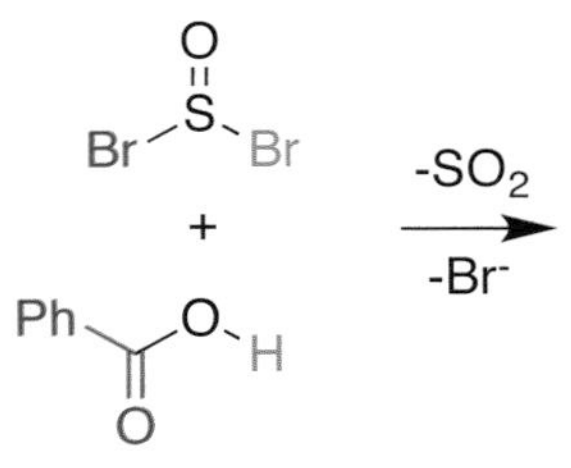

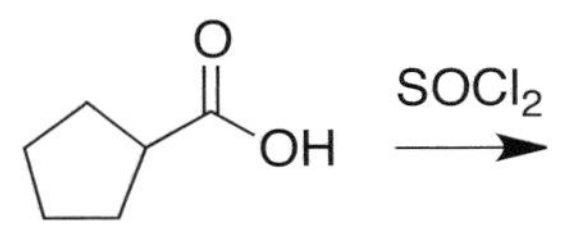

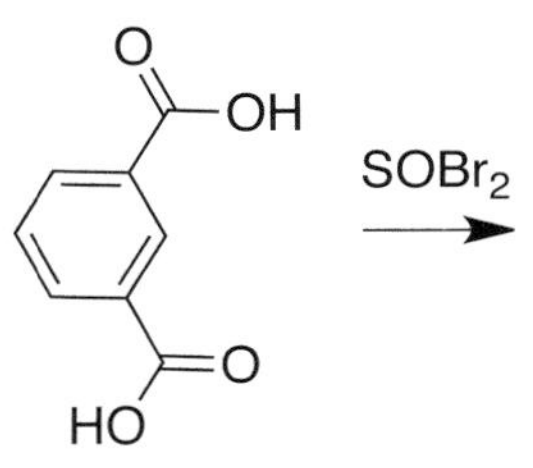

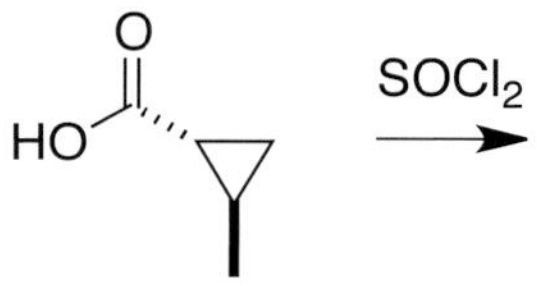

HO—C(=O)—▵   SOCl₂ →

HO₂C(CH₂)₅CO₂H   SOBr₂ →

_____   _____

A kind of anhydride intermediate is formed in these reactions when thionyl halides react with carboxylic acids. Predict the structures of those intermediates for the following reactions.

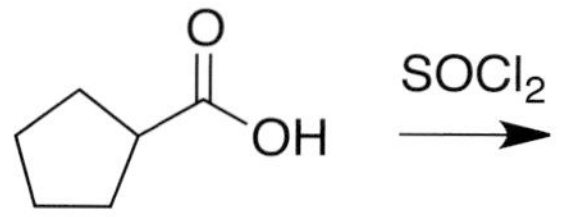

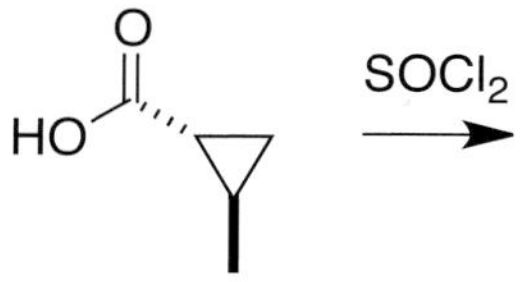

(cyclopentane-C(=O)-OH)   SOCl₂ →

HO—C(=O)—▵   SOCl₂ →

_____   _____
sulfonyl anhydride   *sulfonyl anhydride*
intermediate   *intermediate*

Intermediates in the reactions above are sulfonyl anhydrides. Draw the carboxylic acids that the following sulfonyl anhydrides can be formed from.

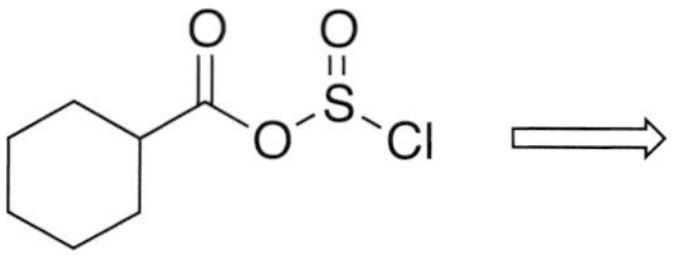

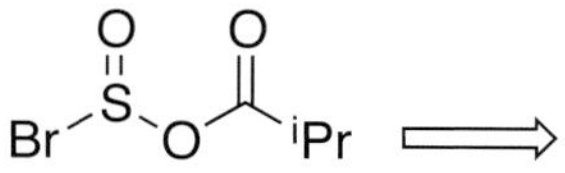

(cyclohexane-C(=O)-O-S(=O)-Cl) ⟹

Br-S(=O)(=O)-O-C(=O)-iPr ⟹

_____   _____

Draw a mechanism for thionyl bromide mediated conversion of the carboxylic acid shown below, into the corresponding benzoyl bromide.

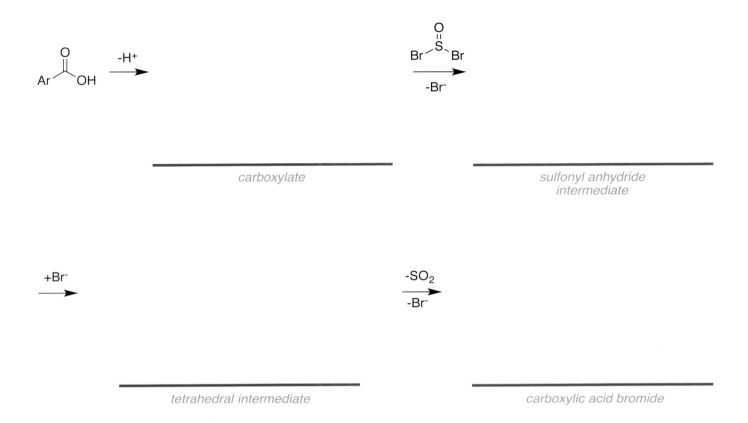

carboxylate

sulfonyl anhydride intermediate

tetrahedral intermediate

carboxylic acid bromide

E Activation By Forming Anhydrides

Symmetrical Anhydrides

Some dehydrating agents can be used to abstract one molecule of water from *1 / 2 / 3* molecule(s) of carboxylic acid to give *1 / 2 / 3* molecule(s) of a symmetrical anhydride.

Without worrying about the phosphorus-containing by-products, show the symmetrical carboxylic acid anhydrides formed in the following reactions.

Symmetrical / unsymmetrical anhydrides can be formed by dehydrating carboxylic acids, but *symmetrical / unsymmetrical* ones cannot be isolated in pure form via this approach.

Show the organic products of the following reactions.

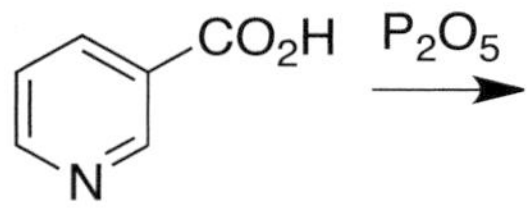

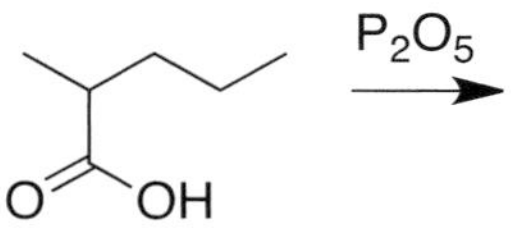

_____   _____

Draw acetic anhydride (which is *symmetrical / unsymmetrical*) and the *symmetrical / unsymmetrical* anhydride from acetic acid and propionic acid.

_____   **_____**

acetic anhydride   *anhydride from ethanoic and propionic acids*

Unsymmetrical And Mixed Anhydrides

Symmetrical anhydrides are made from *1 / 2 / 3* molecule(s) of the same carboxylic acid, but anhydrides from two different carboxylic acid molecules are called *unsymmetrical / asymmetric*.

Mixed anhydrides are formed from a carboxylic acid and another *carboxylic acid / type of acid*.

Unmodified carboxylic acids *are / are not* good acylating agents; however, they can be modified in one step, *in situ*, to give anhydride derivatives that *can / cannot* be used for effective acylation.

Draw an arrow pointing towards the more reactive carbonyl in each of the following anhydrides, circle any that are unsymmetrical, and put a box around those that are mixed.

eg

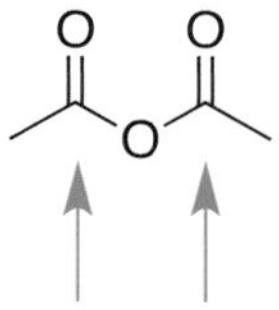

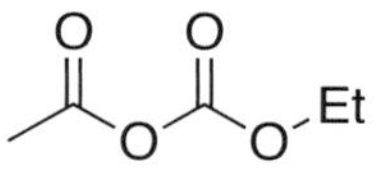

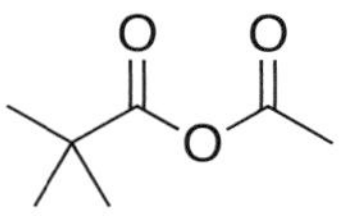

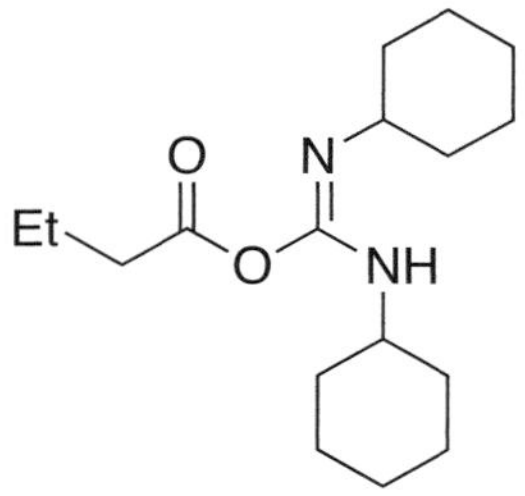

Most unsymmetrical anhydrides could react with nucleophiles at either carbon and the outcome of those two reactions would be *the same / different*, but reactions of mixed anhydrides tend to occur with more selectivity.

Some unsymmetrical anhydride *derivatives* enable every molecule of the starting carboxylic acid to be used as acylating agent, and the other, hopefully less interesting, side of the anhydride-like compound to be displaced.

Formation Of Unsymmetrical Anhydride Derivatives Using Carbodiimides

Even though carboxylic acids are not acylating agents, they can be changed into acylating agents simply by mixing with activating agents, like carbodiimides.

Ultimately, carbodiimides take an oxygen from the carboxylic acid to form a *thiourea / urea / carbamate*.

Complete the following mechanism that outlines activation of ethanoic acid with *N,N'*-dicyclohexylcarbodiimide (DCC) then reaction with methylamine to give an amide. Complete the mechanism showing curly arrows to depict electron flow.

combination

-H⁺, +H⁺

tetrahedral intermediate

Activation of carboxylic acids with diimide reagents is frequently used in coupling amino acids together in syntheses of *RNA / DNA / peptides*, and many other amide syntheses.

Predict the products of the following reactions.

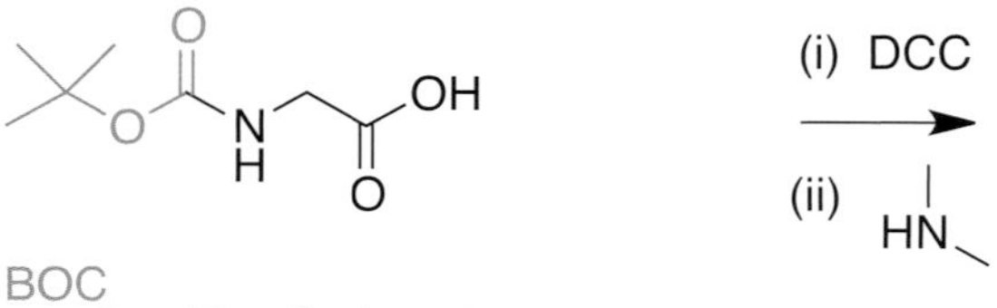
O
OH
O
N
H
O
(i) DCC
(ii)
HN

BOC
tert-ButylOxyCarbonyl

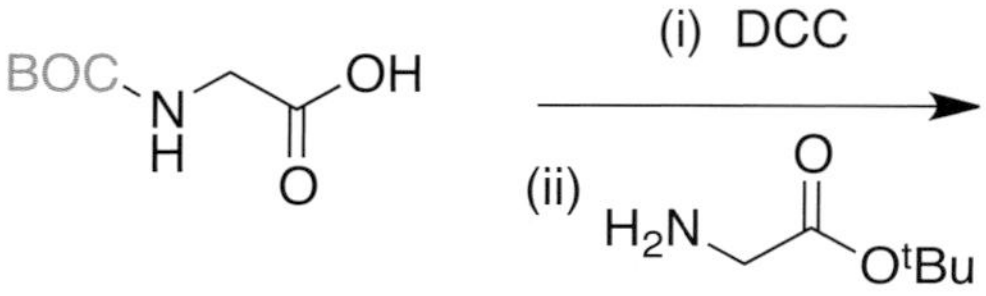
BOC
N
H
OH
O
(i) DCC
(ii)
H_2N
O
O^tBu

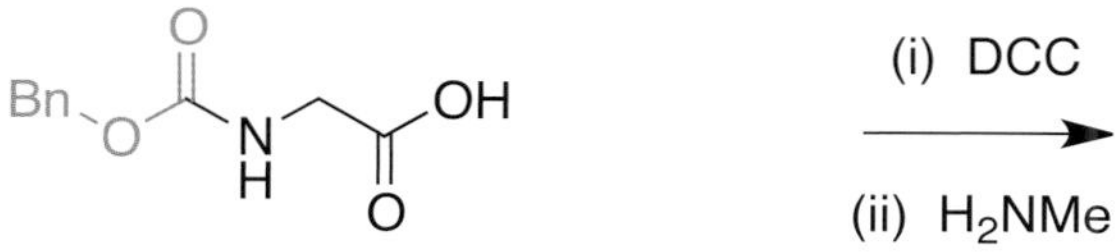
Bn
O
O
N
H
OH
O
(i) DCC
(ii) H_2NMe

CBZ
CarboxyBenZyl

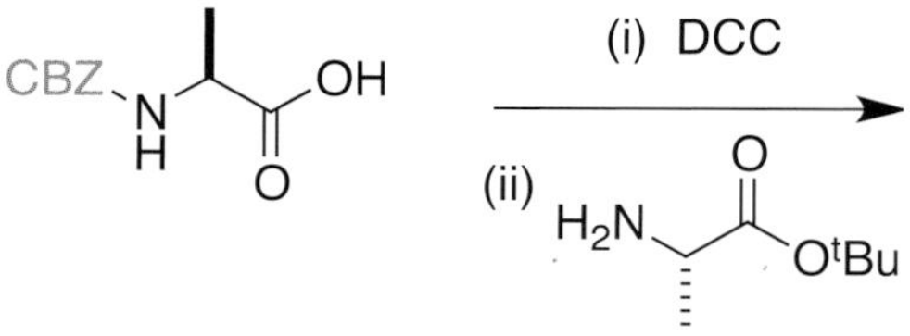
CBZ
N
H
OH
O
(i) DCC
(ii)
H_2N
O
O^tBu

F Activation Of *Phosphate* Acids In Cells Via Phosphate Anhydrides

Formation Of Mixed Anhydrides Of Phosphorus Acids

Intracellular acylation reactions can proceed via *unsymmetrical / mixed* anhydrides like acyl phosphates, derived from phosphoric acids. Complete the following diagrams.

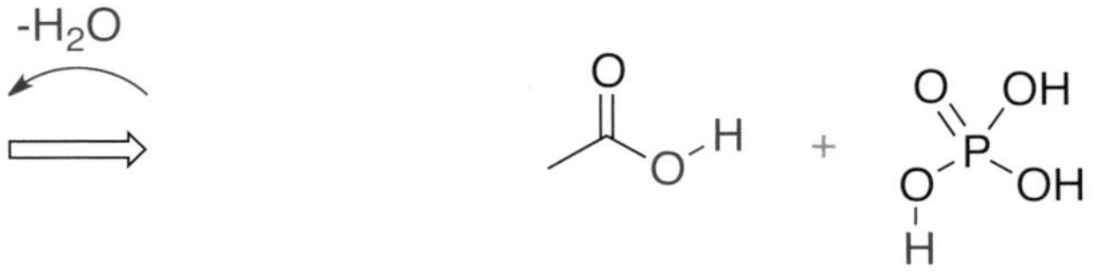

----

acyl phosphate

Blue coloring in the diagram above implies water attacks the *carbonyl / P-atom* of the acyl phosphate; this is a reasonable hypothesis because phosphate is a *better / worse* leaving group than acetate.

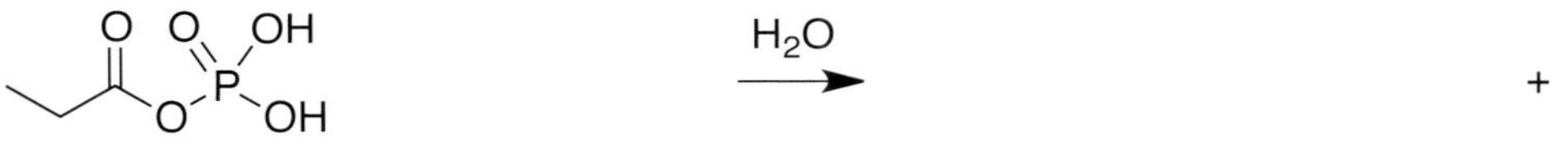

----

carboxylic and phosphoric acids

Hydroxyl groups in acylphosphates are acidic, so they are *protonated / deprotonated* in most environments.

196

Acyl adenylate is the mixed anhydride of acetic acid and adenosine monophosphate (AMP); draw this compound.

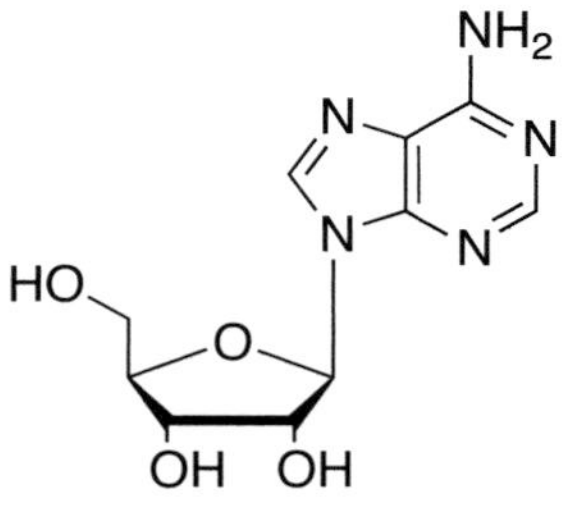

adenosine

---

acyl adenylate

Draw adenosine monophosphate (AMP), adenosine diphosphate (ADP), and adenosine triphosphate (ATP). Two of these, *AMP / ADP / ATP*, contain anhydrides of phosphoric acid.

AMP

ADP

ATP

Show curly arrows to indicate the mode of attack of a carboxylate on ATP that would result in formation of AMP and acyl pyrophosphate.

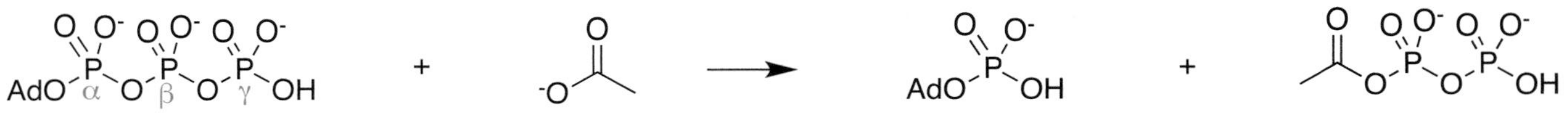

AMP and acyl pyrophosphate

The process shown above involved attack of the carboxylate on the α / β / γ phosphorus. ADP and acyl {mono}phosphate would be formed from attack of the carboxylate on the α / β / γ phosphorus.

Negatively charged phosphate groups *attract / repel* anionic nucleophiles so these reactions are *faster / slower* if encapsulated in an enzyme active site that balances the charges by forming ion pairs.

14 Introducing, The Amino Acids!

from chapter(s) _____ in the recommended text

A Introduction

Focus

Amino acids have several common features, but also each has some distinct properties because of their different side-chains.

Reasons To Care

Combinations of the 20 genetically-encoded amino acid building blocks impart diverse properties to peptides and proteins that impact some of the most interesting molecular interactions in living systems. It is necessary to know what the amino acids are, their ionization states at different pHs, a test that can be applied to detect free *N*-termini, and methods that can be used to isolate optically active samples from racemic forms.

a

-Arg-Gly-Asp-

b

H-Tyr-Gly-Gly-Phe-Met-OH

Figure 1. Even small sequences of amino acids can have important biological properties. **a** The RGD sequence involved in binding the cell surface protein family called *integrins* in cell-cell and cell-matrix recognition processes. **b** Opiate peptide *Met-enkephalin*.

Concepts Involved

acids and bases • condensation of amines with carbonyls • kinetic differentiation of enantiomers

Objective

This section introduces the amino acids as families based on similar properties of their side chains (hydrophobic, hydrophilic, acidic, basic *etc*), and lays foundations to understand syntheses and properties of peptides and proteins, as outlined in the next section.

B Nomenclature And Conventions

Amino acids are best drawn with the *N*-terminus on the *left / right*, and the *C*-terminus on the *left / right*.

Gly is the simplest amino acid, $HO_2CCH_2NH_2$, because it has no side-chain.

Even though it is the convention to show amino acids and peptides in uncharged states, in reality at neutral pH they exist with a *N*-terminal *ammonium / carboxylate* and a *C*-terminal *carboxylate / ammonium*.

Draw Gly without charges, and indicate the *N*- and *C*-termini, then show its *apolar / zwitterionic* form.

_____

glycine, neutral form

_____

glycine, charged form

Draw *cis*- and *trans*-forms of the amide in H-Gly-NHMe and their amide bond resonance structures. Rotation about the CO-NHMe bond is *fast / slow* compared with rotation about a RCH₂-NHMe in an amine because of *resonance / hybridization*.

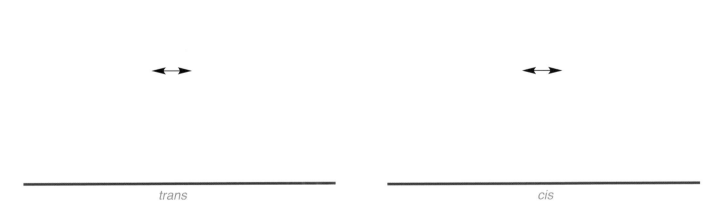

_____

trans

_____

cis

The amide bond is essentially *tetrahedral / flat* because of this resonance, and the H-Gly-NHMe has considerable $sp^3 / sp^2 / sp$ character.

In some ways, amide bonds in peptides and proteins resemble *alkynes / alkenes / alkanes*.

Usually, the preferred conformer of amide bonds in peptides and proteins is *cis / trans* for steric reasons. *Cis* and *trans* nomenclature in peptides refers to the orientation of the atoms in the peptide backbone, and this *is / is not* the same as those set by the priority rules.

There are *20 / 40 / 10* genetically encoded amino acids in proteins.

Learning the amino acid structures requires memorization, but some concepts can help. First, draw the amino acids with their amine group on the left, begin a zigzag chain with the first bond "zagging" downwards; if this convention is followed then the configuration of the first genetically encoded amino acid in the sequence has its side chains pointing back.

Second, learn the amino acids by categories of side chains. For instance, the *four* amino acids with *aliphatic / aromatic* side chains: Ala, Val (^{i}Pr side chain), Leu (^{i}PrCH$_2$), Ile {(*S*)-CHMeEt}, and Pro {which is (*S*)-pyrrolidine 2-carboxylic acid}.

The carbon between the NH and CO of an amino acid is the $C\alpha$ / $C\beta$ / $C\gamma$ and the first atom in any *side chain* attached to it is labeled $C\alpha$ / $C\beta$ / $C\gamma$.

Third, note any peculiarities in each group of amino acids. In the group above, for instance, isoleucine has a chiral center in the side chain, at $C\alpha$ / $C\beta$ / $C\gamma$.

C Amino Acids With Lipophilic Side Chains

Draw the amide *cis* and *trans* forms of Me-Ala-NHMe (alanine, Ala, has a methyl side chain), label the $C\alpha$ and $C\beta$ atoms, and indicate the bond rotations that ϕ, ψ and ω describe.

trans   *cis*

Each amino acid can be represented by a three- and a one-letter code.

alanine, Ala, A   *valine, Val, V*   *leucine, Leu, L*   *isoleucine, Ile, I*

All genetically encoded amino acids have *L- / D-*configurations; these relate to *the configuration of glyceraldehyde / to R and S-nomenclature.*

Proline is an "odd-ball": it is the only amino acid that is a *tertiary / secondary / primary* amine. Draw the *cis* and *trans* isomers of Me-Pro-NHMe.

_____   _____
              trans   *cis*

Peptides that contain proline are *more / less* likely to populate conformers in solution that have *cis*-amide bonds than ones that do not have a Pro residue.

D Alcohol And Thiol Amino Acids

Two amino acids contain side chains with alcohols: *Ser / Thr* (CH_2OH side chain) and *Ser / Thr* {(R)-CH(OH)Me}, and two contain sulfur: *Met / Cys* (CH_2SH) and *Ser / Thr / Cys / Met* (CH_2CH_2SMe).

Draw Ser, Thr, Cys, and Met: in each case, deduce the configuration at Cα (*R* or *S*).

_____   _____   _____   _____
   serine   *threonine*   *cysteine*   *methionine*

One of the amino acids, *Ser (S) / Thr (T) / Cys (C) / Met (M)*, has a different configuration than all the other genetically encoded amino acids, because

_____   _____ .

E Acidic Amino Acids And Their Derivatives

Two amino acids have carboxylic acids in their side chains, Asp (CH_2CO_2H) and Glu ($CH_2CH_2CO_2H$), and two (Asn) and (Gln) feature the corresponding primary amides.

Draw Asp, Glu, Asn, and Gln in neutral forms (*ie* not as ammonium/carboxylates that they exist as at neutral pH), and indicate the most acidic proton in each case (*ie* side-chain or main-chain acid group?).

_____   _____   _____   _____
       D   *E*   *N*   *Q*

Inductive effects from the amine-*N* of Asp and Glu make their main chain CO_2H protons *more / less* acidic than the carboxylic acid in the side chain.

F Basic Amino Acids

Three amino acids have *basic* side chains: *H/ K/ R* {CH_2(4-imidazoyl); pKa of conjugate acid 6.4}, *His / Lys / Arg* ($CH_2CH_2CH_2 CH_2NH_2$; pKa of conjugate acid 10.8), and *His / Lys / Arg* ($CH_2CH_2CH_2NHCNHNH_2$; pKa of the conjugate acid of the *guanidine* side chain 12.).

Draw these amino acids in order of decreasing basicity of the side chain in the free base amino acids, and label the side chain atoms of Lys with α, β *etc.*

most basic	*intermediate*	*least basic*

Draw diagrams describing the likely protonation states of His (pKa's 1.82, 9.17, 6.00, and 7.9) at the following pH values.

pH = 0	*4*	*8*	*12*
di-cation			*monoanion*

G Aromatic Amino Acids

Besides His, Phe (CH_2Ph), Tyr ($CH_2C_6H_4OH$; pKa of side chain 10.1), and Trp contain *aromatic* side chains. Draw these amino acids and indicate their one letter codes.

phenylalanine	*tyrosine*	*tryptophan*

The phenolic side chain of tyrosine is a *stronger / weaker* acid than the side-chain carboxylic acids of Asp and Glu.

The *indole / imidazole / pyridine* N-atom of tryptophan *is / is not* significantly basic because it is involved in aromaticity.

H Summary Of Some Structural Types

To review, draw and name four amino acids with hydrophobic side chains, two with acidic side chains, and two with basic side-chains. Show them in their L-configuration (the one found in genetically encoded proteins), with the amine on the left, the acid on the right, and the side-chains pointed downwards.

hydrophobic 1　　　*hydrophobic 2*　　　*hydrophobic 3*　　　*hydrophobic 4*

name: _____

acidic 1　　　　　　　　　　*acidic 2*

basic 1　　　　　　　　　　*basic 2*

I Isoelectric Points

The pH at which an amino acid has no net charge is called *isoelectric / isobestic* point, *ie* its pI value.

Amino acids without ionizable side chains have pI values that are *smaller than / midway between / greater than* the pKa values for their acid and amine groups.

Calculate the pI for alanine for which the pKa of the carboxylic acid group is 2.34, and that of the amine in its ammonium form is 9.62.

_____

structure of alanine indicating pKa's

_____

calculation

Calculation of pI values for amino acids *with ionizable side chains* is based on the *average / greatest* pKa of the two similarly ionizing groups.

Calculate the pI of Lys. This residue has three pKa values: 2.18, 8.9, 10.79 (the side chain amine is the most basic one, show which groups these pKa levels are associated with).

_____

structure of Lys indicating pKa's

_____

calculation

Calculate the pI for glutamic acid that has pKa values of: 2.19, 4.2, 9.67 (the $C^{\alpha}HCO_2H$ group is the most acidic).

_____

structure of glutamic acid indicating pKa's

_____

calculation

Classify each of the following amino acids:

Asp, *acidic / neutral / basic*   Asn, *acidic / neutral / basic*   Arg, *acidic / neutral / basic*

Glu, *acidic / neutral / basic*   Gln, *acidic / neutral / basic*

Ser, *acidic / neutral / basic*   Thr, *acidic / neutral / basic*

Select amino acids from the following sets that have:

the *highest* pI value *Asn / Arg / Thr / Asp* the *lowest* pI value *Glu / Arg / Ser / Asn*
most *negative* charge at pH 6 *Glu / Arg / Ser / Asn* most *positive* charge at pH 2 *Glu / Lys / Tyr / Asn*

Migratory aptitude in media placed under an electrical potential tends to be proportional to *mass / charge / mass divided by charge*.

In electrophoresis at pH 4, *Glu / Lys / Tyr / Asn* will migrate to the negative electrode faster than the others.

An amino acid pI value of 6.4 will migrate *to the negative electrode / to the positive electrode / not at all* in electrophoresis at pH 6.4.

If that same amino acid is subject to electrophoresis at pH 8 it will *migrate to the negative electrode / migrate to the positive electrode / not migrate at all*.

J The Ninhydrin Test

Ninhydrin stains primary amines, including amino acids, deep blue.

Of the three carbonyls in ninhydrin the most reactive is (are) the *central / peripheral* one(s).

Draw ninhydrin hydrate, and the condensation product it forms with one equivalent of a primary amine.

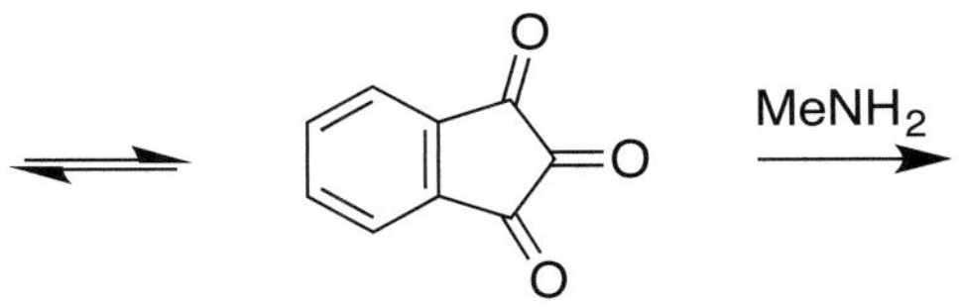

hydrate *ninhydrin* *imine*

Draw the mechanism for the imine formation here:

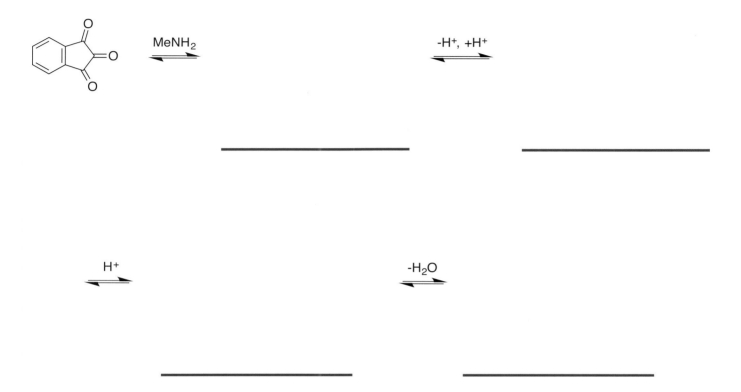

MeNH$_2$

-H$^+$, +H$^+$

H$^+$

-H$_2$O

The ninhydrin test detects amino acids (*eg* after separation via electrophoresis) with primary amines (*ie* does not work well for *proline / alanine*).

In solid phase peptide synthesis, for instance, the ninhydrin test can reveal if all the *amine / alcohol* groups on a supported peptide have been coupled, or if there are some unreacted ones available.

Proline *does / does not* have a primary amine group; it stains brown.

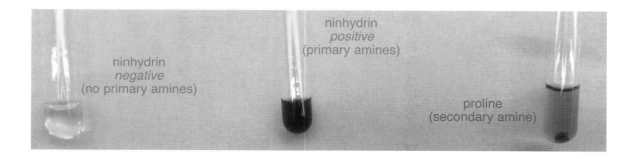

ninhydrin
negative
(no primary amines)

ninhydrin
positive
(primary amines)

proline
(secondary amine)

Deduce a mechanism for the formation of the purple dye illustrated below from Val (do not show the mechanism of imine formation, that is already shown in the last question).

-H$_2$O

-CO$_2$

hydrolysis

imine

imine enolate

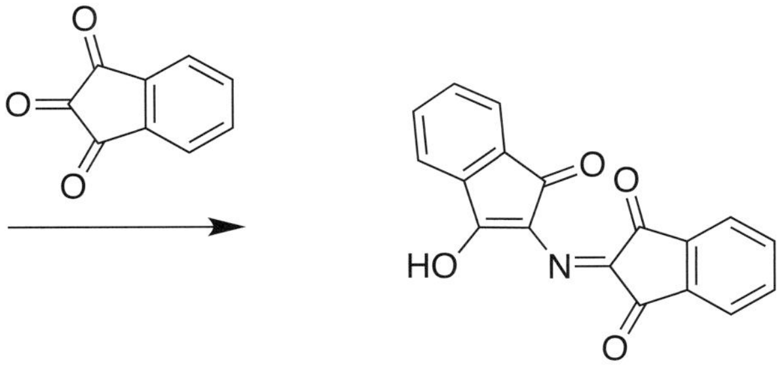

amine

purple

When a tiny amount of amino acid is reacted with ninhydrin a deep *purple / yellow / orange* color forms immediately; that color *can / cannot* be quantified by UV.

The ninhydrin test can be used as a qualitative check from the presence of free amine at peptide *N*-termini, *and / but not* to quantitate the amount of that amine.

K Kinetic Resolutions Of Amino Acids

Kinetic resolutions involve fast reaction of one enantiomer relative to the other so that starting material enriched in one configuration may be recovered from product enriched in the other.

In a *perfect / poor* kinetic resolution, all one antipode of the starting material would remain unreacted, while all the other would be turned into product.

Illustrate kinetic resolution of racemic *N*-acetyl Leu being preferentially hydrolyzed to the free (*S*)-amino acid by pig kidney aminoacylase.

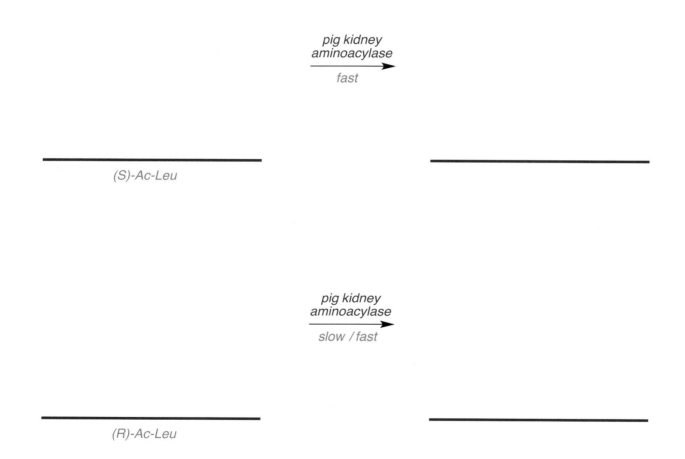

*pig kidney
aminoacylase*
$\xrightarrow{}$
fast

(S)-Ac-Leu

*pig kidney
aminoacylase*
$\xrightarrow{}$
slow / fast

(R)-Ac-Leu

The maximum yield of almost enantiomerically pure reactant after the reaction above is *100 % / just under 0 % / 2 %*.

The maximum yield of almost enantiomerically pure product in this reaction is *100 % / just under 0 % / 2 %*.

The enantiomeric excess of the product in these reactions *increases / decreases* with conversion, while that of the starting material *increases / decreases*.

15 Peptide Syntheses

from chapter(s) _____ in the recommended text

A Introduction

Focus

If amino acids were *C*-activated without any *N*-protection, then they would dimerize, cyclodimerize, oligomerize, and polymerize in uncontrollable ways. Sequence-specific syntheses of peptides require coupling of appropriately *N*-protected units with *C*-protected ones.

Epimerization can be avoided by adding single amino acids to the *N*-terminus of a growing chain, but only if the protection on the amino acid is a carbamate and not an amide. Certain side-chains must be deprotected, and others must be "insulated" from reactive cations in deprotection conditions by using scavengers. Then there is the special case where the *C*-terminal protecting group on the growing chain is a polymeric support, *ie* solid phase methods. These aspects of peptide synthesis are the focus of this section.

conventional peptide synthesis can be performed like this .....

N-terminal carbamate protection ◄- - - - - - - - - - - - - - - *synthesis in C- to N-direction*   *C-terminal protection*

but not like this .....

N-terminal amide protection   *synthesis in N- to C-direction* - - - - - - - - - - - - - ►

Reasons To Care

Researchers in all branches of the biological and biomedical sciences may need peptides or modified peptides for use in their research.

Concepts Involved

activation of carboxylic acids • reactions of activated acids with amines • aromaticity

Objective

Understanding the possibilities and limitations of this aspect of organic chemistry so that it might be applied later.

B Solution Phase Methods

The Need For Protection

Reactions Of Unprotected Amino Acids

Carboxylic acids *do / do not* combine with amines to form amides in the absence of activating agents.

If, in an attempt to make the dipeptide H-Met-Phe-OH, methionine and phenylalanine were mixed, and thionyl chloride was added this would first convert the carboxylic acids to *acid / alkyl* chlorides, then four possible linear dipeptides would form; draw them using the same nomenclature (three letter codes).

H-Met-Phe-OH

| *dipeptide* | *dipeptide* | *dipeptide* | *dipeptide* |

There are also three possible cyclic by-products, *diketopiperazines*, in the reaction above; show these:

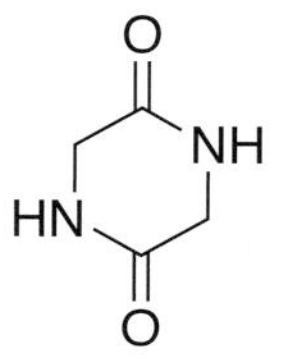

diketopiperazine   *symmetrical diketopiperazine*   *unsymmetrical diketopiperazine*

Polymeric materials *would / would not* also be produced in this reaction.

Overall, this route would be a(n) *satisfactory / impractical* synthesis of a particular linear dipeptide because of separation issues.

The problem is that the building blocks can react using the amine and/or acid functionalities. To solve this problem it is necessary to *C- / N-* protect one of the fragments and *C- / N-* protect the other.

Reactions Of Protected Amino Acids

Predict the products of the following reactions, where P and P' are *N-* and *C*-protecting groups.

P-Met-Cl + H-Gly-P' $\longrightarrow$ P-Phe-Cl + H-Pro-P' $\longrightarrow$

Illustrative Protection: BOC/^{t}Bu

N-BOC Protected Amino Acids

Tert-butyloxycarbonyl, ^{t}BuOCO- or BOC-, groups are used to protect *amines / carboxylic acids* so that they no longer become nucleophilic.

BOC groups are added in much the same way as acid chlorides or acid anhydrides add to *amines / carboxylic acids*.

Draw full structures for the products of the following reactions:

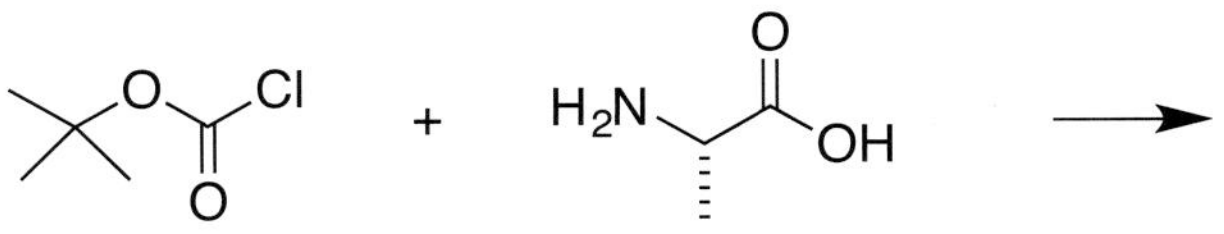

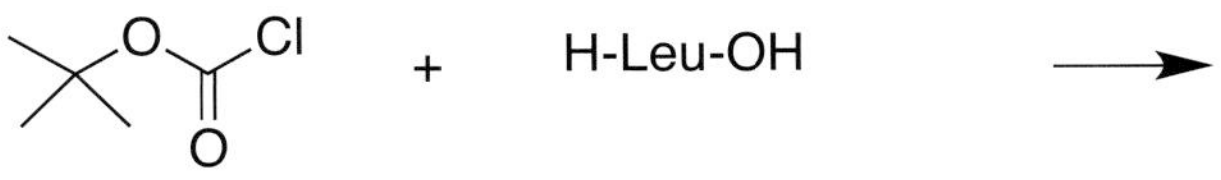

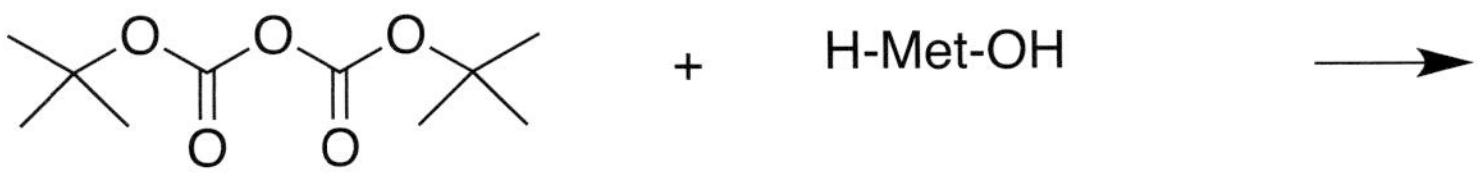

H-Leu-OH

H-Met-OH

H-Val-OH $\xrightarrow{\text{(BOC)}_2\text{O}}$

BOC groups can be removed from amines by treatment with *trifluoroacetic (TFA) / citric* acid.

BOC removal involves protonation of the carbonyl group, then formation of a *tert*-butyl carbocation and carbon *dioxide / monoxide*.

212

Show the mechanism for BOC-deprotection of BOC-Phe-OH using TFA.

$\xrightarrow{H^+}$

$\longrightarrow$

_____
BOC-Phe-OH

_____

$\xrightarrow{-CO_2}$

+

_____
unstable carbamate

_____
amino acid

_____
carbocation

Give the products of the following reactions

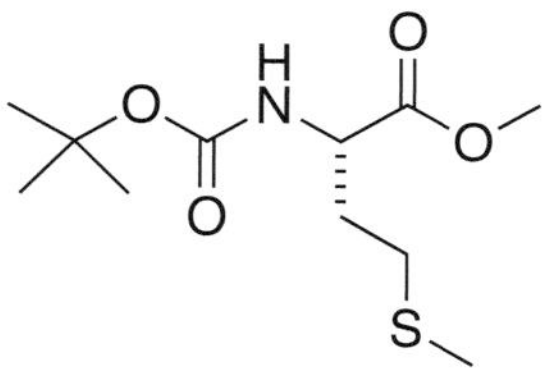

$\xrightarrow{CF_3CO_2H}$

_____

BOC-Val-Ala-OH $\xrightarrow{TFA}$

_____

tert-Butyl cations generated in removal of BOC groups can react with amino acid starting materials or peptide products to give *desirable / undesirable* by-products.

Scavengers like *HSiEt$_3$ / SiMe$_4$* may be added in BOC removal to "mop-up" ^{t}Bu cations to prevent these carbocations reacting with nucleophilic groups on the peptide product.

Two of the following compounds are more reactive to electrophiles, like ^{t}Bu cations, in electrophilic aromatic substitution reactions than the other one; circle those two reactive aromatic systems.

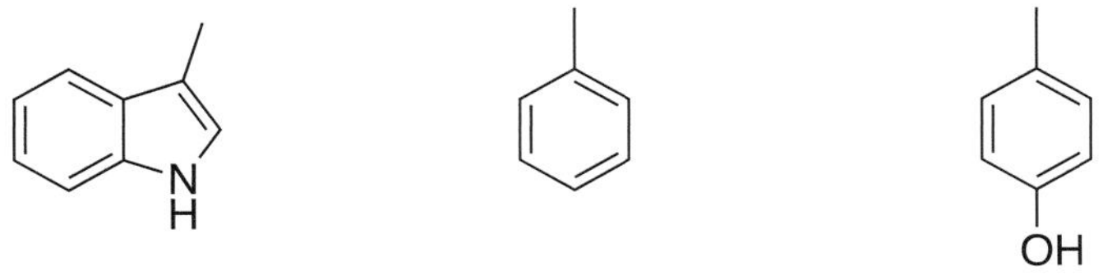

Which *two* of the following amino acids have nucleophilic side chains that might most *easily* react with carbocations: *Ala / Tyr / Phe / Leu / Met / Trp*. Circle those amino acids.

Predict the products of the following reactions (*ie* likely by-products in peptide syntheses).

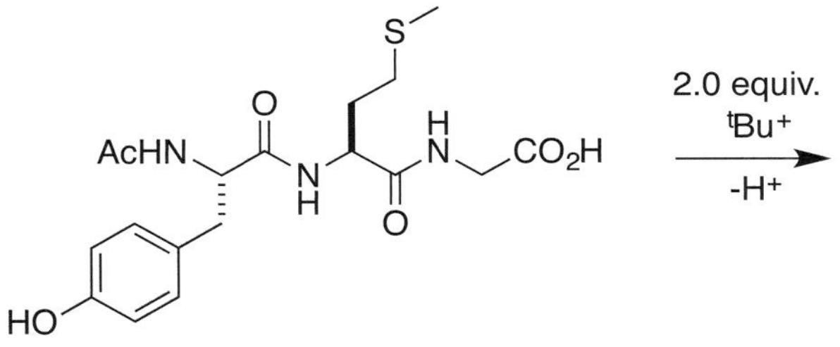

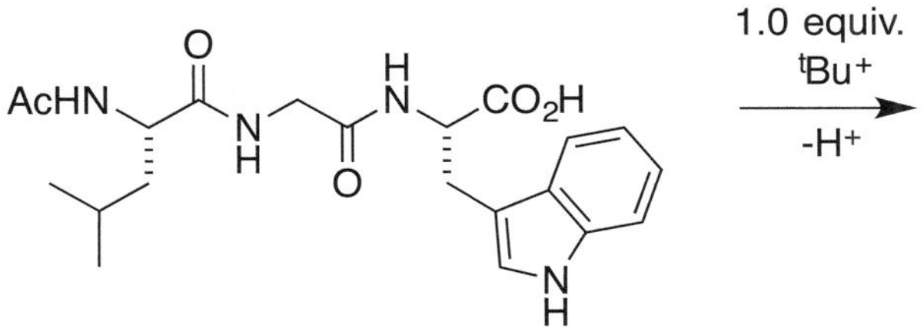

2.0 equiv.
^{t}Bu$^+$
———————→
-H$^+$

1.0 equiv.
^{t}Bu$^+$
———————→
-H$^+$

Reactions like these *usually / never* require a scavenger to prevent formation of by-products.

Show the mechanism for BOC-deprotection of BOC-Try(Bn)-OH using TFA, and indicate the product formed via reaction of the ^{t}butyl cation with HSiEt$_3$.

BOC-Tyr(Bn)-OH

H$^+$ →

→

-CO$_2$ →

+

unstable carbamate

amino acid

carbocation

HSiEt$_3$ →

carbocation

by-product

C-Protection Of Amino Acids With ^{t}Bu-Groups

Trifluoroacetic acid also removes *tert*-butyl groups from ^{t}Bu-esters, via protonation of the carbonyl group. Draw this mechanism for Ac-Met-O^{t}Bu.

H$^+$ →

+

Ac-Met-O^{t}Bu

by-product cation

1-Adamantyl esters *can / cannot* be cleaved as rapidly under the same conditions as *tert*-butyl esters.

tert-Butyl carbocations are generated in these reactions, hence scavengers *are / are not* sometimes necessary for *C*-deprotection of peptides containing nucleophilic groups.

Show the products of the following (use abbreviations and three letter codes for the amino acids).

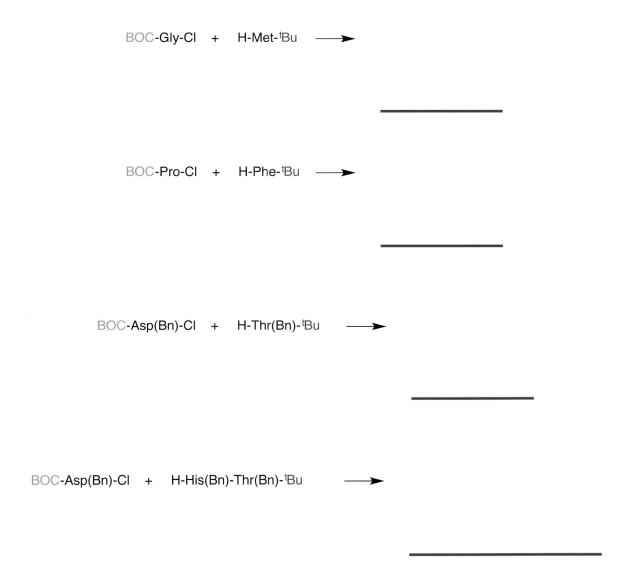

BOC-Gly-Cl   +   H-Met-ᵗBu   ⟶

_____

BOC-Pro-Cl   +   H-Phe-ᵗBu   ⟶

_____

BOC-Asp(Bn)-Cl   +   H-Thr(Bn)-ᵗBu   ⟶

_____

BOC-Asp(Bn)-Cl   +   H-His(Bn)-Thr(Bn)-ᵗBu   ⟶

_____

Activation Of *N*-Protected Amino Acids

In practice, amino acid chlorides are slightly too *reactive / unreactive* for routine peptide syntheses.

Peptide syntheses tend to feature *in situ* activation of *N*-protected amino acids using *carbodiimide / amine* reagents.

Unfortunately, the by-product from activating amino acids with DCC, ie *dicyclohexylurea / dicyclohexylcarbamate*, is relatively insoluble in most solvents making it difficult to wash away.

Ethyl (3-dimethylaminopropyl) carbodiimide, EDCI, is often used in place of DCC because *it is more active / the by-products can be protonated and are water-soluble*.

Draw activation of BOC-Phe-OH (draw a structure below that shows the carboxylic acid) with EDCI, then reaction with H-Ala-O^{t}Bu, hence deduce the structure of the by-product that forms with this reagent.

Let _____ be represented as $R^1\!-\!N\!\!=\!\!\bullet\!\!=\!\!N\!-\!R^2$

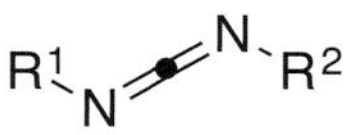

_____
EDCI

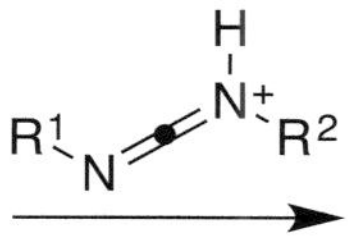

$R^1\!-\!N\!\!=\!\!\bullet\!\!=\!\!\overset{\overset{H}{|}}{N^+}\!-\!R^2$
$\longrightarrow$

$H_2N\!-\!\overset{O}{\underset{}{C}}\!-\!O^tBu$
$\longrightarrow$

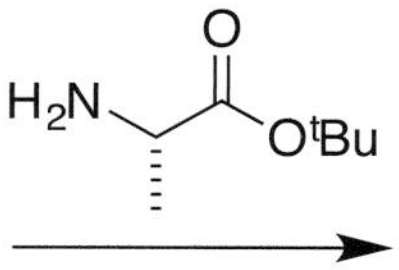

_____
BOC-Phe-O⁻

_____

+

_____
BOC-Phe-Ala-O^{t}Bu

_____
by-product

The Epimerization Problem

One of the challenges in peptide synthesis is retaining the configurations of the chiral-$C\alpha$ centers. It is economically viable to begin with optically pure amino acids in peptide syntheses. However if they racemize (applies to all except Thr and Ile, which *decompose / epimerize*) in the carboxylate activation process then coupling with optically pure *C*-protected amino acids will result in the formation of *enantiomeric / epimeric* products.

Mixtures of epimers tend to be *easy / difficult* to separate into their isomeric components.

Racemization of activated amino acids can occur if a carbonyl group on the *N*-terminus cyclizes by attack of its *O*-atom on the activated intermediate to give an *azlactone / hydantoin*.

Show this cyclization for an activated form of Ac-Ala-X and for BOC-Ala-X (where X is a leaving group; draw the full structures of the amino acids), and compare the inductive effects of Me *vs* the ^{t}BuO to predict which would form the undesired cyclic intermediate faster.

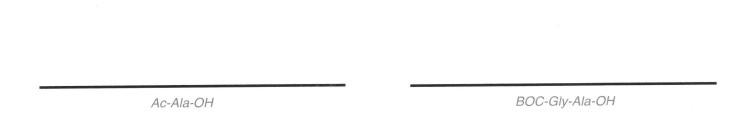

azlactone
forms rapidly / slowly

azlactone
forms rapidly / slowly

Enolization of the azlactone products *is / is not* driven by aromatic stabilization in the product and simultaneous *loss / retention* of amino acid stereochemistry.

The acyl group in the first example is representative of any amide bond in a peptide, but the carbonyl group of the BOC group is not an amide but a(n) *urea / carbamate*.

Carbonyl C=O atoms are *more / less* nucleophilic in amides than in carbamates.

Draw the full structures of Ac-Ala-OH and BOC-Gly-Ala-OH, and circle the amide bonds in both structures that can form azlactones.

Ac-Ala-OH

BOC-Gly-Ala-OH

Strategies In Solution Phase Syntheses That Avoid Epimerization

Boc-Gly-Ala-OH *will / will not* tend to epimerize when activated at the *C*-terminus.

In general, any peptide *will / will not* tend to epimerize when activated on the *C*-terminus.

Consider the two possible solution phase syntheses of BOC-Ile-Val-Ala-O^{t}Bu using the final couplings at the positions shown. Indicate which route is more prone to epimerization, and circle the amino acid in that structure that is most prone to epimerization.

BOC-Ile⦚Val-Ala-O^{t}Bu   BOC-Ile-Val⦚Ala-O^{t}Bu

more / less prone to racemization   *more / less prone to racemization*

circle the one amino acid in one of these structures that is most vulnerable to epimerization

In conclusion, solution phase syntheses usually *are / are not* best performed by adding activated *N*-carbamate-protected amino acids to a growing peptide chain.

In other words, solution-phase peptide syntheses are optimally performed in the *C- to N- / N- to C-* direction.

C Solid Phase Peptide Syntheses

In solution phase syntheses, by-products *are / are not* mixed with the desired product at the end of the reaction.

Purification from by-products *is / is not* usually required at each stage of solution phase syntheses.

If one end of a peptide were attached to an insoluble polymer, then this would make it *harder / easier* to purify because the by-products could be used in excess then washed away after the reaction is complete; these are the major *disadvantages / advantages* of *solid phase* peptide syntheses.

Solid phase syntheses *are / are not* optimally performed by activating the *C*-terminus of a growing peptide chain and adding a *C*-protected amino acid ester, because of epimerization issues (see discussion of solution phase syntheses).

In solid phase peptide syntheses, it is best to attach the polymer to the *C / N*-terminus.

Polystyrene is often used as a support for solid phase peptide syntheses; it is modified so that some of the phenyls are *para*-substituted with chloromethyl (-CH$_2$Cl) groups.

Show the structure of styrene, polystyrene, and the copolymer of styrene and (4-chloromethylphenyl)ethene.

styrene   *polystyrene*   *"4-chloromethylpolystyrene"*

In typical solid phase syntheses, *N*-protected amino acids are added to “4-chloromethylpolystyrene” (Merrifield’s resin) via a(n) *S_N2 / E2* reaction to attach it to the polymer surface via a benzylic ester linkage.

Show attachment of BOC-Pro-OH to 4-chloromethylpolystyrene with curly arrows.

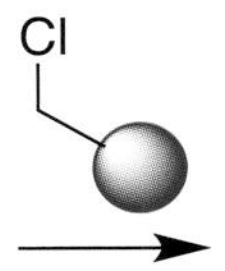
Cl

BOC-Pro-OH

The next step in a solid phase synthesis is removal of the BOC group by treatment with *TFA / THF* often in the *presence / absence* of a scavenger; this *does / does not* cleave the benzylic ester that connects the peptide to the polymer support.

Each cycle of *N*-deprotection and addition of an activated amino acid, elongates the peptide by one residue at the *C / N*-terminus. Show the products of the following reactions (draw unabbreviated structures).

tBu
O
H
N
O
O
O
CO2Bn
TFA
BOC-Ala-OH
EDCI

BOC-Asp(Bn)-support

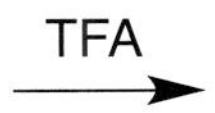
TFA

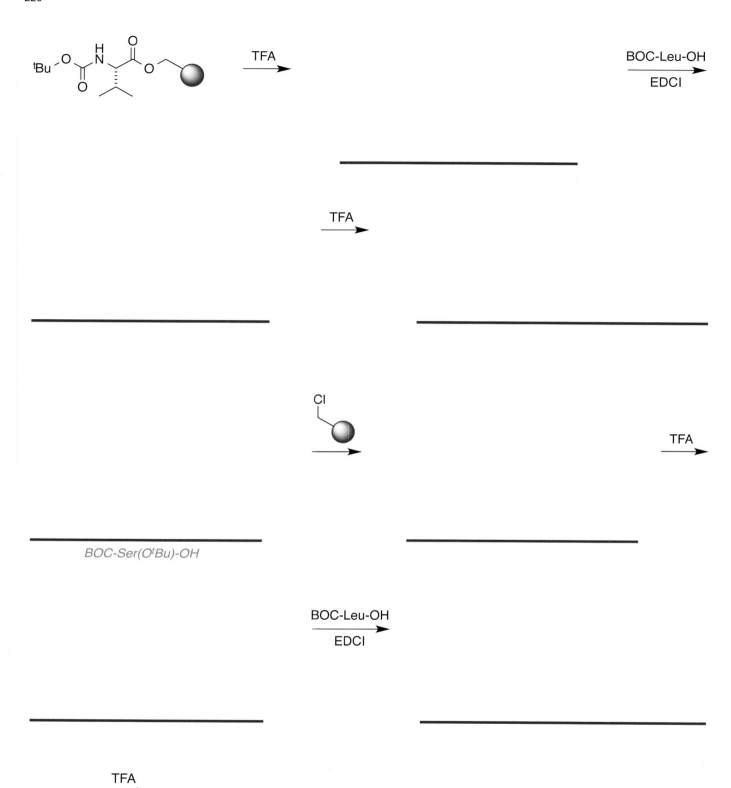

BOC-Ser(O^{t}Bu)-OH

BOC-Leu-OH
EDCI

TFA

When all the amino acids in the desired sequence have been added, the last step is to cleave the desired peptide (and often the *N*-terminal BOC group). This can be achieved by treatment with a mixture containing *HF / HOAc* and scavengers. Show this process for generation of the parent peptide from BOC-Gly-Ala-Met-Pro-polystyrene.

draw peptide

Illustrate how solid phase syntheses featuring poly(4-chloromethylphenylethene) could be used to make H-Leu-Gly-Gly-Phe-Met-OH (use one letter codes throughout, do not draw full structures):

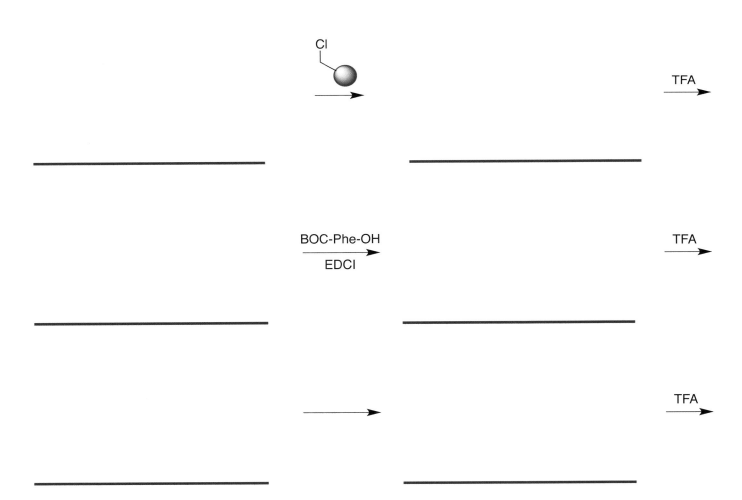

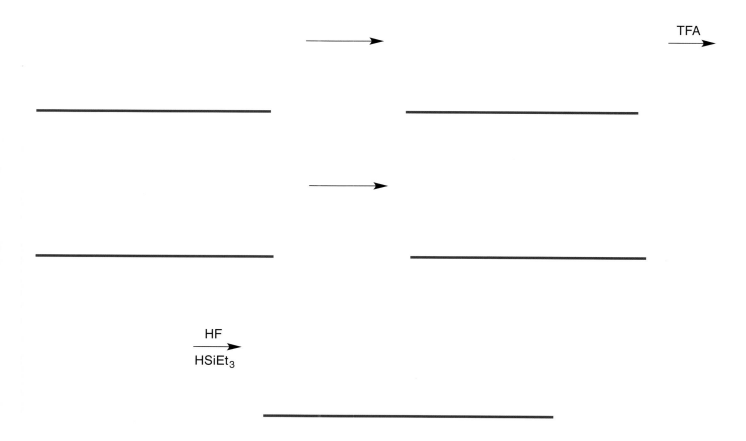

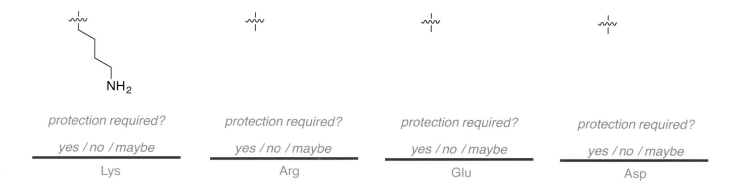

D Side-chain Protection Of Amino Acids

Activated *N*-protected amino acids *may / may not* couple to nucleophilic amino acid side chains on the growing peptide chain, hence side chain protection *is / is not* required.

If side chain protection is used, then it is *desirable / undesirable* that those side chain protecting groups would be cleaved in removal of the main chain *N*-protecting group.

If side chain protection is used, then it is often *desirable / undesirable* that those side chain protecting groups would be cleaved in removal of the peptide from the polymer support in the final purification step.

Draw the side chains for the following amino acids and indicate which ones might need to be protected during amide bond forming steps.

protection required?

yes / no / maybe

Lys

protection required?

yes / no / maybe

Arg

protection required?

yes / no / maybe

Glu

protection required?

yes / no / maybe

Asp

protection required?

yes / no / maybe

Tyr

protection required?

yes / no / maybe

Trp

protection required?

yes / no / maybe

Ser

protection required?

yes / no / maybe

Thr

protection required?

yes / no / maybe

Cys

protection required?

yes / no / maybe

Gln

protection required?

yes / no / maybe

Asn

protection required?

yes / no / maybe

Phe

E The FMOC Approach

The BOC-approach to peptide uses acid to remove the BOC, and *HF / HOAc / citric acid* to remove other protecting groups (usually benzyl-based ones) from the side-chains and *C*-termini.

FMOC *N*-protection is *acid / base* labile, and removal of protection from side-chains and the *C*-termini is via *HF / HOAc / TFA*.

Draw the structures of these three FMOC-protected amino acids.

FMOC-Glu(*t*Bu)-OH

FMOC-Lys(BOC)-OH

FMOC-Ser(*t*Bu)-OH

16 Peptides And Proteins

from chapter(s) _____ in the recommended text

A Introduction

Focus

Short peptides do not tend to form predominant conformations in solution, but as the number of amino acids involved increases, so do the cumulative diverse inter-residue interactions. Eventually these cumulative interactions resolve into dominant conformational shapes, tertiary structures. Secondary structure motifs (*eg* helices and turns) may be recognizable within these states, and the tertiary structures may assemble into complexes having definite quaternary structures. This section is about the factors that contribute to the wonderful diversity of structures that exist for peptides and proteins.

Reasons To Care

Every year the number of protein crystal structures solved increases, and these data are having a profound impact on biology and the biomedical sciences.

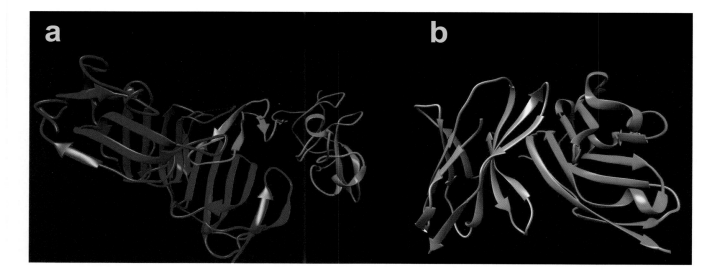

Figure 1. a Interaction between two proteins (uPAR, blue and uPA red) that play key roles in cancer metastasis. uPA complexes by inserting a sheet-turn-sheet motif into a large cavity in uPAR formed by β-sheets. **b** Complex of the "checkpoint proteins" PD1 and PDL1 (yellow and red) that are pivotal to some contemporary immunotherapies of melanoma and other forms of cancer.

Concepts

conformational preferences • proteases • mass spectrometry • primary, secondary, tertiary, and quaternary structures of peptides and proteins.

Objective

This section is to illustrate that the basis of protein science is chemistry.

B Nomenclature And Conventions

Peptides and proteins are composed of amino acids joined by *amide / ester* bonds.

Conventionally, peptides are drawn with *N*-termini on the *left / right*, and the *C*-termini on the *left / right*.

Draw the *tripeptide* (Gly)$_3$ and indicate the *N*- and *C*-termini (begin with the first bond on the left "zagging" down).

triglycine

This tripeptide can be represented as H-Gly-Gly-Gly-OH where the H- indicates a primary (*ie* unsubstituted) *N*-terminal *acid / amide / amine*, and the -OH shows a *C*-terminal carboxylic *acid / amine*.

Even though it is the convention to show peptide in the way indicated above, at neutral pH peptides exist with a *N*-terminal *ammonium / carboxylate* and a *C*-terminal *carboxylate / ammonium*.

Usually, the preferred conformer of amide bonds in peptides and proteins is *cis / trans* (based on the *priority rules / peptide polyamide backbone*).

In some ways, amide bonds in peptides and proteins resemble *alkynes / alkenes / alkanes*.

Dihedral angles in peptides and proteins describe their *local / average* conformations of amino acids in those structures.

These dihedral angles are denoted by Greek symbols like $\phi / \psi / \omega$ (the *N-Cα* dihedral), $\phi / \psi / \omega$ (*Cα-CO*), and $\phi / \psi / \omega$ (*CO-NH*).

Of these dihedral angles, there is *least* variation in $\phi / \psi / \omega$ because of amide resonance.

Draw the amide *cis* and *trans* forms of MeCO-Ala-NHMe (alanine, Ala, has a methyl side chain), label the Cα and Cβ atoms, and indicate the bond rotations that ϕ, ψ and ω describe.

trans

cis

C Primary Structures

Primary structures are the *sequence of amino acids / evolutional origins* of peptides and proteins.

Primary structures of naturally occurring peptides reveal the *sequence / glycosylation state* of DNA that encodes for their syntheses.

Homology is the word used to describe the *similarity / shape* of protein primary sequences. Highly homologous primary sequences may indicate the proteins involved *fold into similar shapes / have similar toxicities*.

Elucidation Via The Edman Degradation

The order of amino acids in peptides and proteins is their *primary / secondary / tertiary* structure.

This order can be determined via an iterative chemical procedure called *The Edman Degradation*, involving two steps. The first step is addition of the free *N*-terminus to phenyl isothiocyanate (PhNCS) to form a thiourea. Show this for H-Ala-Phe-OMe.

+

———

——— ———

PhNCS   H-Ala-Phe-OMe

The second step in the Edman degradation involves *O*-protonation to activate the amide carbonyl causing attack of the *C=S* on the proximal amide *C=O*, formation of a tetrahedral intermediate, then collapse of this to liberate a five-membered ring heterocycle, leaving a free *N*-terminus of the peptide now containing one less amino acid. Rearrangement of the liberated heterocycle gives a thiohydantoin bearing the side-chain of the parent amino acid. Show those final products for the following:

HCl

protonate
and cyclize

———

——— ——— ———

amino acid _____   initial cyclization product   rearranged cyclized product

Chromatographic / crystallographic analysis of the liberated *thiohydantoins* is used to deduce the *N*-terminal amino acid at the start of the process (versus a set of standards with the amino acid side chains of each of the protein amino acids). Repetition of the process allows the protein to be sequenced.

Edman sequencing *does / does not* require the *N*-terminus to be a free primary amine.

If there are disulfide linkages in the substrate, then these must first be reduced to the thio form, then reacted with an alkylating agent to allow these residues to be calibrated in the chromatographic analysis.

It *is / is not* possible to perform an Edman degradation on *polymer supported* peptides.

It *is / is not* possible to perform a complete Edman degradation on *cyclic* peptides.

Draw the first three thiohydantions formed in Edman degradation of H-Met-Pro-Arg-Ala-OH.

first thiohydantoin	*second thiohydantion*	*third thiohydantoin*

There are limits to the number of amino acids that can be sequenced in Edman degradation because small amounts of impurities accumulate increasing signal-to-noise in the HPLC analysis. Consequently, proteins are "cut" into overlapping smaller fragments, these fragments can be sequenced, and ordered by comparing regions overlap. There are two main strategies for cutting peptides: enzymatic and chemical.

Elucidation Via *Enzymatic* Cleavage And Mass Spectrometry

Fragmentation patterns of peptides in *ultraviolet spectroscopy / mass spectrometry* (particularly MS-MS) often allow their primary sequences to be elucidated.

Sequencing in this way is easier for shorter peptides than longer ones, so *proteases / esterases* are often used to cleave proteins *randomly / at predictable sites* so that the fragments can be sequenced.

Endopeptidases are enzymes that catalyze hydrolysis of peptide bonds *within / only at the end* of a chain.

Positions of cleavage *vary / are invariant* for different endopeptidases.

Trypsin

Trypsin tends to cleave only on the *C*-terminal side of Lys and Arg residues. Show the peptide fragments that would be formed when this enzyme is used to digest:

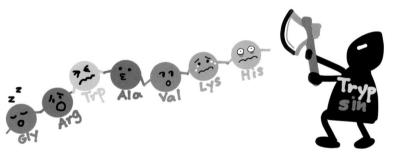

H-Pro-Ala-Pro-Gly-Arg-Trp-Ala-His-Gln-Met-Val-Lys-His-Lys-Pro-Trp-Pro-Ser-Tyr-Thr-Ala-OH

1

fragment 1:

_____

fragment 2:

_____

fragment 3:

_____

fragment 4:

_____

Chymotrypsin

Chymotrypsin is an endopeptidase that cleaves only on the *C*-terminal side of amino acids that have side chains containing six membered rings. Predict the fragments that would be formed in exhaustive degradation of peptide **1**.

fragment 1:

_____

fragment 2:

_____

fragment 3:

_____

fragment 4:

_____

Elastase

Elastase is an endopeptidase that cleaves only on the *C*-terminal side of the smallest amino acids, *ie* Gly and Ala. Predict the fragments that would be formed in elastase-mediated degradation of peptide **1**.

fragment 1:

_____

fragment 2:

_____

fragment 3:

_____

fragment 4:

_____

In fact, a few of the fragments above probably would *not* be formed in appreciable amounts because those endopeptidases mentioned do not cleave amide bonds to proline. Proline is the only amino acid that contains a cyclic secondary amine, and this limits its accessibility to most proteases. Circle the fragments from the three endopeptidases above that are therefore unlikely to form.

Elucidation Via Cyanogen Bromide Cleavage And Mass Spectrometry

Selective, *C*-terminal cleavage of *methionine / threonine / arginine* residues is effected by cyanogen bromide, Br-CN, in aqueous acid.

In this reaction, the *S*-atom of the side-chain of *methionine / threonine / arginine* adds to the nitrile and eliminates the bromide; this creates a sulfonium group (R_2S^+CN) that can be displaced (giving a sulfide) by nucleophilic attack of the Met amide *C=O* on the methionine $C\gamma$ / $C\beta$ / $C\alpha$ atom.

Hydrolysis of the *C=N* bond of the *iminolactone / hydantoin* produced gives cleavage of the peptide chain, and creates a lactone on the *N*-terminal side.

Show the mechanism for cyanogen bromide cleavage of Ac-Met-Ala-NH$_2$ (dipeptide with *N*-terminal acyl group and *C*-terminal amide; draw out the peptide chain).

Br-CN $\longrightarrow$ cyclization $\longrightarrow$

_____   _____
        Ac-Met-Ala-NH$_2$ *sulfonium salt*

hydrolysis $\longrightarrow$

_____   _____   _____
        iminolactone   *lactone*   *Ala-NH$_2$*

Show the products of the following reactions using three letter amino acid abbreviations, but also clearly showing the termini effected by the cyanogen bromide cleavage.

H-Pro-Ala-Met-Val-Lys-Met-Lys-NH$_2$ $\xrightarrow{\text{BrCN}}$

                                 +   +

_____   _____   _____

H-Pro-Ala-Pro-Gly-Arg-Trp-Ala-His-Gln-Met-Val-Lys-His-Lys-Pro-Trp-Pro-Ser-Tyr-Thr-Ala-OH $\xrightarrow{\text{BrCN}}$

                                 +

_____   _____

D Secondary Structures

Highlight those of the following parameters that do *not* facilitate folding of peptides and proteins into strongly favored three-dimensional conformations:

hydrogen bonding between residues   shielding of hydrophobic residues from aqueous surroundings

entropy gains   placing hydrophilic residues at the core   placing hydrophilic residues at the periphery

ionic interactions between charged side-chains   stacking of aromatic rings

packing of one chain against another   overlap of orbitals containing C$\underline{O}$ lone pairs with other CO π^* orbitals

increased temperature   addition of high concentrations of guanidine hydrochloride

The folded shape of a large peptide or protein folds is called its *primary / secondary / tertiary* structure. Within that structure there may be motifs of recognizable *primary / secondary / tertiary* structures.

Types Of Helices

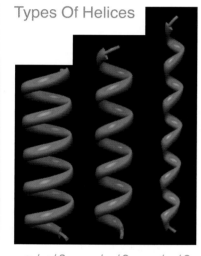

Amino acid blocks that coil into spring-like arrangements are called *helices / sheets / turns*.

Almost invariably, these helical arrangements from L-amino acids spiral in a *right / left* handed corkscrew when viewed from *the C-terminus / the N-terminus / does not matter*.

Crystallographic studies reveal the "tightness" of these spring-like helical regions. Of all helical peptides, the *least / most* common, α-helices, have *3.0 / 3.6 / 4.0* amino acid residues per coil of the helix.

α-Helices are intermediate between π-helices that are the most compressed (least tightly wound) and 3_{10}-which are the most tightly wound. Label the three helices shown here as α, π, or 3_{10}.

His / Glu / Pro is rarely found in α, π, or 3_{10} helices because of the cyclic structure of this residue. However, it is formed in special polyproline helices found in *cholesterol / collagen / citric acid*.

α / π / 3_{10} α / π / 3_{10} α / π / 3_{10}

Other elements of secondary structure include β-sheets. These are sandwich-like regions involving H-bonded sections of amino acids.

Parallel β-sheets have the strands running in *the same / opposite* directions.

Anti-parallel β-sheets have the strands running in *the same / opposite* directions.

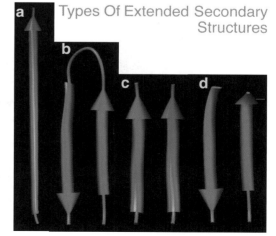

Types Of Extended Secondary Structures

Turns are secondary structure elements in which the strand loops back on itself / the configuration of the amino acids changes.

If the strand forms a U-shape then they are *γ-turns / β-turns*, while *γ-turns / β-turns* are more V-shape.

β-Turns are frequently used to connect two strands to form *parallel / antiparallel* β-sheets.

From the picture of extended secondary structures assign the labeled secondary structures as:

sheet-turn-sheet / parallel β-sheet / antiparallel β-sheet / β-strand

a _____   b _____   c _____   d _____

The following structure depicts a nerve growth factor protein; place a square around a turn region, a rectangle around a sheet region, and a circle around a helical region.

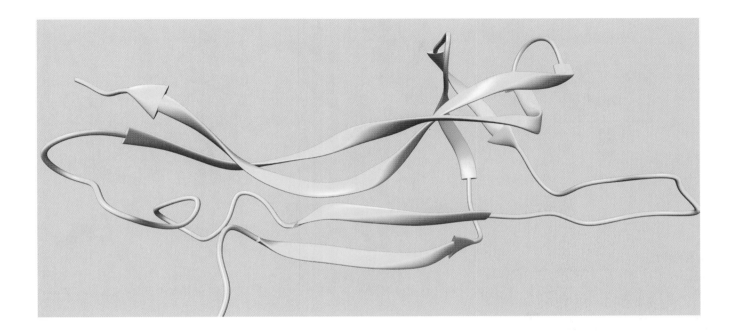

Identify the boxed structures in the following proteins as turns, helices, or sheets.

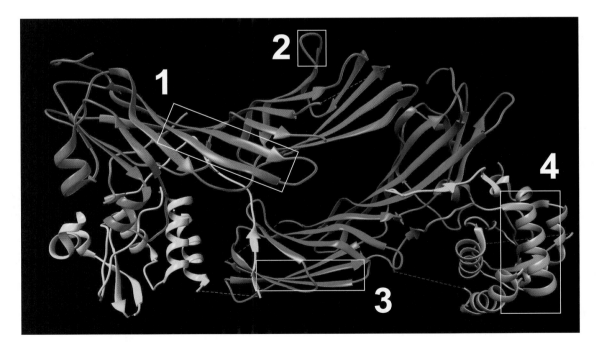

turn / helix /sheet	*turn / helix /sheet*	*turn / helix /sheet*	*turn / helix /sheet*
1	2	3	4

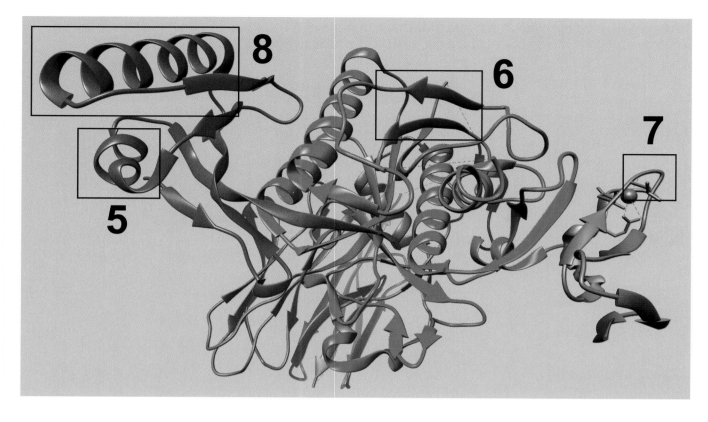

| turn / helix /sheet | turn / helix /sheet | turn / helix /sheet | turn / helix /sheet |
| 5 | 6 | 7 | 8 |

E Tertiary And Quaternary Structures

Tertiary structure is the shape of a protein as a whole formed when the secondary structures assemble.

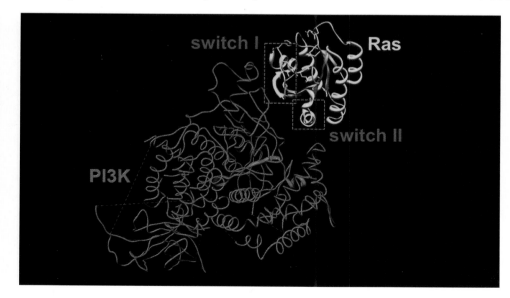

Quaternary structures form when protein units assemble into a macromolecular dimers or oligomers; these protein units usually *are / are not* covalently bound to each other (Figure 1).

Figure 1. Complex of the protein RAS with another one called PI3K. This illustrates the tertiary structures of both proteins, and the quaternary structure of the complex formed between them. RAS regions at the interface are called switch 1 and switch 2 domains. Mutations in RAS are common in cancer, and can be induced by cigarette smoke.

F Constraints On Peptide And Protein Structures

Relatively unconstrained rotation about the ϕ and ψ bonds means most peptides of less than about 20 – 30 amino acids *do / do not* fold into recognizable shapes.

Some longer peptides, and many proteins can fold into different shapes. These shapes can be enforced by cyclization via an amide bond formed between the *C*- and *N*-termini. Illustrate this using amino acid abbreviations for the cyclic peptide from Orn, Leu, Phe, Pro, Val, D-Orn, Leu, Phe, Pro, Val (in that order; this is called gramicidin S. Fill in the molecular structures of L- and D-Orn as indicated.

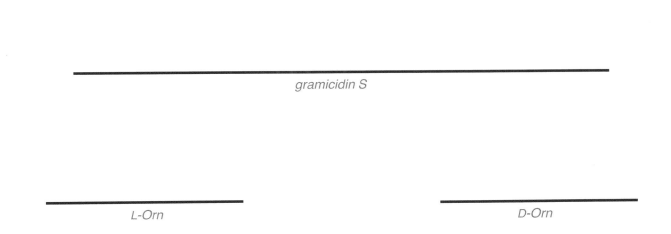

gramicidin S

L-Orn   *D-Orn*

Another way peptides and proteins are made more rigid is via formation of *disulfide bonds* between side chains of *Met / Cys / Ser* residues.

Chemically, disulfide bonds may be formed from thio-containing side-chains using many different mild *oxidizing / reducing* agents.

Reactions of thiols with halogens via a mechanism that involves nucleophilic attack of thiolates on the halogen, then nucleophilic attack on the halo-sulfur compound formed are easy to envisage. Draw the product of BOC-Cys-Cys-O^{t}Bu oxidation (use the BOC and ^{t}Bu abbreviations, but do not abbreviate the amino acids).

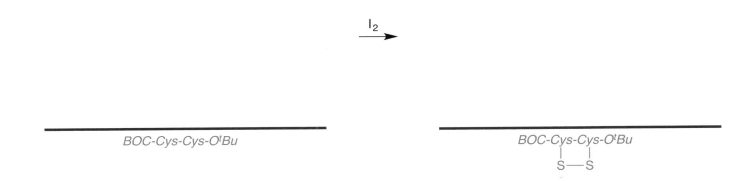

$$\xrightarrow{\text{I}_2}$$

BOC-Cys-Cys-O^{t}Bu   *BOC-Cys-Cys-O^{t}Bu*
                                          | |
                                          S — S

Use nomenclature like in the last question (*ie* using three letter codes) to denote the structure of H-Cys-Tyr-Ile-Gln-Asn-Cys-Pro-Leu-Gly-NH$_2$ after disulfide bond formation.

Indicate all the intramolecular disulfide linked peptides that might arise from oxidizing Ac-Cys-Ala-Cys-Ala-Cys-Ala-Cys-OH (use one letter codes; we count four including two diastereomers where the same Cys residues are linked).

It *is / is not* necessary to control disulfide bond formation when forming compounds like this.

Control of disulfide bond formation *could / could not* be done by using different Cys *S*-protecting groups, chemoselective deprotection, and separate oxidation steps.

Part 4:
Towards Understanding Syntheses Of Natural Products

17 Hydridic Reductions

from chapter(s) _____ in the recommended text

A Introduction

Focus

In the presence of the right catalysts, hydrogen tends to add across non-polarized double bonds (*eg* alkenes and alkynes) easily. However, if the bond is polarized then stepwise addition of hydride then proton is usually the favored reduction strategy. This section focuses on reductions of polarized functional groups via hydridic mechanisms.

all give net addition of H$_2$ after protonation

(EWG = Electron Withdrawing Group)

Reasons To Care

Many organic reactions involve oxidation state changes and net addition of hydrogen is one of the most common reduction pathways. Sometimes in the lab, and almost invariably *in vivo*, it is not practical to achieve reduction using hydrogen gas. Organic chemists therefore achieve many reduction reactions by addition of hydridic agents then acidic work-up, while NADH and similar "gentle" reducing agents are used in Nature.

Concepts Involved

additions of nucleophiles to aldehydes and ketones • acylation reactions • oxidation and reduction processes

Objective

Hydridic reactions can be made to appear quite complex if we try to draw arrows to explain how a reagent "lets go" of a hydride and what becomes of the reagent residues. However, these issues are unimportant relative to the basic idea: addition of hydride placing the negative charge on an electronegative atom, then protonation. This section is designed to convey that simple concept.

B Mechanism

Stepwise reduction of unsaturated bonds can occur via addition of hydride, then a proton. Draw this generic process for the following substrates using clear curly arrows.

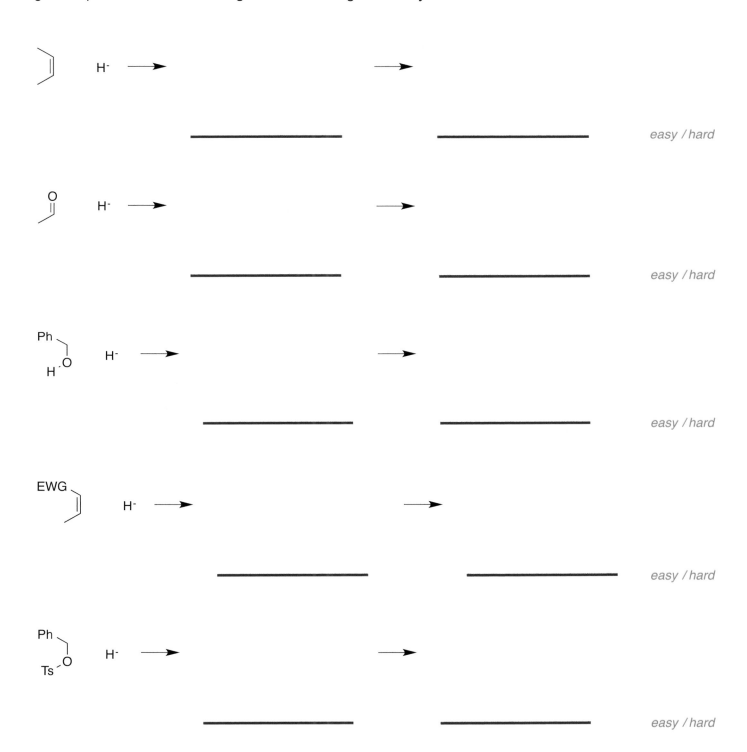

Three of the processes shown above are easy relative to the other two, indicate which ones. It follows that it is *easy / hard* to reduce aldehydes and ketones to alcohols, but *easy / hard* to reduce them to alkanes using hydridic agents.

Write the structures of a tosyl group (Ts) and a tosylate (TsO⁻).

Tosyl groups / tosylates are relatively good leaving groups in nucleophilic substitutions but *tosyl groups / tosylates* are not.

Hydrogenations and hydrogenolysis reactions are basically *radical / ionic* processes favoring different types of substrates, so it is usually possible to use these and hydridic agents to selectively reduce functional groups that tend to favor homolytic or heterolytic additions, respectively.

This is the basis of many *chemoselective / regioselective* reductions in organic chemistry.

Ts	TsO⁻

Just as there are many heterogeneous catalysts for adding hydrogen, there are many homogeneous reagents for adding hydride and they can have widely different properties.

Some simple metal hydrides, LiH, NaH and KH *do / do not* tend to be suitable for hydridic reductions.

For this section, assume an appropriate hydridic agent is used to deliver the number of hydrides indicated.

C Substrate Scope

One-step Reductions

Fill in the gaps for the following mechanisms, and write clear curly arrows to describe the reaction flow.

Ph—C(=O)   H⁻ →   H⁺ →

_____
alkoxide

_____

(cyclohexanone)   H⁻ →   H⁺ →

_____
alkoxide

_____

The preferred reagent for hydridic reduction of aldehydes and ketones is, in fact, *NaBH₄ / LiAlH₄ / NaH* because it is sufficiently reactive but not so much that it interacts violently with water.

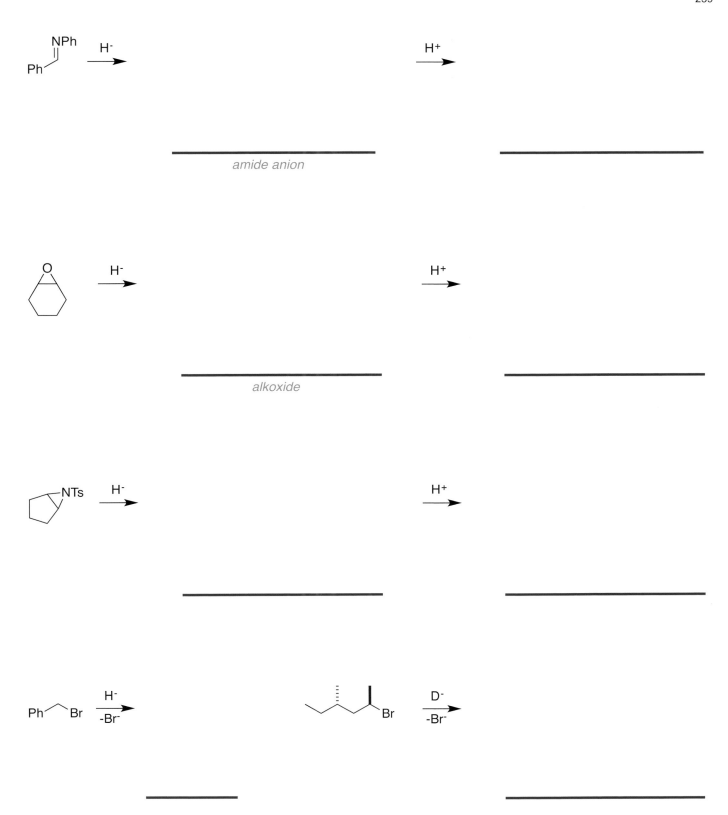

It takes *1 / 2* reduction steps to bring functional groups at the acid oxidation level down to the alcohol one.

Two-step Reductions

Show the mechanisms of the following reactions, using clear curly arrows. The true leaving group in many of these reactions will not be a free hydroxide, alkoxide, *etc.*, but the mechanisms are simplified to convey the concept of hydridic reduction.

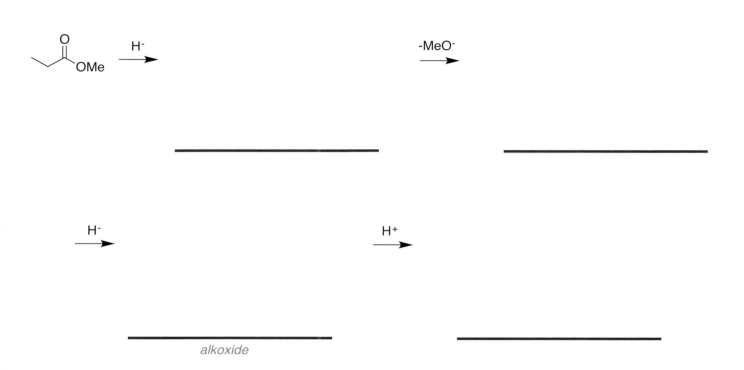

———————————————————

———————————————————

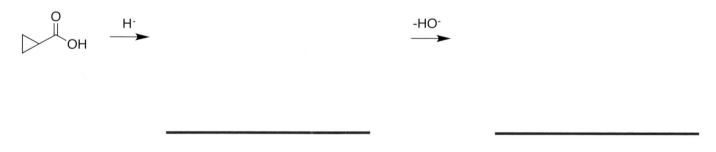

alkoxide

———————————————————

———————————————————

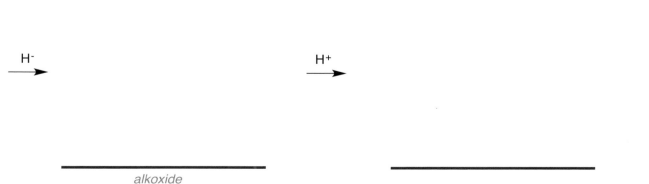

alkoxide

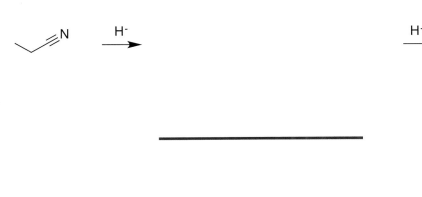

Predict the products of the following reactions.

(i) H⁻
(ii) H⁺

(i) 2H⁻
(ii) 2H⁺

(i) H⁻
(ii) H⁺

sulfide / sulfone

(i) H⁻
(ii) H⁺

imine / amine

CH₃CH₂CH₂C≡N	$\xrightarrow[\text{(ii) H}^+]{\text{(i) H}^-}$	_____

Ph−C≡N	$\xrightarrow[\text{(ii) 2H}^+]{\text{(i) 2H}^-}$	_____

CH₃COCH₂COCH₃	$\xrightarrow[\text{(ii) 2H}^+]{\text{(i) 2H}^-}$	_____

HCOO-propyl	$\xrightarrow[\text{-MeOH}]{\text{(i) 2H}^-~\text{(ii) 2H}^+}$	_____

(γ-butyrolactone)	$\xrightarrow[\text{(ii) 2H}^+]{\text{(i) 2H}^-}$	_____

(δ-valerolactone)	$\xrightarrow[\text{(ii) H}^+]{\text{(i) H}^-}$	_____

CH₃CH₂CH₂COOH	$\xrightarrow[\text{-OH}_2]{\text{(i) 2H}^-~\text{(ii) 2H}^+}$	_____

Ph−CO−OMe	$\xrightarrow[\text{-MeOH}]{\text{(i) 2H}^-~\text{(ii) 2H}^+}$	_____

244

Difference Between Hydridic Reductions Of Amides And Esters

Outline mechanisms for the following hydridic reductions using clear curly arrows to depict electron flow.

a

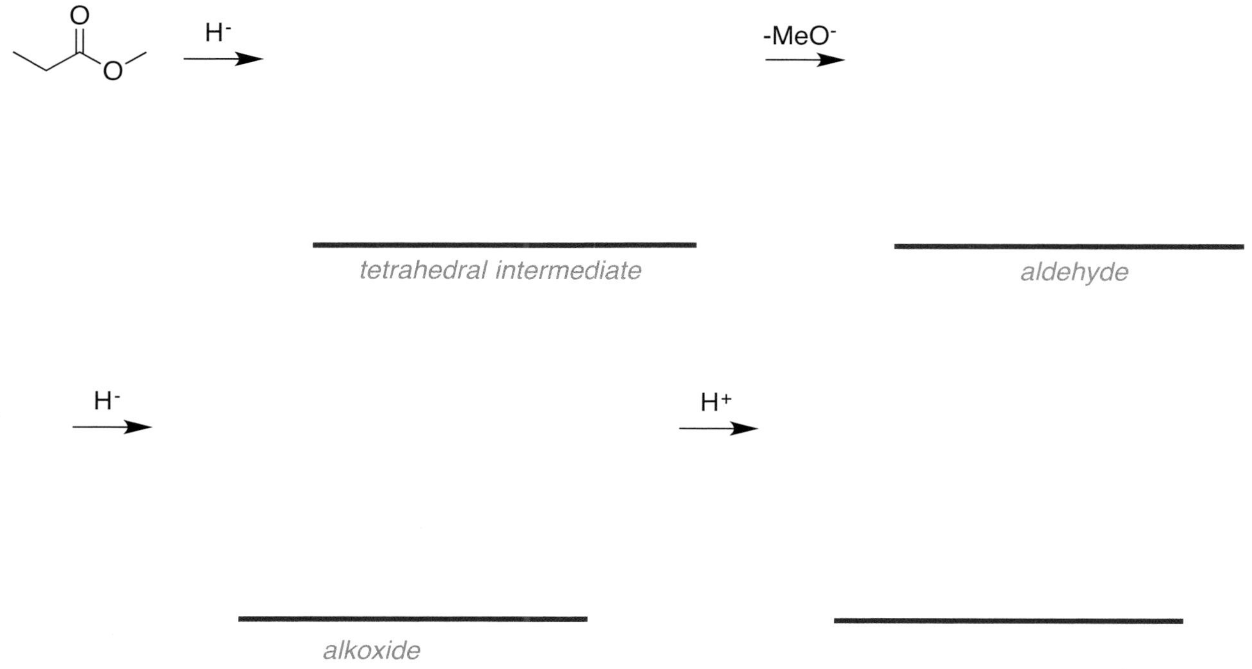

H⁻ →

-MeO⁻ →

_____
tetrahedral intermediate

_____
aldehyde

H⁻ →

H⁺ →

_____
alkoxide

_____

b

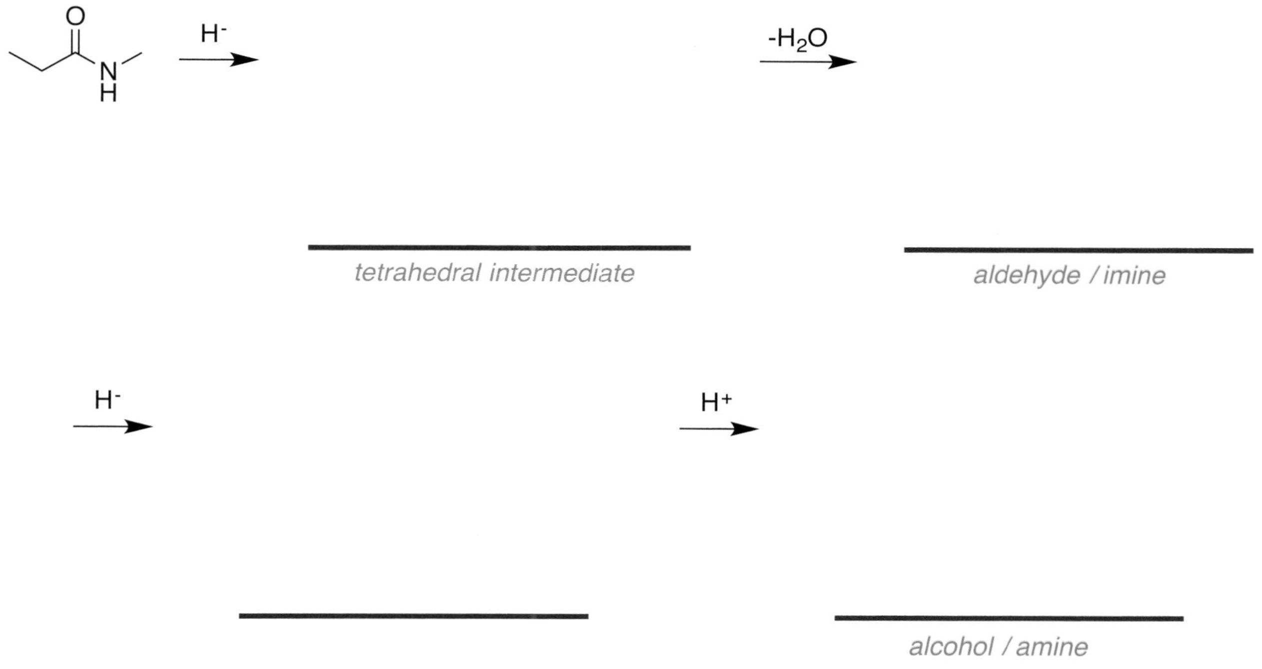

H⁻ →

-H₂O →

_____
tetrahedral intermediate

_____
aldehyde / imine

H⁻ →

H⁺ →

_____

_____
alcohol / amine

c

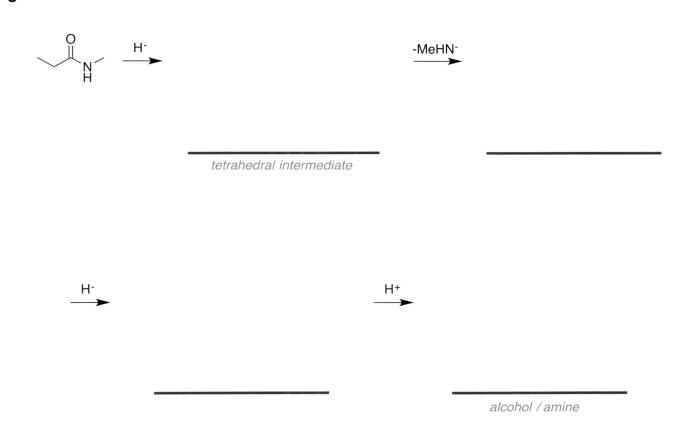

tetrahedral intermediate

alcohol / amine

Pathway **a** is the one followed in reductions of esters. If reductions of amides followed the same route then they would proceed via pathway **c**; however, mechanism **b** is an alternative that differs from that for reduction of esters.

Highlight the first point of divergence in the mechanism above by circling that step.

In fact, hydridic reduction of amides tends to proceed via mechanism *b / c*. Suggest reasons:

_____

_____.

D NADH: A Hydride Source *In Vivo*

Research the full name and structure of NADH, hence complete the following diagram.

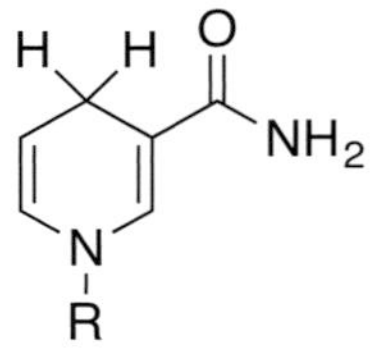

R =

_____

NADH full name: _____

Draw arrows to express how NADH might donate a hydride to a protonated ketone.

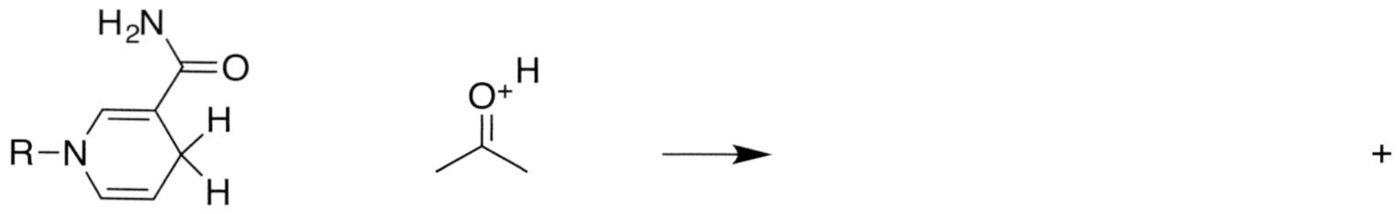

→   +

_____   _____

by-product full name:

_____

_____

The by-product in this reaction is *aluminum alkoxides / nicotine / NAD*.

Draw the product of this ketone reduction.

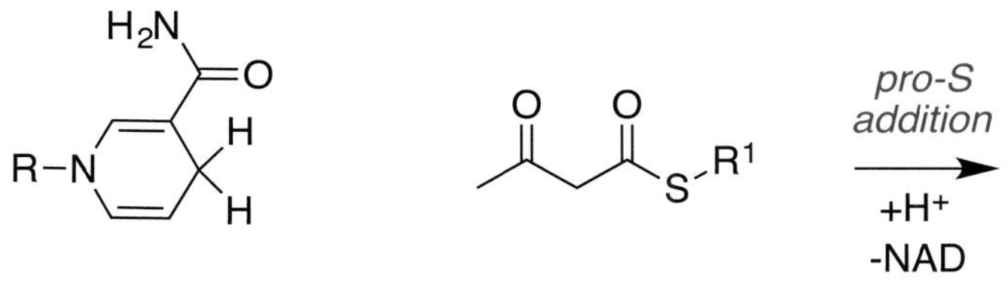

H₂N

R–N

H
H

O

O

S–R¹

pro-S
addition

+H⁺
–NAD

18 Reductions Via Electrons And Radicals

from chapter(s) _____ in the recommended text

A Introduction

Focus

The first workbook in this series, and in this book up until here, has dealt almost exclusively with mechanisms that involve flow of two electrons. This section focuses on reactions involving movements of single unpaired electrons, *ie* radicals. The simplest radical is an electron, generated in, for instance, solutions of alkali metals in ammonia. Neutral radicals in organic chemistry may be involved in many processes characterized by a series of initiation, propagation, and (non-productive) chain termination steps. The focus of this section is on illustrative types of both processes.

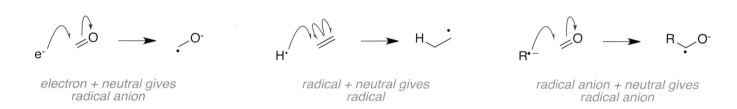

electron + neutral gives
radical anion

radical + neutral gives
radical

radical anion + neutral gives
radical anion

Reasons To Care

Most organic reactions in biological systems involve flow of electrons in sets of two, but some do not. For instance, formation of "reactive oxygen species" in and around cells leads to multiple complex reactions that can be detrimental to cell survival when the cell is stressed (*eg* during inflammation). In drug metabolism, the cytochrome p40 enzymes tend to use a battery of radical reactions to remove alien organic molecules from the system.

Concepts

fish-hook curly arrows • reductions and oxidations • chain reactions

Objective

This section uses some synthetic radical reactions that are well controlled and give predominant products to illustrate how.

B Reductions Via Free Electrons

Addition Of One Electron

Radicals are entities with an unpaired electron, and an isolated electron is a radical. However, it might more accurately be called a *radical cation / radical anion* since it is not neutral.

Isolated electrons are different to hydrogen radicals because the latter have nuclei consisting of a *proton / neutron / both* orbited by a single unpaired electron.

If an electron adds to a carbonyl group in a neutral molecule, then the product will be a *radical cation / radical anion / neutral radical*. Show this process carefully using fishhook arrows.

Addition Of One Electron Then Protonation

If a proton adds to a radical anion, then the product is *a radical / an anion*. Show this for the following steps.

_____

_____

_____

_____

If an electron were to add to a radical anion then the product would be a *diradical anion / dianion*, but this addition is unlikely because of the electrostatic repulsion between the electron and the radical anion. This mechanism is shown in some books, but it is probably incorrect.

When a free electron adds to a radical the product is *a radical / an anion / a radical anion*. Show this for the following, showing clear fishhook arrows to depict the electron flow.

_____

_____

_____

_____

Overall, if double bonds undergo addition of an electron, a proton, an electron, then a proton again, then the net effect is *addition of two hydrogens / oxidation*.

Show this mechanism for the following reductions.

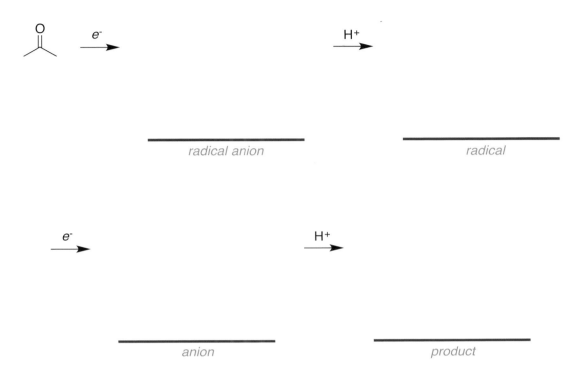

radical anion   radical

anion   product

In fact, the reaction may take a different course if, for instance, the radicals self-couple before an electron adds, but these outcomes are dependent on the source of the electrons, and the conditions.

A way to generate single electrons is to use salts like samarium diiodide, SmI_2, that readily *oxidize / reduce*, to Sm(3+) salts in this particular case.

Another is to dissolve sodium in mercury to give *sodium amalgam / sodium potassium alloy* where electrons liberated from the sodium are dispersed in the metallic solvent. This form of sodium can be used in the presence of protic solvents.

Amines and ammonia are not ideal media for substrates that may react with them (*eg* aldehydes), but for others it is ideal.

Sodium dissolves in liquid ammonia giving an intense *inky-blue / green* solution.

Ammonia is protic, so it is conceivable that electrons in ammonia would be protonated by the solvent; draw fishhook arrows to show this.

$$Na \xrightarrow[-Na^+]{NH_3} e^- \xrightarrow{H-NH_2} H^{\cdot} + {}^{\cdot\cdot}NH_2$$

hydride   radical
radical   anion

This process is *not* the dominant one; presumably formation of hydrogen radicals and *N*-centered radical anions is kinetically or thermodynamically unfavorable. However, when an electron adds to a double bond, then the product is a radical *anion / cation*, and this *can* be protonated by ammonia.

Cycles Of Electron Addition Then Protonation

Reduction of internal alkynes in sodium/ammonia is interesting because the intermediate radical anion adopts a *trans / cis*-geometry, and this is maintained in the product of the reaction.

Reduction of alkynes via stepwise addition of electrons is *equivalent / complimentary* to hydrogenation with respect to double bond geometry of the alkene product.

Show mechanisms for the following reductions.

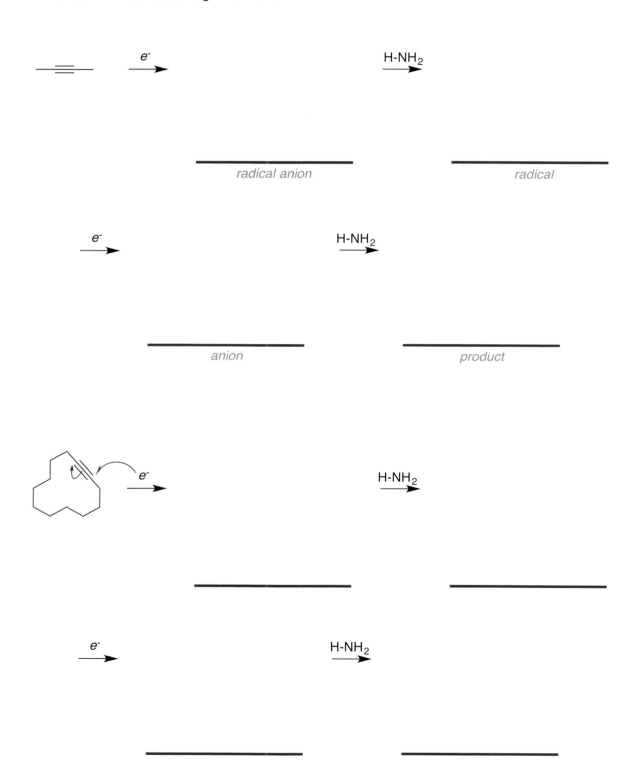

radical anion   radical

anion   product

One electron reduction of aromatic compounds in liquid ammonia gives cyclohexadienyl radical anions. Subsequently, they can add a proton to form *an anion / a radical*, then another electron to form *an anion / a radical / a radical anion* then finally a proton to achieve *1 / 2 / 4* electron reduction overall.

Show this process by carefully adding arrows to the following.

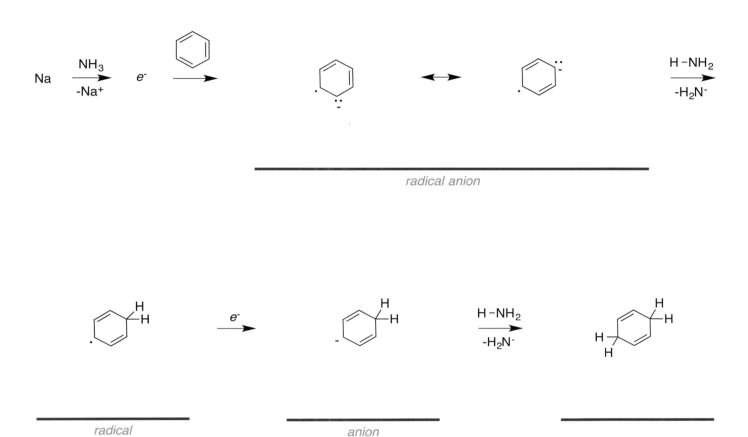

radical anion

radical   anion

Protonation on the central carbon of the pentadienyl anion fragment is presumably favorable because that is where the *LUMO / HOMO* has the greatest orbital size.

This process, the Birch reduction, produces *conjugated / non-conjugated* dienes from aromatic compounds.

Complete the following, for dissolving metal reduction of 1,4-dimethylbenzene, consider the stability of the two possible radical anion and anion intermediates, hence predict the regioselectivity of the reduction.

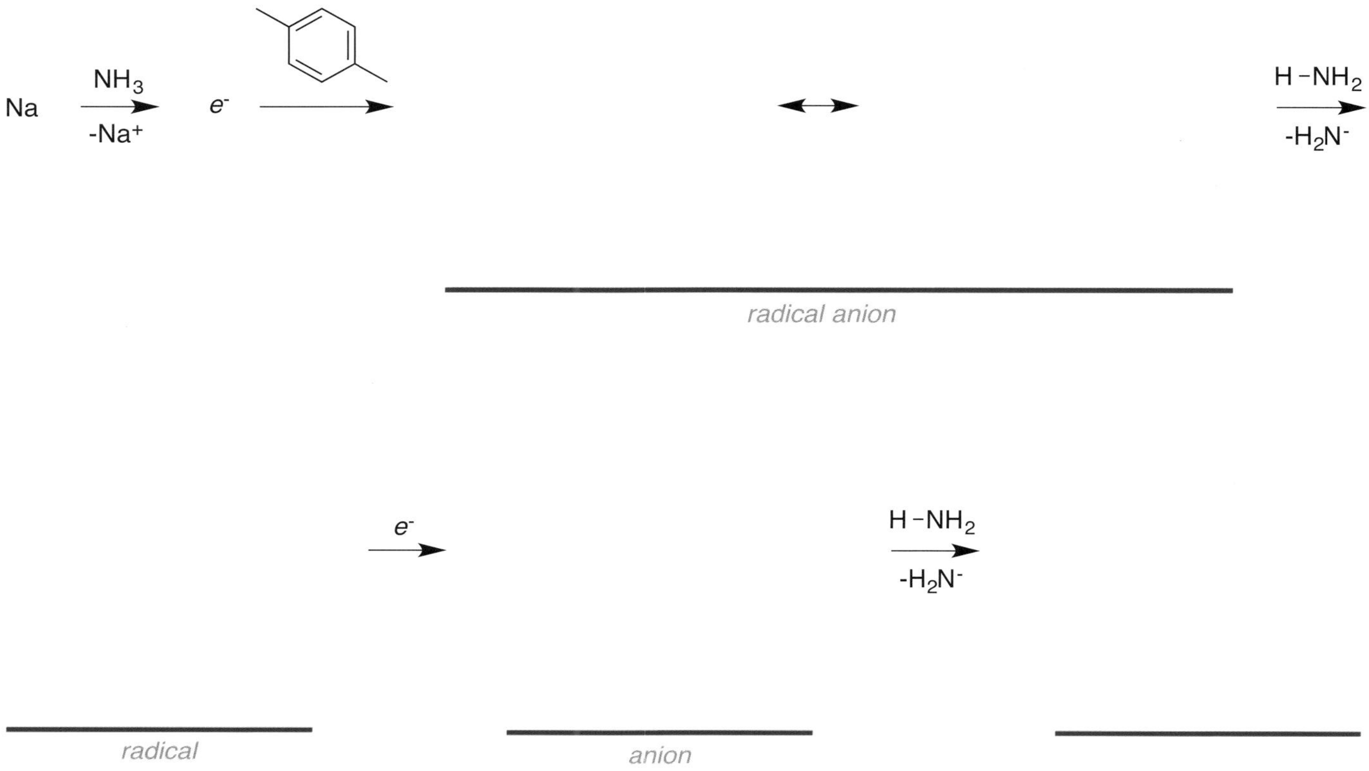

Na $\xrightarrow[\text{-Na}^+]{\text{NH}_3}$ e⁻ $\xrightarrow{\hspace{2cm}}$ $\longleftrightarrow$ $\xrightarrow[\text{-H}_2\text{N}^-]{\text{H-NH}_2}$

_____
radical anion

e⁻ $\xrightarrow{\hspace{1cm}}$ $\xrightarrow[\text{-H}_2\text{N}^-]{\text{H-NH}_2}$

_____   _____   _____
radical   *anion*

C Reductions Via Other Radicals

Reductions can also be achieved using radical reactions. Imagine a hypothetical process wherein a hydrogen radical attacks iodoethane *on the iodine* to give a *C*-based radical. If that radical then combined with another hydride the overall effect would be net *oxidation / reduction* of the substrate.

Show this by placing clear fishhook arrows on the following diagram.

$\xrightarrow[\text{-HI}]{\text{H}^\bullet}$ $\xrightarrow{\text{H}^\bullet}$

This reaction does *not* work efficiently. Outcomes of radical reactions are dominated by relative reaction rates, ie *kinetic / thermodynamic* effects.

Catalytic / stoichiometric / more than stoichiometric amounts of hydrogen radical are required for the reaction above, and at such concentrations they would irreversibly recombine to hydrogen.

Reagents that can dissociate to form hydrogen radicals are used to overcome the problem outlined above. In the case of trialkyltin hydrides, the $R_3Sn\bullet$ that is formed can remove the iodide.

Complete the following mechanism showing clear curly arrows; label each step from the choices indicated.

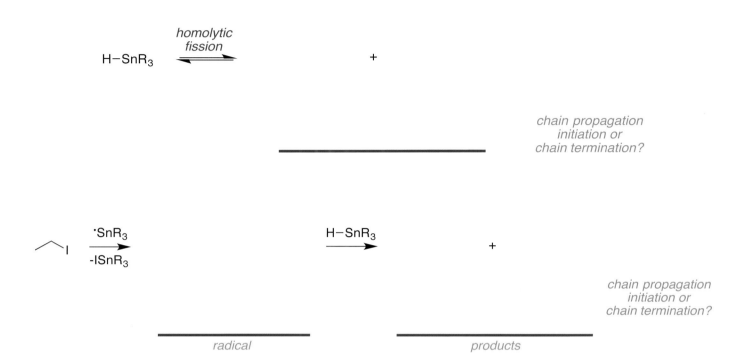

Consumption of one trialkyltin radical by reaction with the iodide leads to generation of *another tin radical / hydride*.

Every SnR$_3$• that enters the process via the first transformation can be *used only once / regenerated many times*.

The overall reaction is temporarily slowed when hydrogen atoms collide with SnR$_3$•, or when two SnR$_3$• radicals combine; it is permanently retarded when hydrogen radicals combine to give hydrogen, but this will happen rarely because their concentration is *high / low*. Complete the following.

Show the mechanism for the following reaction.

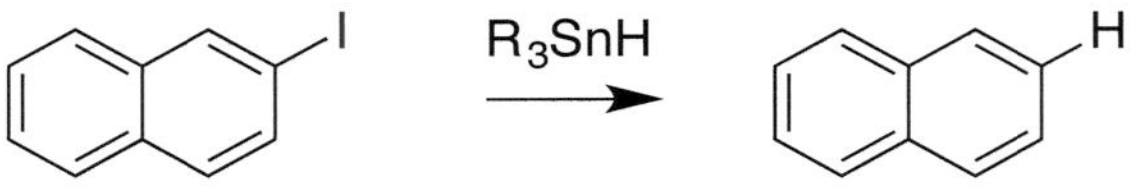

chain initiation

$$H-SnR_3 \rightleftarrows \text{homolytic fission} \quad\quad +$$

_____

chain propagation

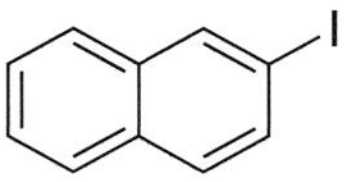

$$\xrightarrow[\text{-ISnR}_3]{\cdot SnR_3} \quad\quad \xrightarrow{H-SnR_3} \quad\quad +$$

_____ _____
radical   *products*

chain termination

$$H\cdot \quad \cdot H \rightleftarrows \text{homolytic fusion}$$

_____

$$H\cdot \quad \cdot SnR_3 \rightleftarrows \text{homolytic fusion} \quad\quad R_3Sn\cdot \quad \cdot SnR_3 \rightleftarrows \text{homolytic fusion}$$

_____   _____

The chain initiation and termination steps *would / would not* change as the substrate is varied.

D Biosynthesis Of Prostaglandin H₂ (PGH₂)

Complete the following mechanism showing clear curly arrows throughout.

arachidonic acid

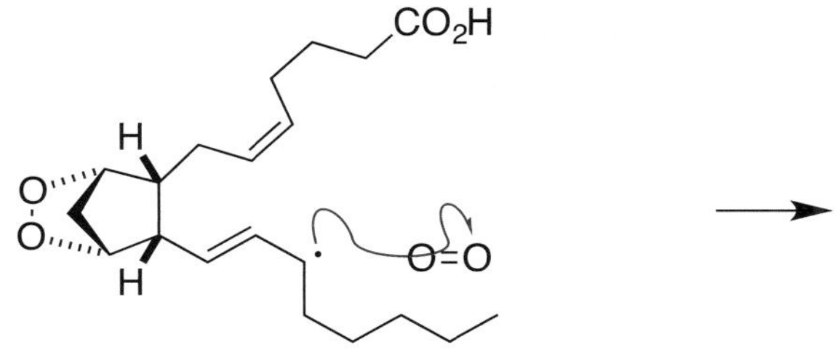

$+ \; O=O$

$+ \; O=O$

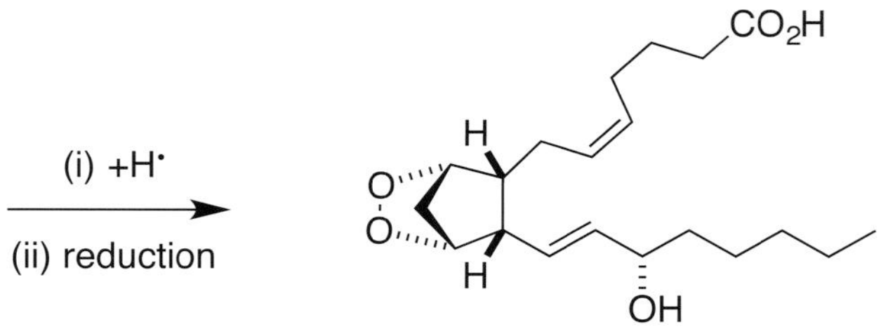

$$\xrightarrow{\text{(i) +H}^\bullet \quad \text{(ii) reduction}}$$

prostaglandin H_2 (PGH$_2$)

Prostaglandins *dilate blood vessels / inhibit red blood cell aggregation / are secreted in seminal fluid from the prostate gland* (circle all that is true).

E Reactive Oxygen Species

Write mechanisms for the following reactions using clear curly arrows.

$$O=O \xrightarrow{e^-}$$

————————————

superoxide, radical anion

$$^-O–O^- \xrightarrow{2\,H^+}$$

————————————

$$^\bullet O–O^- \xrightarrow{e^-}$$

————————————

peroxide anion

$$^\bullet O–O^- \xrightarrow{H^+}$$

————————————

perhydroxyl radical

Reactive oxygen species are produced in the *endoplasmic reticulum / mitochondria / lysosomes / peroxisomes* of cells (circle all that apply).

19 Oxidations

from chapter(s) _____ in the recommended text

A Introduction

Focus

Oxidation reactions are diverse, but share some characteristics. Many involve addition of oxygen atoms; successive additions of oxygen atoms to amines reveal there is a logical correlation between oxidation and stepwise addition of [O], but it is somewhat obscured by loss of water in only some steps. All oxidations involve reduction of something else (usually a reagent, or sometimes an electrochemical cathode). Alcohol oxidations often involve formation of an "alkoxide" with a metal or some non-metallic elements in high oxidation states; deprotonation and elimination of the entity attached creates a *C=O* bond. Mechanisms can be proposed for these reactions that resemble antiperiplanar E2 processes, or intramolecular synperiplanar eliminations. Aldehyde hydrates can be oxidized in much the same way as alcohols (formation of "alkoxides" then elimination), but this pathway is not open to ketones because they do not have hydrogen atoms attached to the hydrate carbon. In general, oxidations of ketones are harder because they involve cleavage of *C-C* bonds.

some oxidations have steps that resemble E2 eliminations

others involve migration reactions with a similar electron flow

Reasons To Care

Nearly all the reactions discussed in this section are laboratory synthetic methods, but they are a primer for being able to recognize oxidations in all branches of the biological sciences.

Concepts Involved

oxidation and reduction • E2 • *anti-* and *syn*-periplanar • epoxidation • migration reactions

Objective

This section is to highlight common mechanistic features of oxidation reactions, particularly oxidations of alcohols, aldehydes, and ketones.

B Amine Oxidations

Whereas reductions in organic chemistry usually feature adding hydrogens, oxidations involve replacing hydrogen with a heteroatom. There is considerable scope for the types and connectivities of heteroatoms added in oxidation reactions, so there are a lot of different kinds.

Many oxidation reactions involve *increasing / decreasing* the number of oxygen atoms.

Ammonia

Complete the following reaction sequences for oxidation of ammonia to nitric acid showing the intermediates. It involves inserting an oxygen atom between *N - H* bonds. Note that if there are two hydroxyls joined to nitrogen, the compound sometimes *reduces / dehydrates* to a more stable form, *ie* *HO-N-OH* often extrudes *oxygen / water / ammonia*.

Draw out each of the following products in three dimensions.

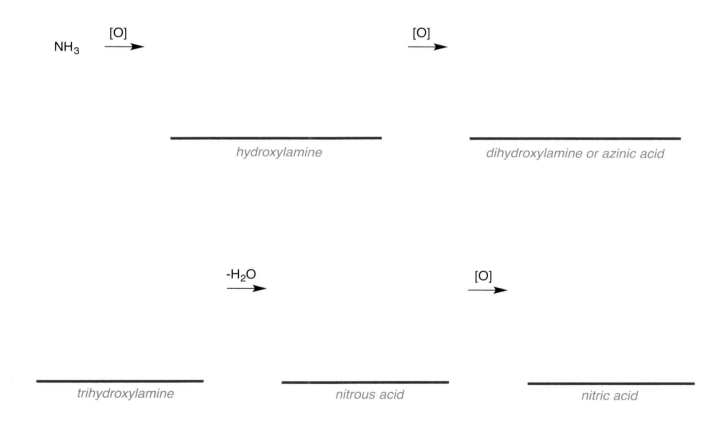

hydroxylamine	*dihydroxylamine or azinic acid*

trihydroxylamine	*nitrous acid*	*nitric acid*

Dihydroxylamine and azinic acid are *resonance forms / tautomers*.

A similar pathway is conceivable for *C-N* bonds with elimination of alcohols; in fact, amine *C-N* *do / do not* tend to be oxidized in the same way as *H-N*, as shown in the following section.

Organic Amines

Deduce the consequences of oxidation of ethylamine in a series of steps in which oxygen atoms are inserted into one or more *N-H* bonds or simply added to *N*-atoms.

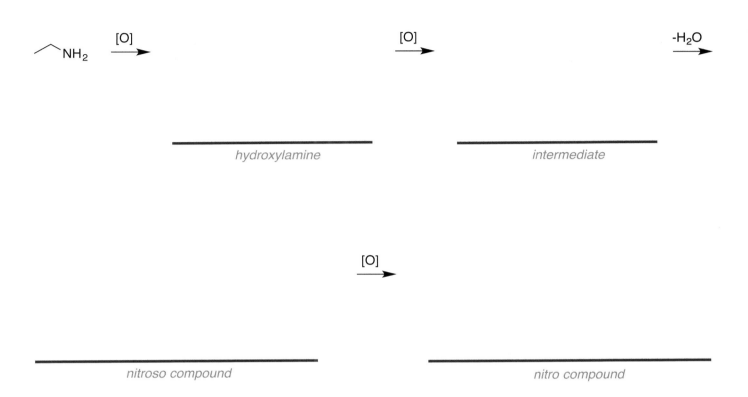

Show the consequences of similar transformations for the secondary amine, pyrrolidine, and the tertiary amine *N*-methylpiperidine, by completing the diagrams below.

Overall, it is *easier / harder* to oxidize bonds to hydrogen than to carbon.

C Oxidations Of Alkenes And Alkynes Via Additions Of Heteroatoms

Modification of $C - C$ unsaturation by forming more than one $C -$ heteroatom bonds, or forming $C - C$ multiple bonds, is *oxidation / reduction*.

For the following additions, show the increase or decrease in oxidation levels at one of the carbons involved in the change (*eg* oxidation of an alcohol to a ketone would be +1, but reducing it to an alkane would be -1).

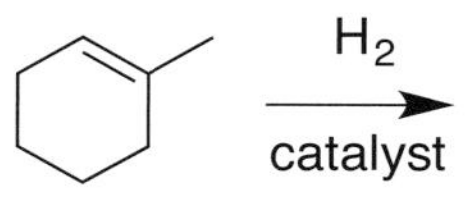

$-2 , -1, 0, +1, +2$

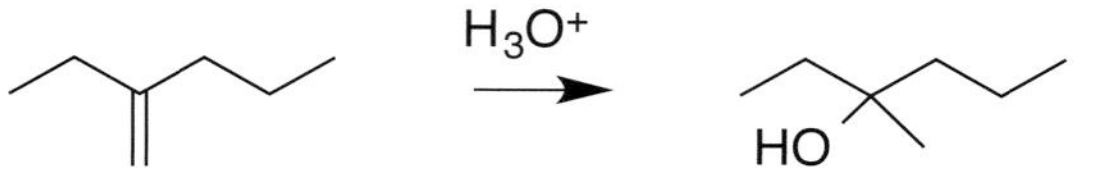

$-2 , -1, 0, +1, +2$

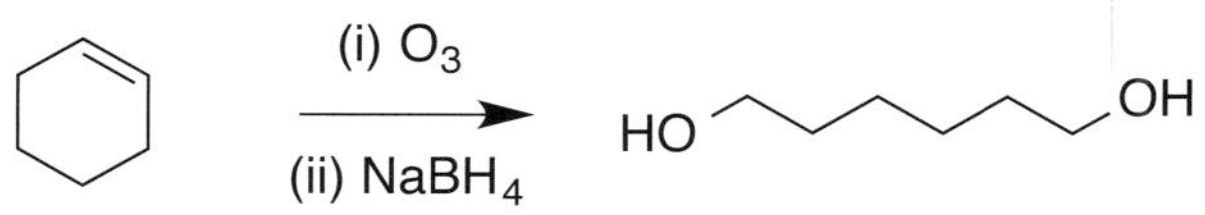

$-2 , -1, 0, +1, +2$

$-2 , -1, 0, +1, +2$

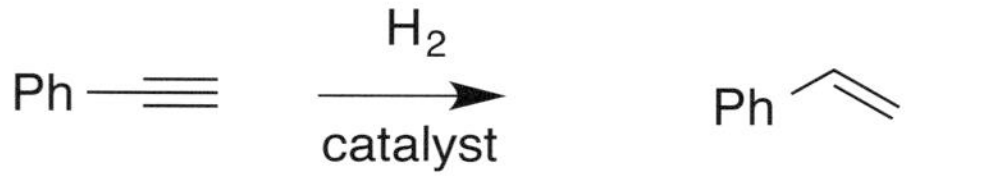

$-2 , -1, 0, +1, +2$

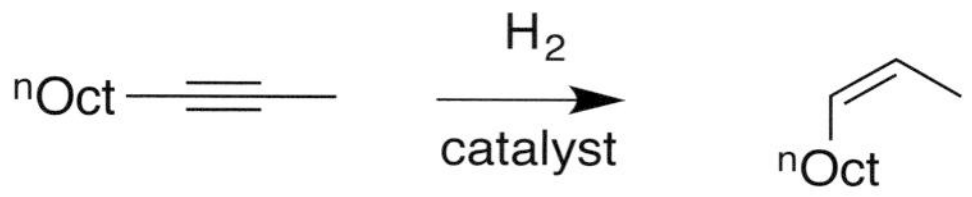

$-2 , -1, 0, +1, +2$

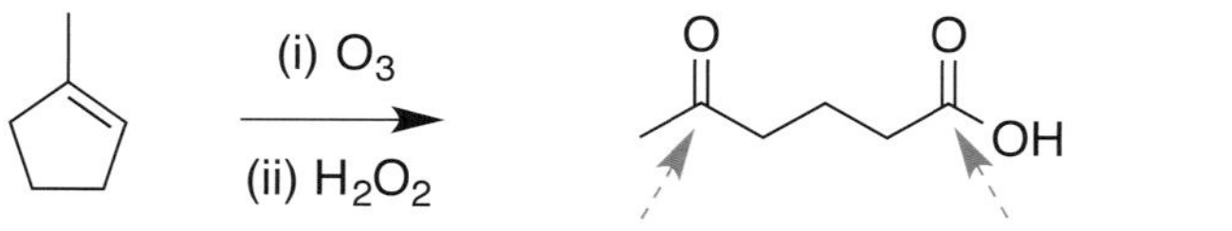

$-2 , -1, 0, +1, +2$ $-2 , -1, 0, +1, +2$

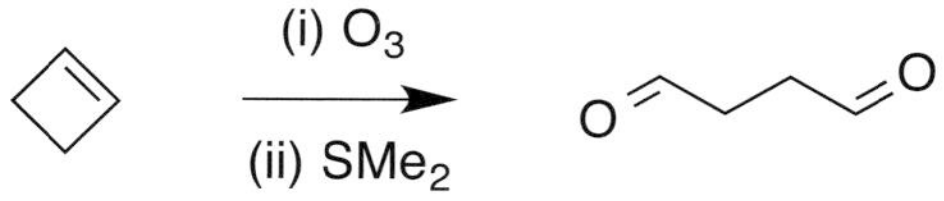

$-2 , -1, 0, +1, +2$

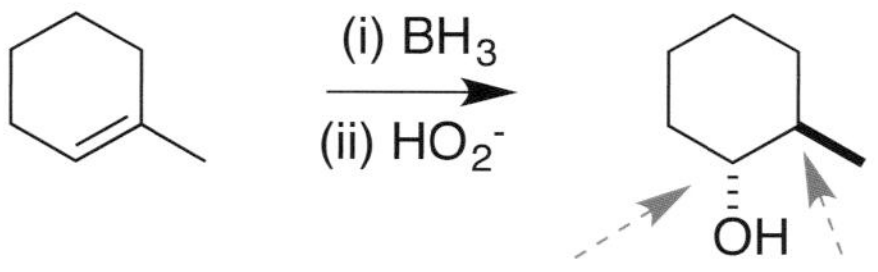

$-2 , -1, 0, +1, +2$ $-2 , -1, 0, +1, +2$

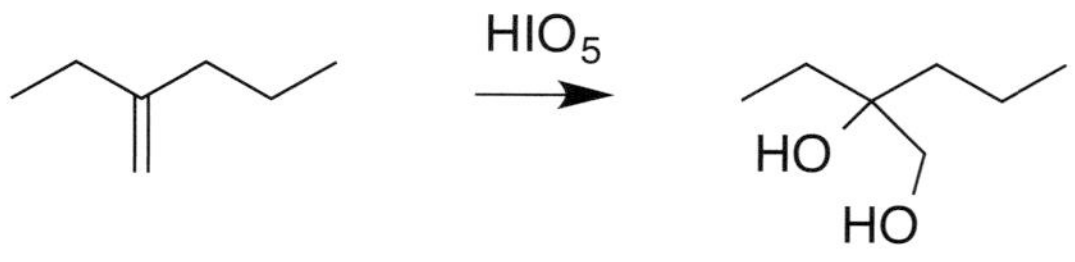

$-2 , -1, 0, +1, +2$

D Oxidation States Of Common Oxidants

Write the oxidation state of the red atoms in the reagents below.

_____   _____   _____   _____   _____   _____   _____   _____

These are relatively *high / low* oxidation states for these elements.

E Dehydrogenation Reactions

Dehydrogenation of alkanes or alcohols is a(n) *reduction / oxidation* reaction.

Catalysts lower the activation barrier for reactions, and *do / do not* influence the thermodynamic states of the reactants and starting materials.

If a hydrogenation catalyst lowers the activation energy barrier for addition of hydrogen to an alkene, it *does / does not* lower it for the reverse reaction.

This is called *The Principle of Microscopic Reversibility / Hammond's postulate*.

In practice, catalysts that mediate hydrogenation of alkenes can also promote dehydrogenation of the alkane products, but only if the *kinetic / thermodynamic* barrier for the reverse reaction can be surmounted under those conditions.

If the kinetic barrier can be surmounted, dehydrogenation product will only be formed in a ratio that reflects the energy difference of the products (including hydrogen) and the starting materials. Dehydrogenation reactions become easier if hydrogen is *enclosed/ removed* from the system.

It is *easier / harder* to find practical catalysts for hydrogenation reactions than dehydrogenation reactions because the energy barrier to the process involving loss of hydrogen is *greater / smaller*.

F Oxidation Of Alcohols

Catalytic Dehydrogenation

There are heterogeneous catalysts that will dehydrogenate, and therefore *oxidize / reduce* alcohols to the corresponding aldehydes or ketones.

Complete the following diagrams.

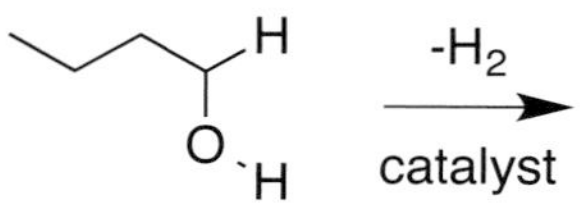

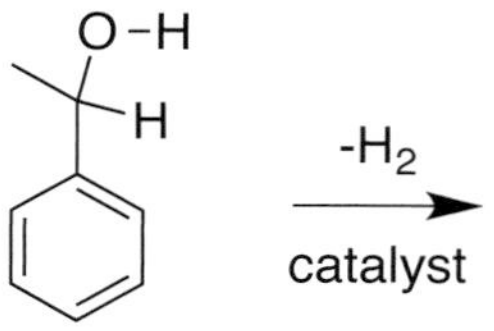

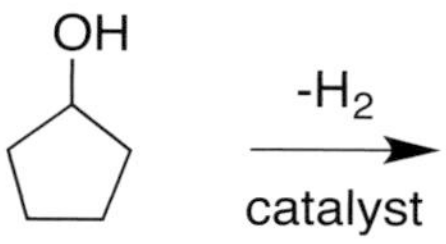

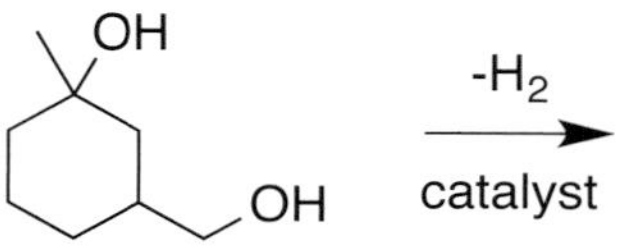

Alcohols have to be *primary / secondary / tertiary* and not *primary / secondary / tertiary* for this reaction to be possible (circle all that apply).

In general, and not just for catalytic dehydrogenation reactions, it is much harder to oxidize *primary / secondary / tertiary* alcohols than *primary / secondary / tertiary* ones.

In laboratory scale chemistry, catalytic dehydrogenations of alcohols are rarely used because there are numerous convenient alternatives that involve elimination from alkoxides.

Elimination From Alkoxides In Many Alcohol Oxidations

Imagine a process in which an alcohol interacts with a metal salt (dicationic, for example) to form an alkoxide. Elimination then occurs via loss of a C$\underline{H}$OH proton to form a carbonyl as follows.

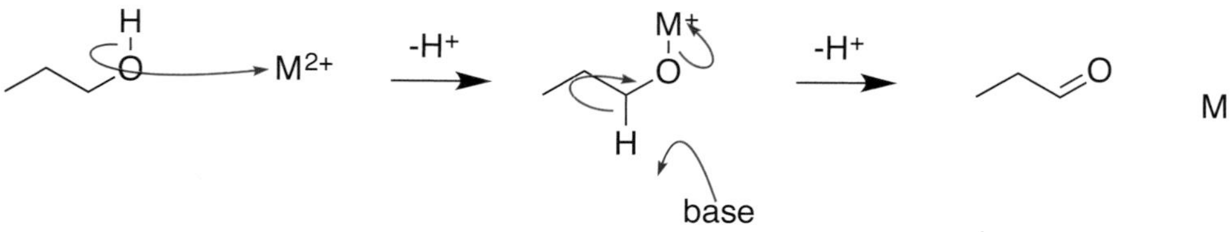

The process shown above is similar to the *E1 / S_N1 / E2 / S_N2* mechanism.

In this process, the metal is *oxidized / reduced*; circle the key arrow that is responsible for that.

Based on that arrow, good oxidants in this process probably involve metals in *high / low* oxidation states, so that it is most easily *oxidized / reduced*.

It is *harder / easier* to change Cr(2+) into Cr(0), that it is to convert Cr(6+) into Cr(4+), for example.

In practice, the "metal" can be a transition metal like manganese, chromium, or ruthenium, but it can also be a non-metallic element in a *high / low* oxidation state.

For the following hypothetical reactions, show clear curly arrows, intermediate and the products, including the heteroatom used to make the alkoxide; it is important to show its oxidation state at the end of the reaction (*eg* what becomes of the S^{2+} in the first reaction).

$$Ph\text{-}CH(OH)\text{-}H \xrightarrow[-H^+]{S^{2+}} \underline{\hspace{6cm}} \xrightarrow[-Hbase]{base} \underline{\hspace{6cm}} + \quad S$$

$$Ph\text{-}CH(OH)\text{-}H \xrightarrow[-H^+]{S^{4+}} \underline{\hspace{6cm}}_{alkoxide} \xrightarrow[-Hbase]{base} \underline{\hspace{6cm}} + \quad S^{2+}$$

$$\text{(2-nitrobenzyl alcohol)} \xrightarrow[-H^+]{Mn^{4+}} \underline{\hspace{6cm}}_{alkoxide} \xrightarrow[-Hbase]{base} \underline{\hspace{6cm}} +$$

$$\text{(4-methylcyclohexanol)} \xrightarrow[-H^+]{I^{5+}} \underline{\hspace{6cm}}_{alkoxide} \xrightarrow[-Hbase]{base} \underline{\hspace{6cm}} +$$

$$\text{(1-methoxy-2-propanol)} \xrightarrow[-H^+]{Ru^{7+}} \underline{\hspace{6cm}}_{alkoxide} \xrightarrow[-Hbase]{base} \underline{\hspace{6cm}} +$$

Draw curly arrows and predict products from oxidation reactions that involve the following key steps; identify for each if the step that removes the proton is intramolecular or intermolecular. In many cases it is uncertain if the reaction is intra- or inter-molecular, so both are shown here.

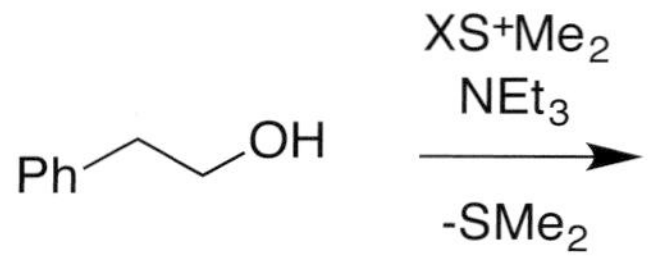

Ph⌣OH

XS^+Me_2
NEt_3
→
$-SMe_2$

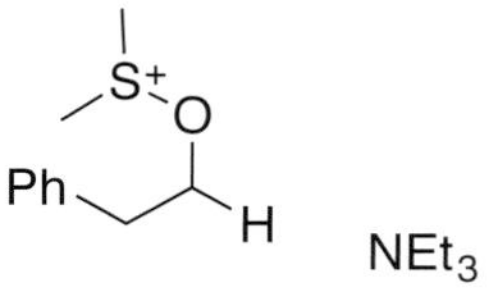

Ph⌣CH(O-S⁺Me₂)H   NEt₃

or

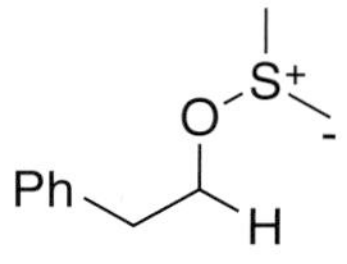

Ph⌣CH(O-S⁺Me₂)H

*intramolecular /
intermolecular*

*intramolecular /
intermolecular*

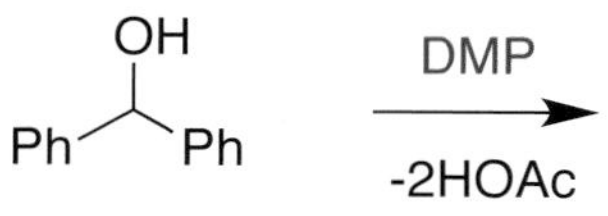

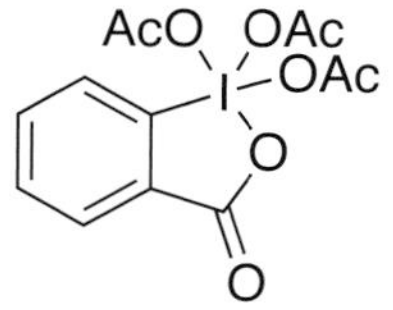

OH
Ph—CH—Ph

DMP
→
-2HOAc

AcO OAc
I—OAc
O
=O

DMP

⁻OAc

AcO OAc
I—O—CH(Ph)H
O—Ph
=O

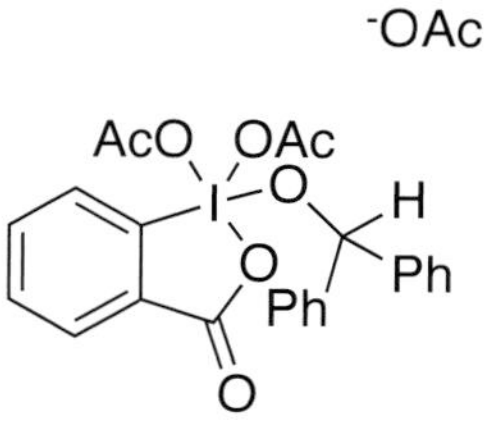

*intramolecular /
intermolecular*

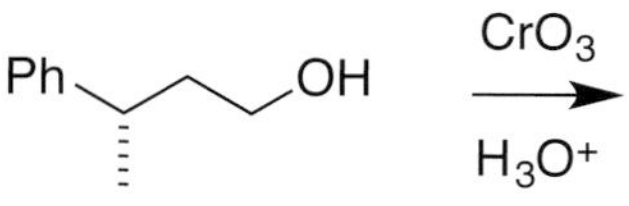

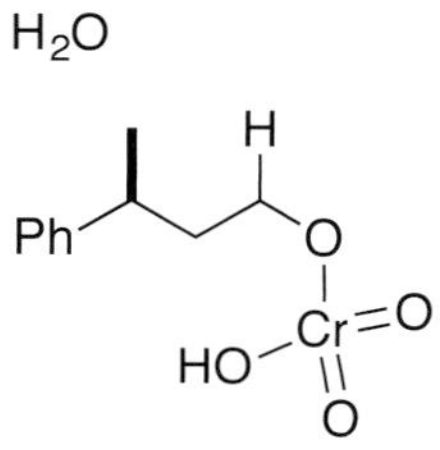

Ph⌣CH₂OH

CrO_3
→
H_3O^+

H_2O

Ph⌣CH(H)—O—Cr(=O)(OH)=O

or

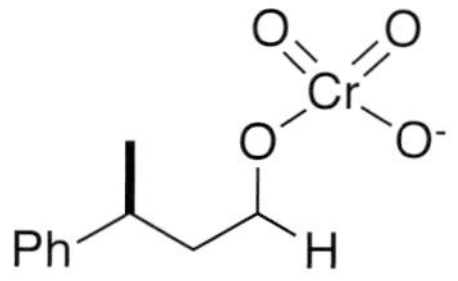

Ph⌣CH(H)—O—Cr(=O)(=O)O⁻

*intramolecular /
intermolecular*

*intramolecular /
intermolecular*

The last example, below, is special because the metal is not reduced, but a ketone ligand is. The initial product is an alkoxide of the product alcohol

OH
Ph
Ph
Al(OiPr)3
MeCOMe
-HOiPr
iPrO
OiPr
Al
O
O
H
Ph
Ph

intramolecular / intermolecular

G Oxidation Of Aldehydes

Aldehydes and ketones often are oxidized under conditions that favor an equilibrium amount of hydrate formation; alkoxides formed from these hydrates may eliminate just as in the previous section, except that the product automatically forms in the acid oxidation state.

Show this process, with clear curly arrows, for the following reactions.

O
Ph
H2O
-H+
Cr6+

hydrate

alkoxide

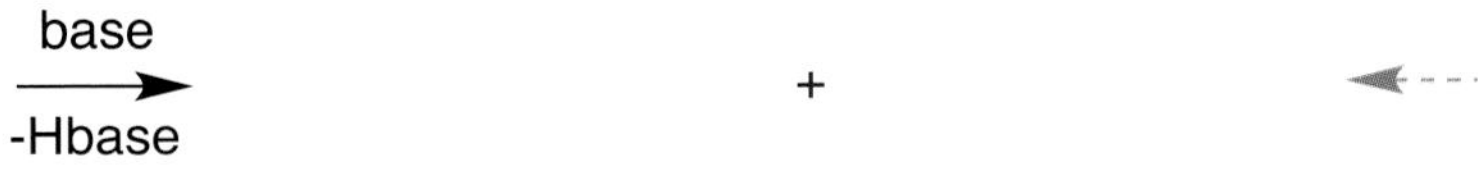
base
-Hbase
+

indicate what happens to the metal here

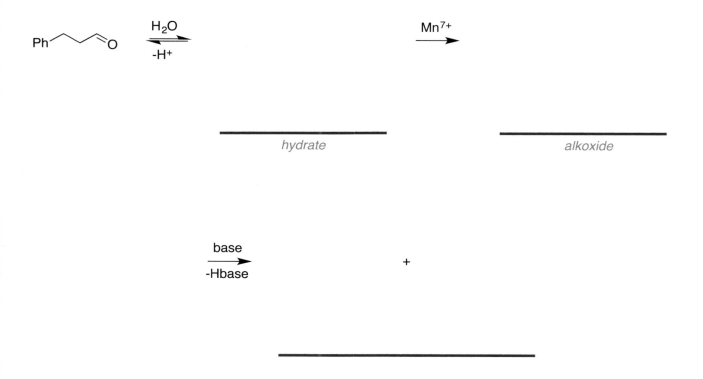

hydrate   _alkoxide_

Ketones _can / cannot_ be oxidized in a similar way because they _have / do not have_ α-C$\underline{H}$ atoms.

The following reaction does _not_ involve hydration, but it has a similar feature. Show the mechanism with clear curly arrows.

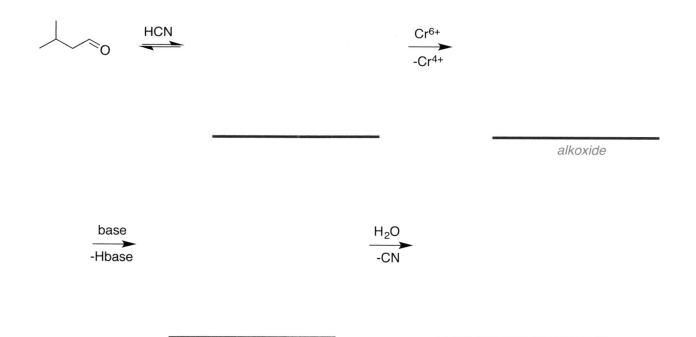

alkoxide

acyl nitrile

Write the structures of chlorous acid HOClO, and hypochlorous acid, HOCl.

_____   _____
           chlorous acid   *hypochlorous acid*

Deduce the mechanism of oxidation of the following aldehyde by chlorous acid that involves intramolecular abstraction of an α–C*H* by an oxygen attached to a chlorine.

$\xrightarrow{H^+}$ $\underset{}{\overset{ClO_2^-}{\rightleftharpoons}}$ $\longrightarrow$

_____   _____   _____
                                         "alkoxide"

H Oxidation Of Ketones

Ketones can be oxidized via attack of peroxide then rearrangement via alkyl migration. This reaction is similar to oxidation of boranes with hydrogen peroxide. Draw curly arrows on the following reactions to illustrate the electron flow.

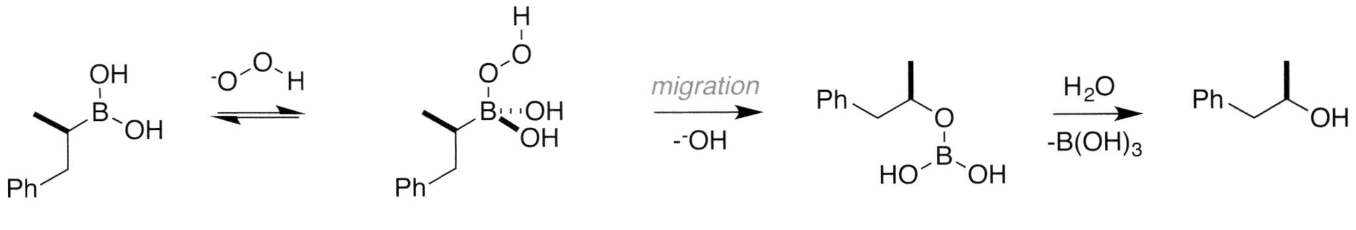

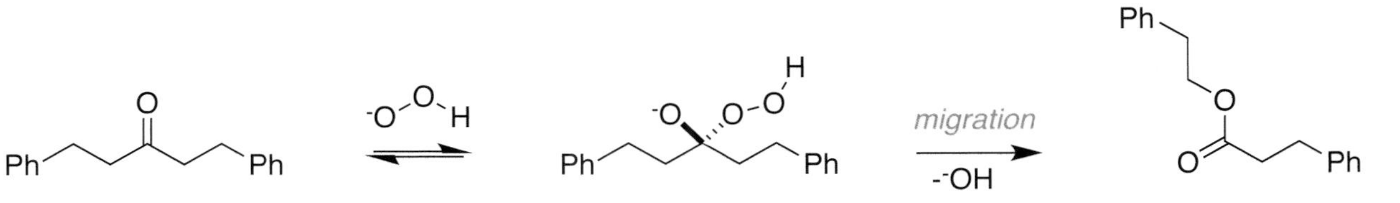

The alignment of the migrating group and the bond cleaved is *syn* / *anti*-periplanar in these migrations. Draw mechanism and predict products for the following reactions where the group best able to support positive charge migrates, and with retention of stereochemistry.

migration

-\-OH

———————————   ———————————

migration

-\-OH

———————————   ———————————

migration

-\-O$_2$CAr

———————————   ———————————

20 Characteristics Of Enols And Enolates

from chapter(s) _____ in the recommended text

A Introduction

Focus
Enols and enolates may form under acidic and basic conditions from many compounds that have a *CH* bond adjacent an electron-withdrawing group. Those electron-withdrawing groups can be selected from numerous different functionalities. Enolization can impact chemical reactivity via deuterium exchange, racemization or epimerization, and isomerism.

Reasons To Care
Nature uses enolates for constructing *C-C* bond frameworks; these are milder reagents than hard-anions like Grignards. Enols and enolates are a gateway to electrophilic attack on those α-*C* atoms. Reactions of enolates (dealt with after this section) are key to *in vivo* construction of huge numbers of natural products.

Concepts
acids and bases • resonance • tautomerism

Objective
This section introduces structures of enols and enolates, and the mechanisms by which they might form.

B Enols Form Under Acidic Conditions

Mechanism Of Formation

Reactions of aldehydes and ketones under acidic conditions tend to involve *protonation / deprotonation* of the carbonyl oxygen as the first step.

Protonation of the carbonyl facilitates removal of an α-C*H* because that enables the electrons to flow directly into the carbonyl oxygen. Consequently, the base used can be as weak as *O*-lone pairs of water, hence this proton loss can occur under *acidic* conditions, resulting in formation of an *enol / enolate*.

Draw the structures in the enolization of the simple aldehydes and ketones below.

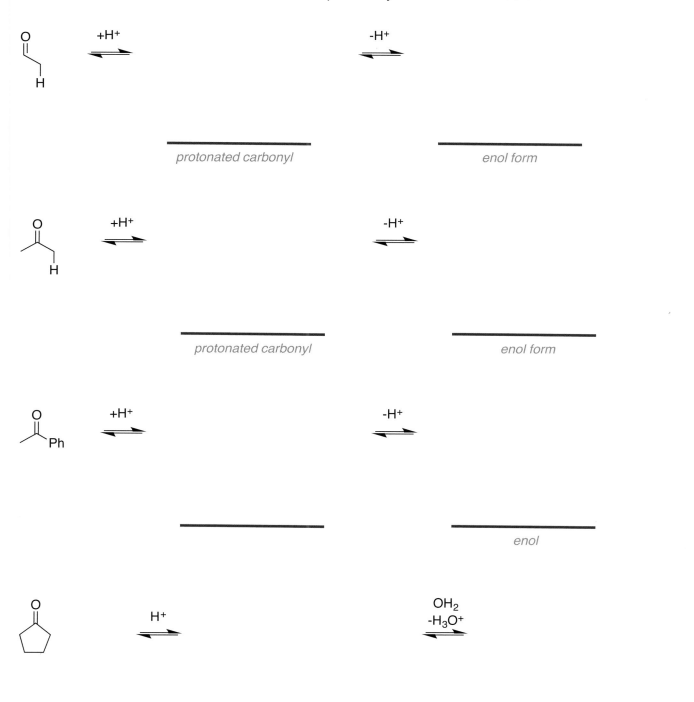

protonated carbonyl   enol form

protonated carbonyl   enol form

enol

Deuterium Exchange

Ketones and aldehydes with enolizable hydrogens exchange these for deuterium when exposed to *deuterons / neutrons / Bosons*.

Illustrate how deuterium is incorporated onto *C*-atoms into the following compounds when they are exposed to D⁺.

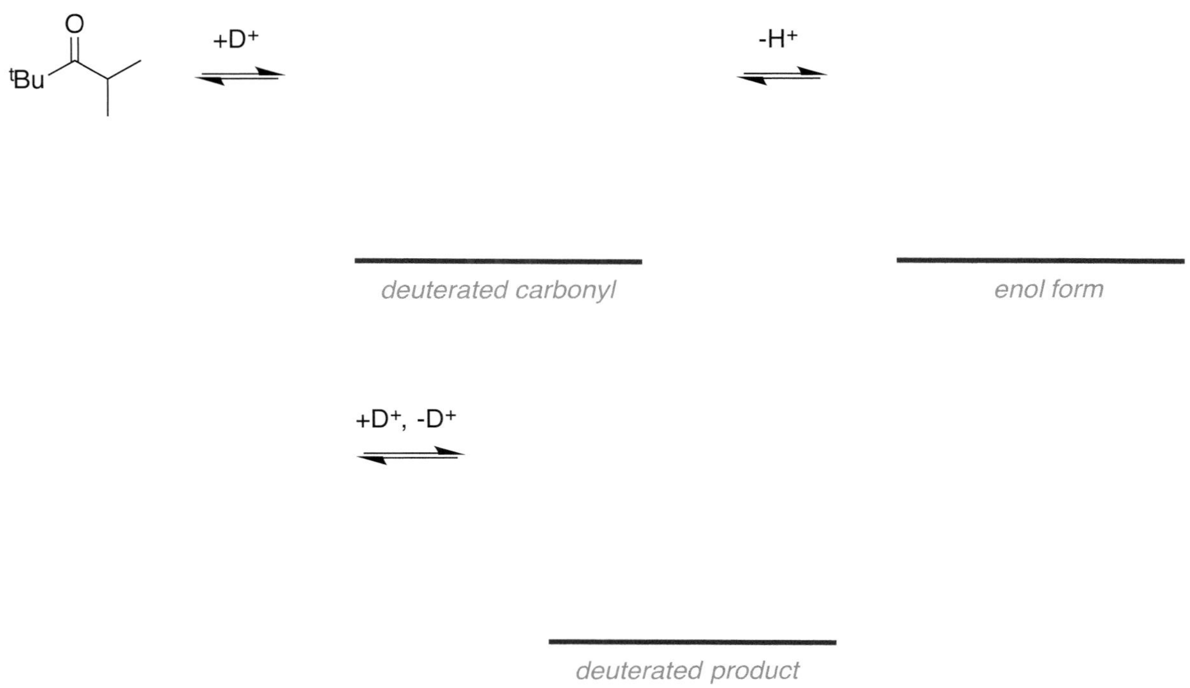

$+D^+$ $-H^+$

_____   _____
deuterated carbonyl   enol form

$+D^+, -D^+$

_____
deuterated product

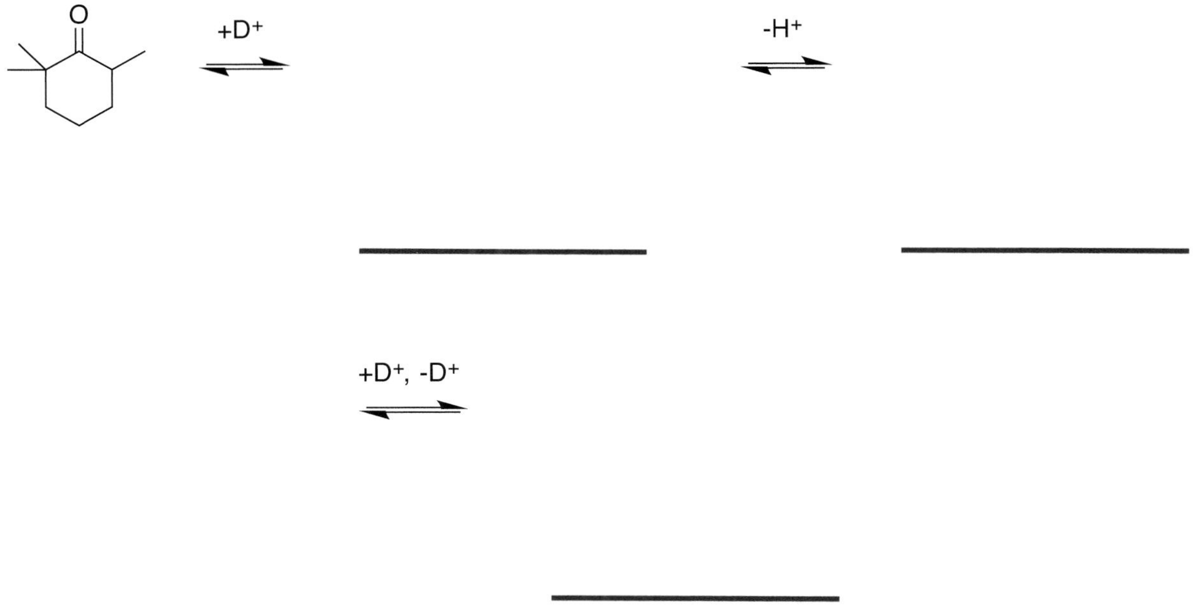

$+D^+$ $-H^+$

_____   _____

$+D^+, -D^+$

_____

Some enols and enolates can have *E*- and *Z*-isomers. Often mixtures are formed and this can be represented using a wavy-line bond; do this in the following example.

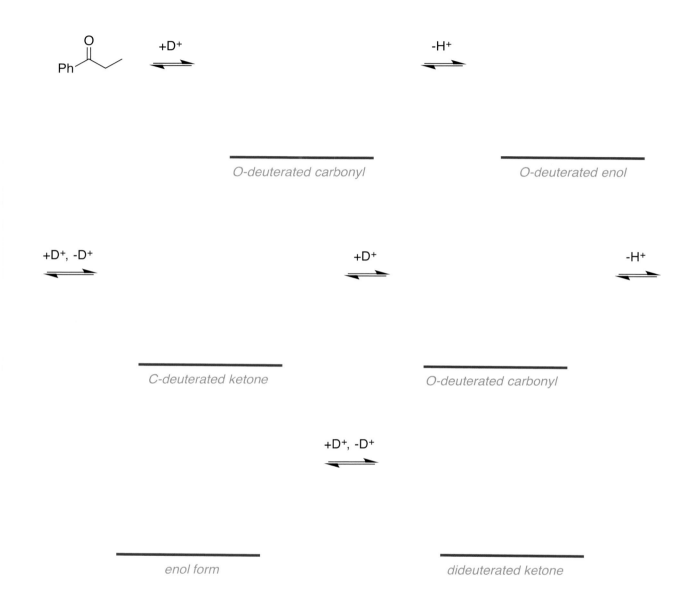

+D⁺

−H⁺

_____ O-deuterated carbonyl

_____ O-deuterated enol

+D⁺, −D⁺

+D⁺

−H⁺

_____ C-deuterated ketone

_____ O-deuterated carbonyl

+D⁺, −D⁺

_____ enol form

_____ dideuterated ketone

Circle carbons in the following molecules that bear H that may exchange with excess D⁺.

In general, when isomers interconvert by changing the position of a hydrogen atom and nothing else, such as going from carbonyl to enol form, this is called *resonance / tautomerism / aromaticity*; it can be achieved via acid or base catalysis.

Enols Of 1,2- And 1,3-Dicarbonyl Compounds

For simple aldehydes and ketones the *enol / keto* form is more abundant in solution.

For acetone the keto : enol ratio is about *1 : 1 / 10^6 : 1 / 1 : 10^6*.

The *enol / keto* form is much more prevalent for some other types of carbonyl compounds. Fill in the structures below and suggest reasons why their enols are more favored than that of acetone.

+H⁺

-H⁺

_____
protonated carbonyl

_____
enol form

reason: _____

_____

_____.

+H⁺

-H⁺

_____

_____

reason: _____

_____

_____.

Enolization of 1,3-dicarbonyl *conjugates / infiltrates* one carbonyl with a double *C=C* bond and sometimes enables *H*-bond stabilization.
Draw enol forms of the following compounds having one or both those attributes.

Show the 1,3-dicarbonyl compounds associated with the following.

Enols Of Other Carbonyl Compounds

Draw the formation of the following enols with clear arrows. Use a wavy-line bond to indicate mixtures of *E*- and *Z*-isomers, or show the configuration if only one is formed.

278

Keto-Enol Tautomers Of Other Compound Types

Draw tautomers of the following compounds, and indicate if they are *keto* or *enol* forms.

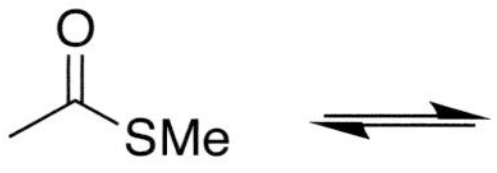

keto / enol

keto / enol

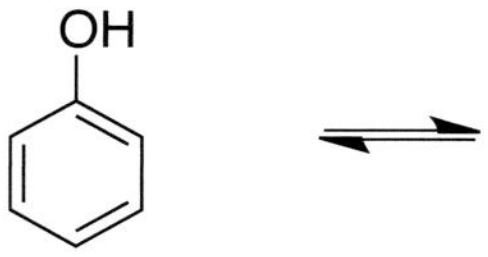

keto / enol

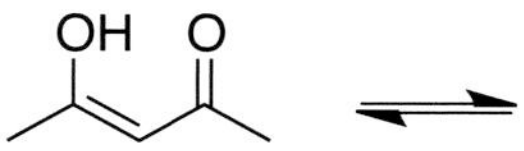

keto / enol

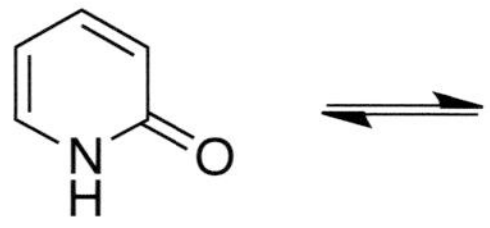

keto / enol

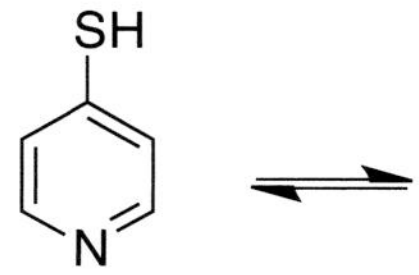

keto / enol

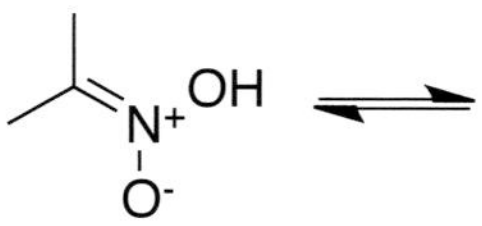

keto / enol

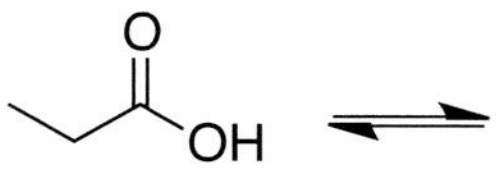

keto / enol

It would be *correct / incorrect* to relate the keto and enol forms above with a double-headed arrow
(⟷) because _____ .

C Enolates Form Under Basic Conditions

Mechanism Of Formation

Base-mediated formation of enolates involves *C*-deprotonation then *O*-protonation. Draw this mechanism for formation of the enol form of ethyl acetate.

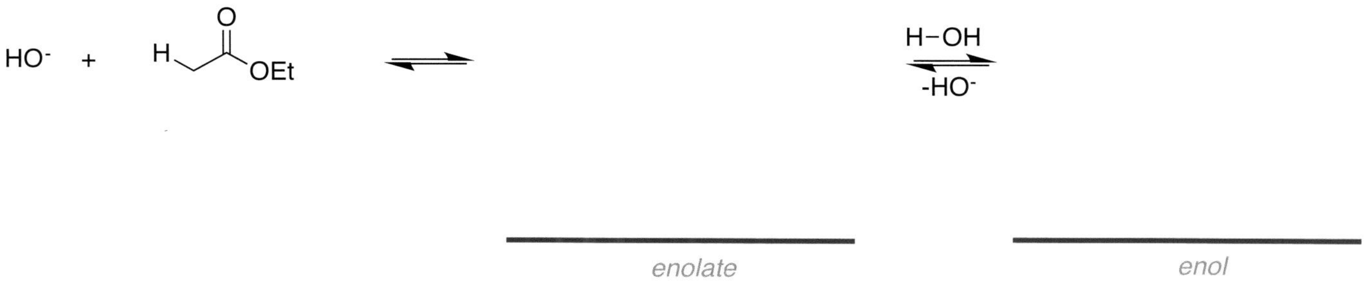

HO⁻ + (H–CH₂–C(=O)–OEt)   ⇌

H–OH / –HO⁻

_____   _____
      enolate   *enol*

Draw similar processes for the following transformations using wavy lines to indicate mixtures of *E*- and *Z*-isomers, or show the configuration if only one is formed.

MeO⁻ + (H–CH₂–C(=O)–OMe)   ⟶

H–OH / –HO⁻

_____   _____

Na⁺ H⁻ + (H–CH(CH₃)–C(=O)–OMe)   ⟶

H–OH / –HO⁻

_____   _____

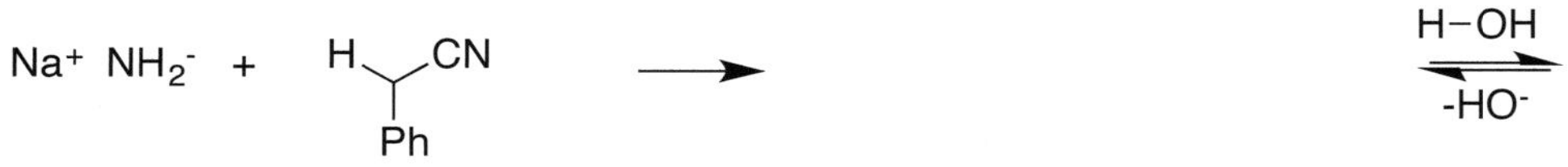

Na⁺ NH₂⁻ + H—CN
                 |
                 Ph

                                              H—OH
                                          ⇌
                                             -HO⁻

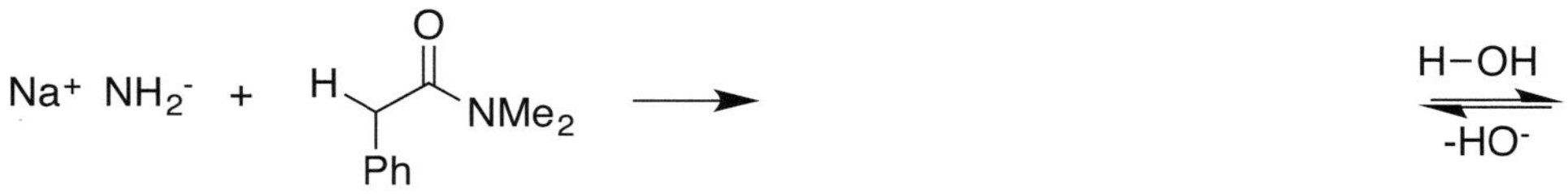

———————————————   ———————————————

Na⁺ NH₂⁻ + H—C(=O)—NMe₂
                 |
                 Ph

                                              H—OH
                                          ⇌
                                             -HO⁻

———————————————   ———————————————

Resonance Structures Of Enolates

Draw resonance structures of the following anions.

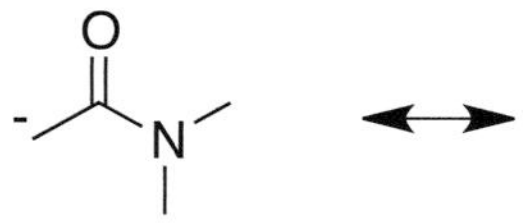

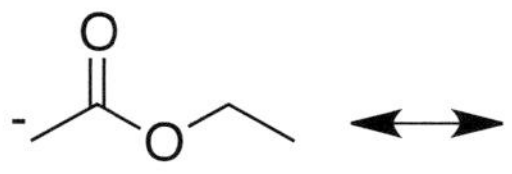

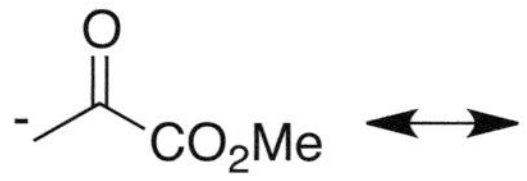

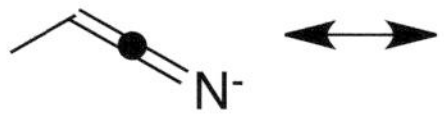

⁻CH₂—C(=O)—N(Me)Me ↔

⁻CH₂—C(=O)—O—CH₂CH₃ ↔

———————————————   ———————————————

⁻CH₂—C(=O)—CO₂Me ↔

CH₃—CH=C=N⁻ ↔

———————————————   ———————————————

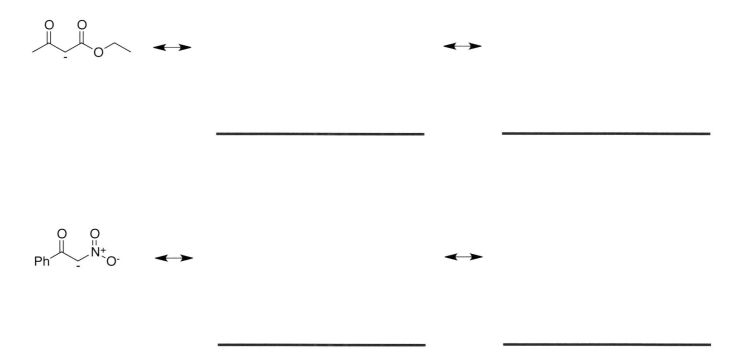

Nitrogen is *more / less* electronegative than carbon so *more / less* able to support a negative charge.

Circle the most acidic hydrogen(s) in the following structures.

It *is / is not* easy to form *C*-enolates from compounds like the last three from the right shown here because they form

_____ .

D Effects Of Enolization

Racemization

Draw enol forms of the following optically active molecules, and indicate if these are also optically active.

optically active / achiral

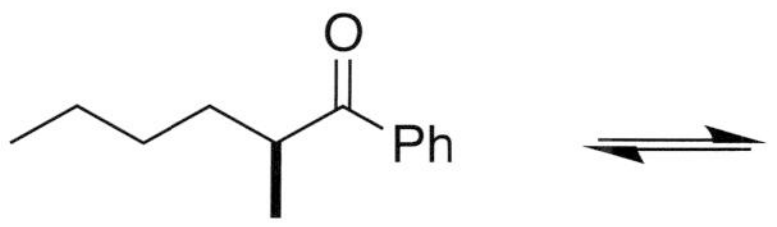

282

optically active / achiral

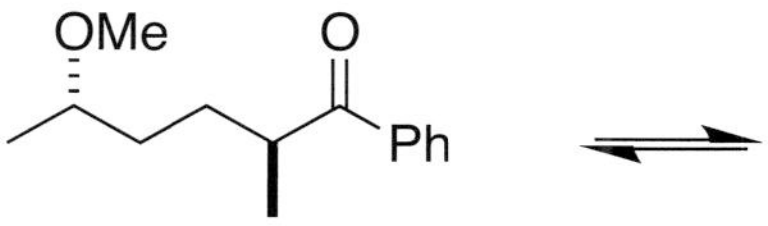

optically active / achiral

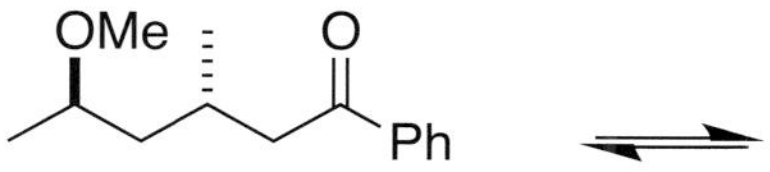

optically active / achiral

In general, α-chiral ketones and aldehydes *can / cannot* racemize or epimerize in the presence of acid or base.

Complete the following to determine if other carbonyl compounds can undergo the same type of process.

ibuprofen

enol

Double Bond Migration

The following compounds can form enolates via deprotonation at the $C\alpha$ then form keto forms by adding protons back to $C\gamma$; the consequences of this is *racemization / migration*. Complete the following diagrams:

enol	_keto_

enol	_keto_

enol	_enol_

keto	_enol_

284

Draw a keto form of ascorbic acid (vitamin C) to indicate why Cβ may have some carbonyl character.

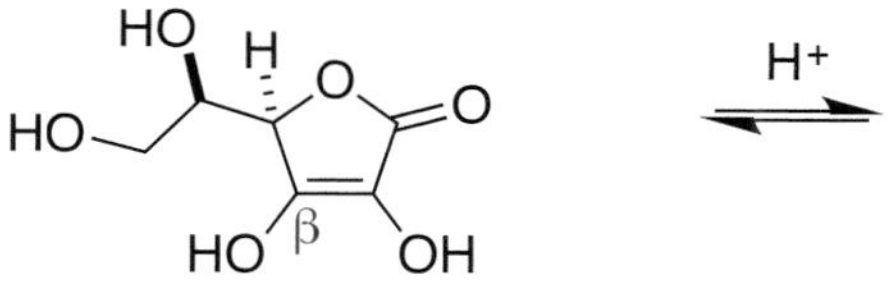

HO H
HO
O
O
HO β OH

ascorbic acid

H+

_____

alternative enol

Draw the enol form that would enable glucose to be isomerized into fructose.

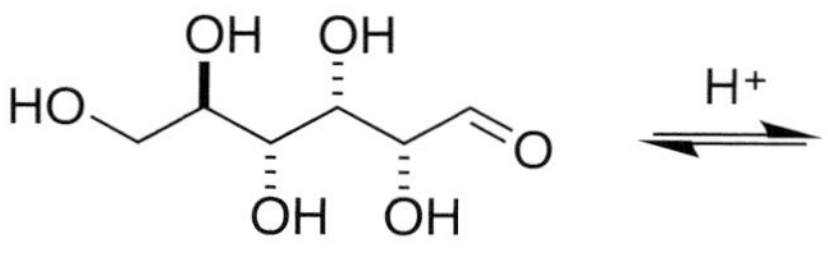

OH OH
HO
O
OH OH

glucose

H+

_____

enol

H+

OH OH
HO
OH
OH O

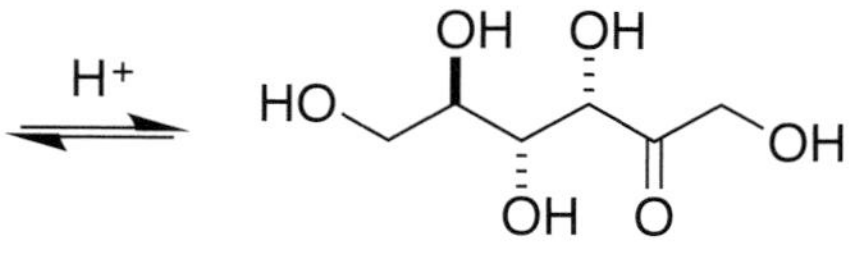

fructose

21 Halogenation Of Enolizable Aldehydes And Ketones

from chapter(s) _____ in the recommended text

A Introduction

Focus

Just as halogenation of alkenes is one of the simplest electrophilic addition mechanisms, halogenation of enols and enolates is also straightforward. However, unlike the corresponding alkene reactions, this is a substitution, not an addition, and the mechanism, and outcomes, are different under acidic and basic conditions.

This section explains why monohalogenation predominates under acidic conditions, but polyhalogenation is possible under basic conditions. Methyl ketones, in fact, can react further, *ie* via "the haloform reaction", losing trihalomethyl anions, CX_3^-, thus generating carboxylic acids. The halogenation processes featured here illustrate how simple electrophiles add to enols and to enolates, and why the outcome is not always the same.

Reasons To Care

Halogenation of enolates is a process that does occur in some living systems, and these transformations are widely used in laboratory syntheses.

Concepts

halogenation of alkenes • resonance • tautomerism • enols and enolates

Objective

Rationalization of halogenation of enols and enolates in terms of the reactivities of the initial product formed, and a gentle introduction into the wider set of reactions of enols and enolates with electrophiles.

B Halogenation Via Enols (Acidic Conditions)

Acidic Conditions Give Monohalogenation

Enols tend to form under neutral or *acidic / basic* conditions, whereas enolates form under *neutral or acidic / basic* conditions.

Enols are *more / less* reactive than *enolates* towards electrophiles because they do *not* have a negative charge.

Show the reaction of phenylethanone with bromine via dissociation of a proton from the enol-*OH* while bromine simultaneously adds to the α-carbon.

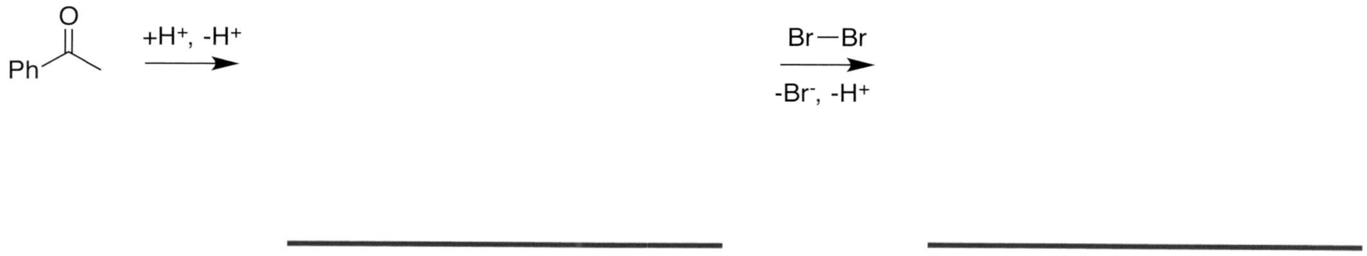

Ph— (O) +H⁺, -H⁺ →   Br—Br → -Br⁻, -H⁺

_____   _____
        enol   *bromoketone*

Another way to represent this reaction is: *O*-deprotonation (rather than just dissociation) with the strongest base available (the solution is neutral or acidic, so this will not be a strong base) and simultaneous reaction with the electrophile.

Draw the same reaction shown above but with bromide deprotonating the enol-*OH* at the same time the carbon of the enol attacks the bromine.

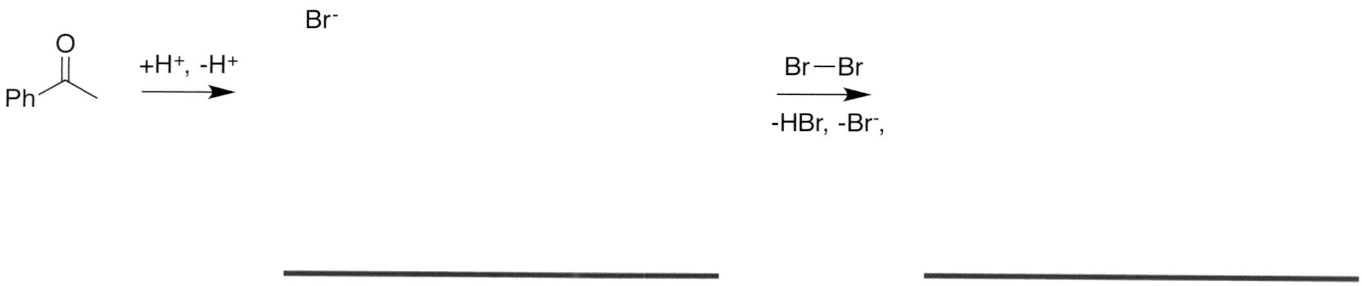

Br⁻

Ph— (O) +H⁺, -H⁺ →   Br—Br → -HBr, -Br⁻,

_____   _____

Consider how likely it is for three friends walking from three different directions to accidentally bump into each other at *exactly* the same time. By analogy, the second representation is *less / more* likely because the process would involve three molecules coming together simultaneously, which is *less / more* statistically favorable.

Complete the following diagram by showing the products; the nitrosylation reaction adds NO$^+$ as an electrophile. NOCl is a pseudo- *halide / base / name*.

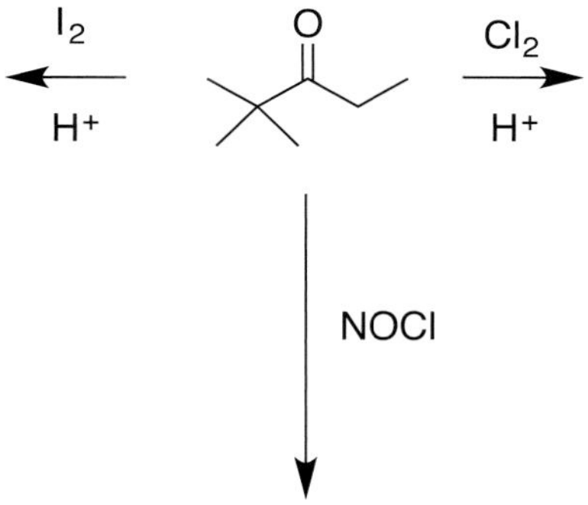

$$\xleftarrow[\text{H}^+]{\text{I}_2} \qquad \text{(ketone)} \qquad \xrightarrow[\text{H}^+]{\text{Cl}_2}$$

$$\downarrow \text{NOCl}$$

_____
monosubstitution

_____
monosubstitution

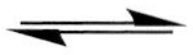

$$\rightleftharpoons$$

_____
nitroso form

_____
oxime tautomer

c Halogenation Via Enolates (Basic Conditions)

Basic Conditions Facilitate Substitution Of More Than One Halogen

Acid- and base-promoted halogenations of carbonyl compounds are mechanistically *different / identical*.

Rank the following enolates in order of decreasing stabilities by showing their resonance forms and circling **1** for the most stable, **2** next, *etc*.

_____
1 / 2 / 3 / 4

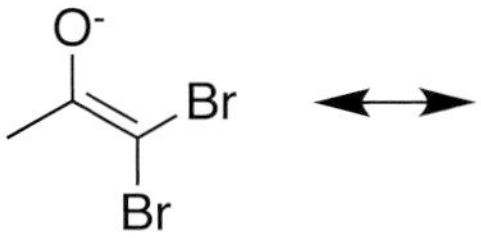

_____
1 / 2 / 3 / 4

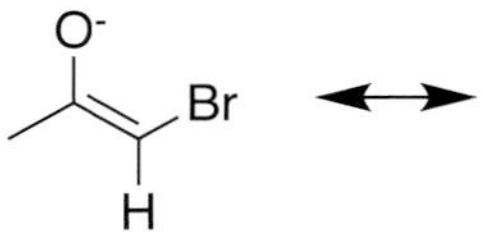

_____
1 / 2 / 3 / 4

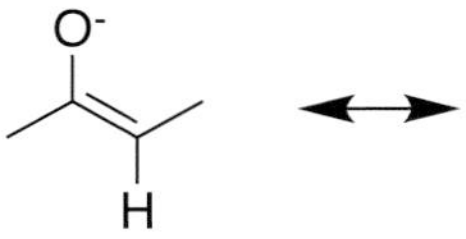

_____
1 / 2 / 3 / 4

Under *basic* conditions, haloketones are *more / less* acidic than the starting materials due to inductive stabilization of the enolate.

Monohaloketone products under basic conditions are *more / less* likely to enolize and react with more halogen electrophile than ones formed under acidic conditions.

Show the mechanism of base-mediated bromination of 2,2-dimethylpentan-3-one to the corresponding dibromoketone.

base →

Br₂ →

base →

_____
2,2-dimethylpentan-3-one

_____
more / less likely to form enolate than starting ketone

Br₂ →

_____
enolate

_____
2,2-dibromo-4,4-dimethylpentan-3-one

Based on the above, methyl ketones under basic conditions *would / would not* react with *three* equivalents of base and halogen to form 1,1,1-trihalomethylketones.

In fact, the final product of the reaction above is *not* 1,1,1-trihalomethylketones. This is because after each substitution the carbonyl group becomes *more / less* electrophilic.

After three substitutions the base can add to the carbonyl and the bulky, inductively stabilized trihalomethyl anion is expelled; this is the *haloform / chloroform* reaction.

Outline the mechanism for reaction of 1-phenylethanone with excess bromine and base, by completing the following diagram.

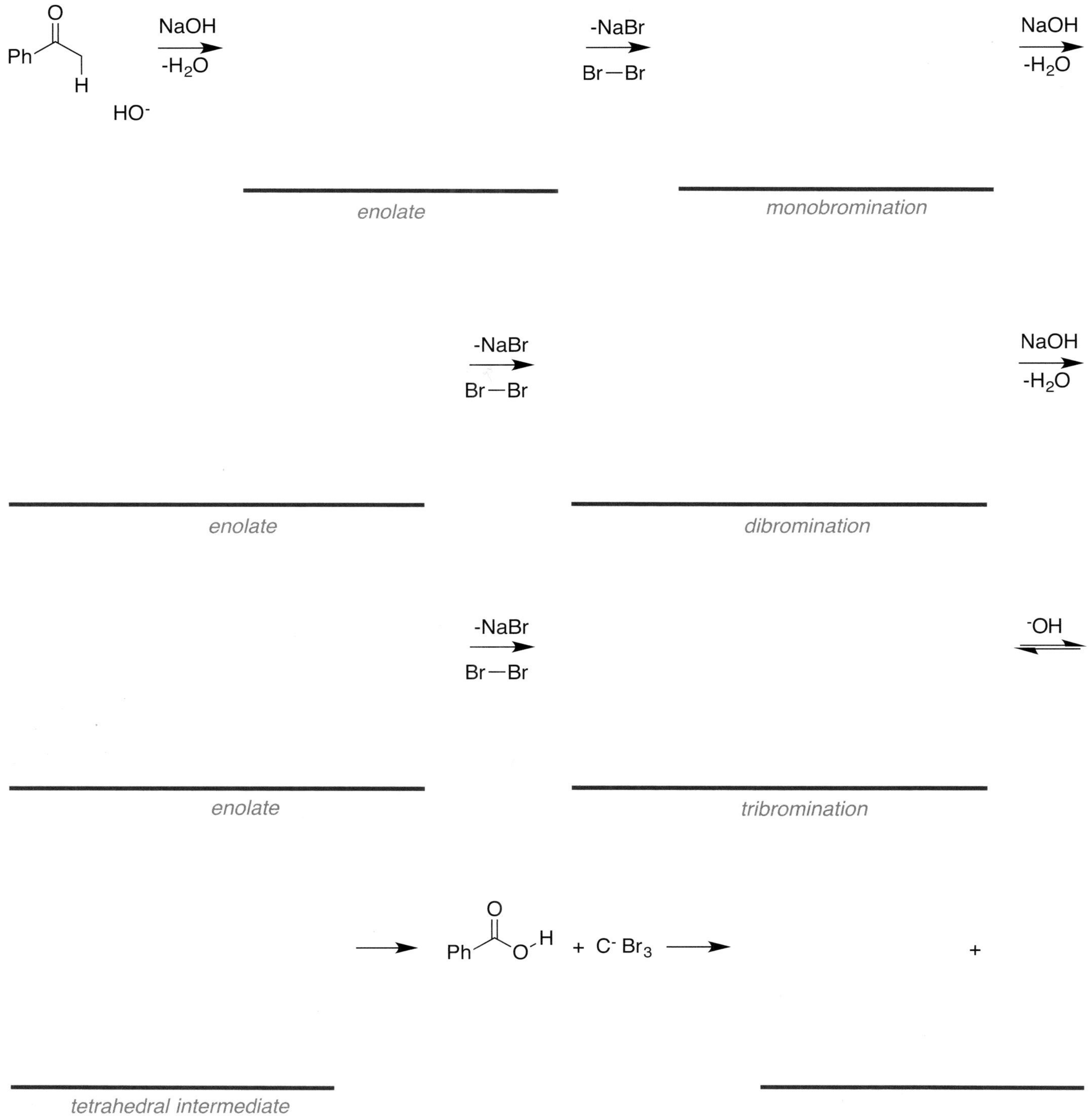

enolate

monobromination

enolate

dibromination

enolate

tribromination

Ph—C(=O)—O—H + C⁻Br₃ ⟶ +

tetrahedral intermediate

Iodoform, I₃CH, is a crystalline solid that precipitates from many organic solvents so treatment with hydroxide and iodine _could / could not_ be used as a visual test for methyl ketones.

290

Outline the mechanism of the following iodoform-generating reaction.

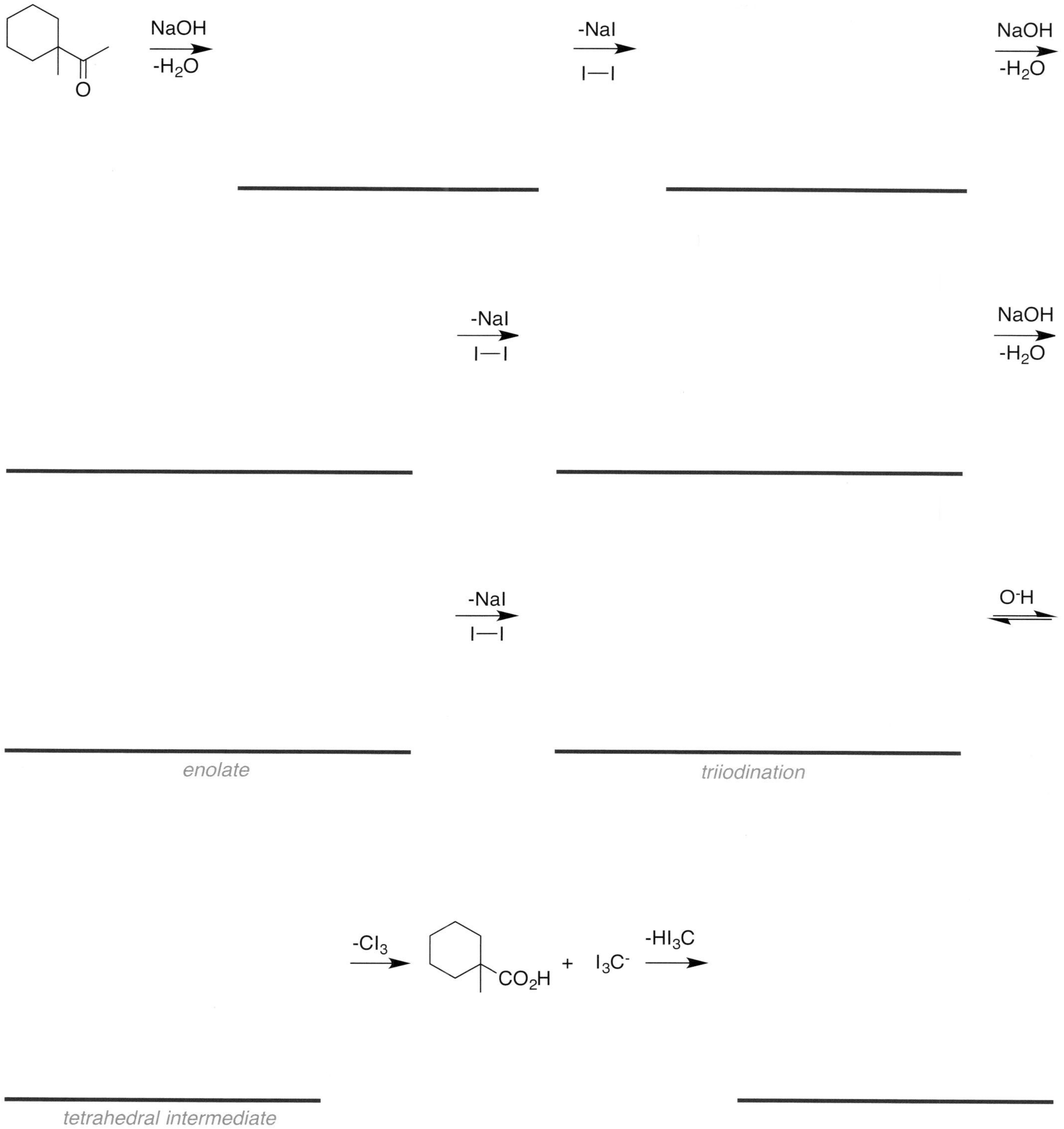

NaOH
-H₂O

-NaI
I—I

NaOH
-H₂O

-NaI
I—I

NaOH
-H₂O

-NaI
I—I

O⁻H

enolate

triiodination

-Cl₃

CO₂H + I₃C⁻

-HI₃C

tetrahedral intermediate

Under *acidic* conditions enolization of the monohaloketone product is *slower / faster* than the ketone starting material because the carbonyl oxygen is less basic than in the starting material.

Which of the following ketones could give iodoform when treated with iodine and hydroxide?

yes / no   yes / no   yes / no   yes / no   yes / no   yes / no   yes / no

D Choosing Acidic Or Basic Conditions For Halogenations

Predict the products of the following halogenation reactions.

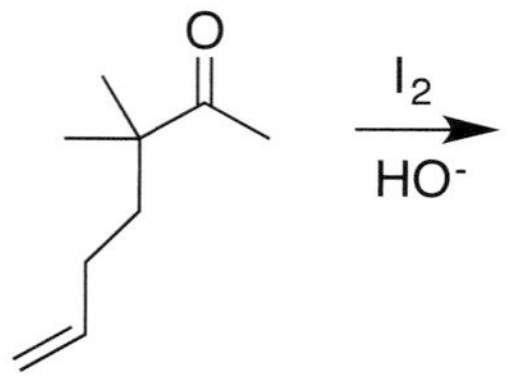

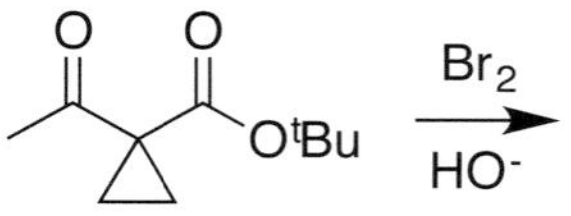

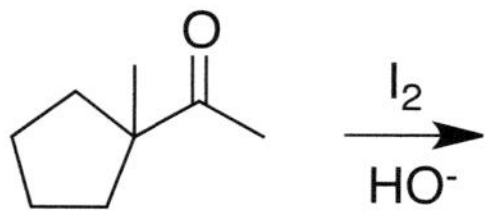

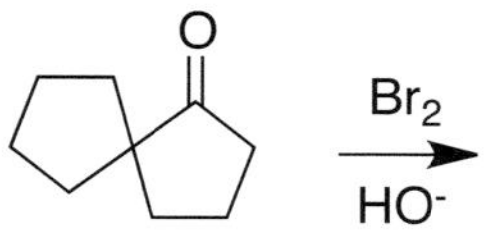

$\xrightarrow[HO^-]{I_2}$

_____

$\xrightarrow[HO^-]{Br_2}$

_____

$\xrightarrow[HO^-]{I_2}$

_____

$\xrightarrow[HO^-]{Br_2}$

_____

Identify the conditions and starting materials for preparation of the following products; all these reactions require halogenation.

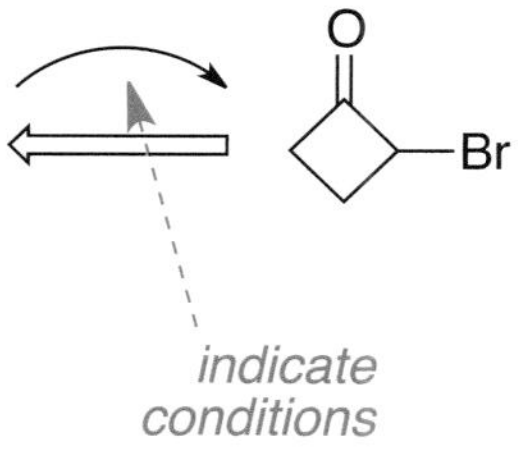

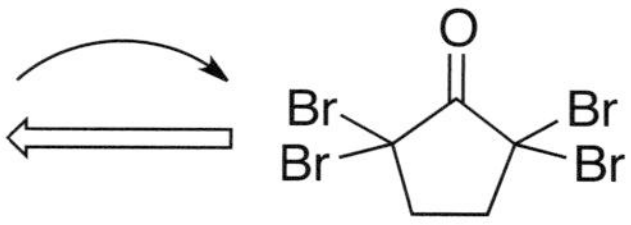

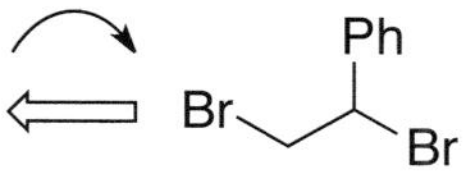

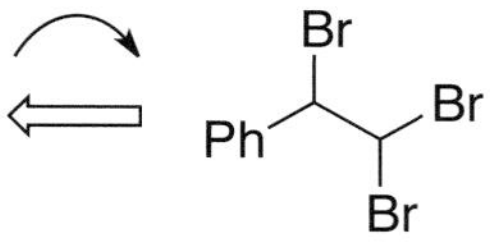

indicate
conditions

_____

_____

_____

_____

_____ _____

Alkene bromination followed by *E1 / E1cb* eliminations are operative in the following reactions (1 equiv of bromine is used). Show starting materials and indicate conditions.

_____ _____

_____

_____

22 Reactions Of Enolizable Compounds With C-Electrophiles

from chapter(s) _____ in the recommended text

A Introduction

Focus

Grignard reagents can be used to build-up carbon frameworks in organic molecules by adding nucleophiles to carbonyl compounds (and some other electrophiles). In addition to this, enolizable carbonyl compounds can be converted to enols, enolates, or some equivalent of these then C-alkylated. The fact that enolizable carbonyl compounds can react as electrophiles (at the carbonyl) or nucleophiles (on the α-C carbon) makes them extremely versatile intermediates in synthetic pathways.

add nucleophiles here please!

electrophiles add here

enolate   hydrazone enolate   silyl enol ether   enamine

Reasons To Care

Alkylation of enolates is used in laboratory syntheses and biosynthesis, but the other strategies are mostly for synthesis laboratories. All these methods, however, illustrate ways in which enolate reactivities may be tuned to give α-C alkylation, as an alternative to nucleophilic additions to carbonyl groups.

Concepts

enolates • enamines • electrophilic attack • construction of the carbon framework of organic molecules

Objective

Practitioners should understand the concept of enolate alkylation, some of the limitations of that approach, and strategies that have been adopted to overcome some of those restrictions.

B α-Alkylation Of Carbonyl Compounds Under Strongly Basic Conditions

C-Alkylation Of Ketones

Stronger bases than HO⁻ drive most ketones to exist predominantly as enolates, but may also be *nucleophilic / electrophilic* enough to react at the carbon of carbonyl groups.

Deprotonation of simple carbonyl compounds in preference to addition to the carbonyl group of these compounds, requires a base that is *strong / weak* and *nucleophilic / non-nucleophilic*.

One strategy to favor deprotonation of carbonyl compounds is to use *small / hindered* alkali metal amides.

Draw products of the following reactions.

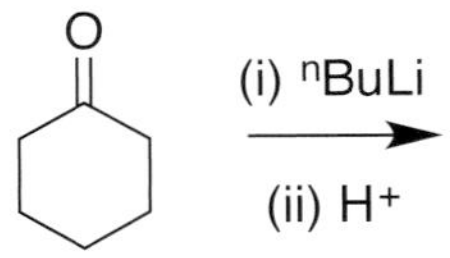

(i) ⁿBuLi
(ii) H⁺

_____

tertiary alcohol

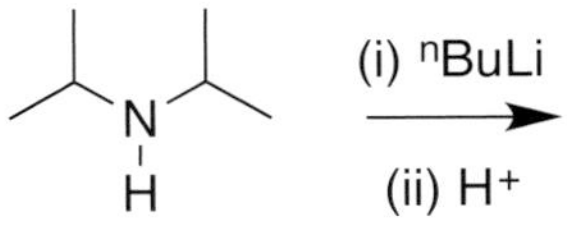

(i) ⁿBuLi
(ii) H⁺

-HNⁱPr₂

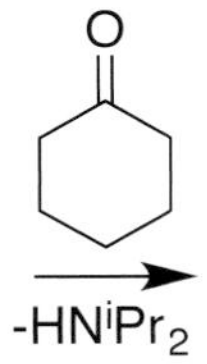

lithium diisopropylamide LDA
pKa 35 / 10 / -5

enolate

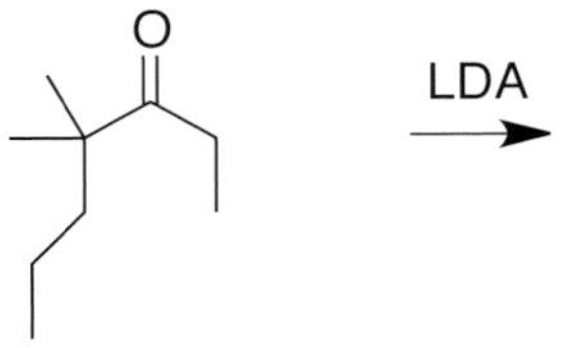

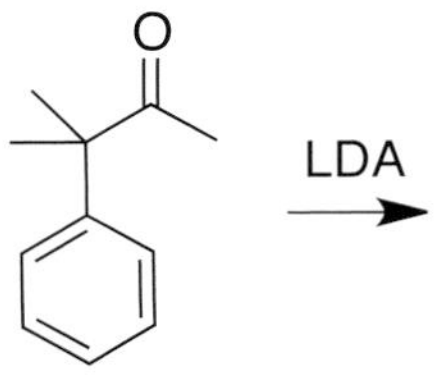

LDA

LDA

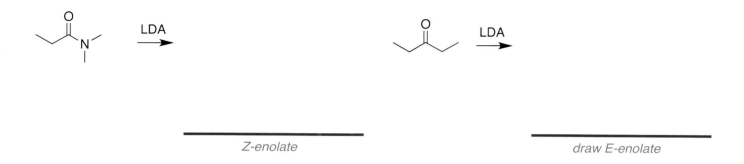

Z-enolate | _draw E-enolate_

Draw the two possible products of monoalkylation of 2-methylcyclopentanone with ethyl bromide.

(i) LDA ← (ii) EtBr   (i) LDA → (ii) EtBr

2,5-dialkyl product | _2,2-dialkyl product_

It is _easy / difficult_ to design conditions so that one of these products is significantly favored over the other.

Ways to overcome this problem include alkylation of anions from hydrazones, from silyl enolates, or to use an enamine and alkylate that under neutral conditions.

Alkylation Of Hydrazones

Hydrazones can have *syn* and *anti*-forms. Under thermodynamic conditions, the most stable (usually the least hindered) isomer is formed.

Show the isomeric hydrazones from 2-methylcyclopentanone.

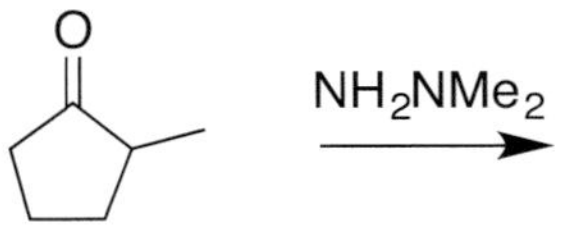

+

_____   _____
syn   more / less stable   *anti   more / less stable*

Alkylation of the following *N,N*-dimethylhydrazone-derived anion gives almost exclusively 2,-dialkyl products, because the hydrazone is mostly *anti* and the lithium cation becomes coordinated at the least hindered site. This is an example of *kinetic / thermodynamic* control.

Illustrate this by completing the diagram below.

_____
anti / syn hydrazone

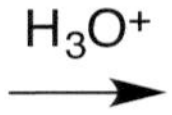

H₃O⁺

_____   _____
alkylation at least hindered carbon   *2,5-dialkylation product*

Silylation and *O*-Methylation Of Aldehydes And Ketones

Silicon – oxygen bonds are relatively *strong / weak* so *Si*-based electrophiles tend to silylate on *O / C -* atoms of enolizable carbonyl compounds.

Silylation of ketones and aldehydes tends to be so facile that only a weak base is required (*eg* a tertiary amine), but stronger bases can be used.

Draw the products of the following reactions.

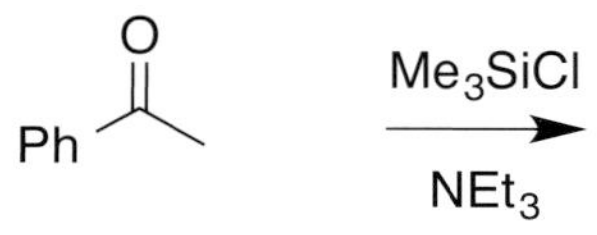

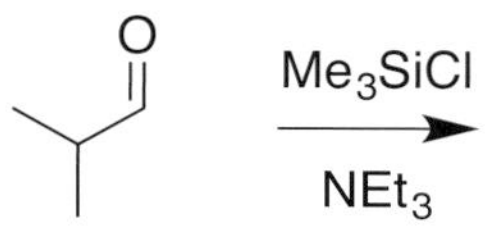

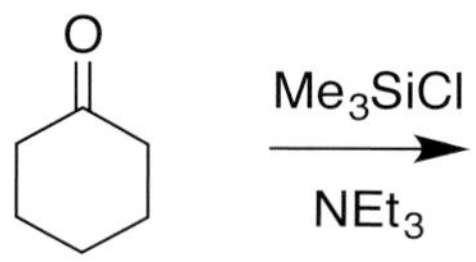

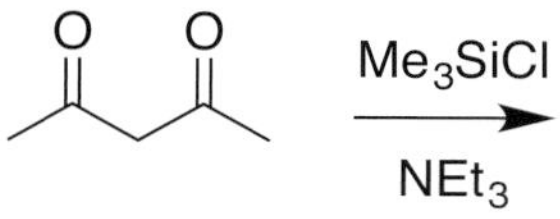

Ph—C(=O)—CH₃ + Me₃SiCl / NEt₃ → _____

(CH₃)₂CH—CHO + Me₃SiCl / NEt₃ → _____

cyclohexanone + Me₃SiCl / NEt₃ → _____

CH₃—C(=O)—CH₂—C(=O)—CH₃ + Me₃SiCl / NEt₃ → _____

disilyl enol ether

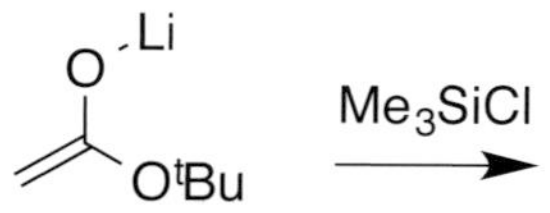

lithium enolate (O⁻Li, O^tBu) + Me₃SiCl → _____

lithium enolate (cyclohexene O⁻Li) + Me₃SiCl → _____

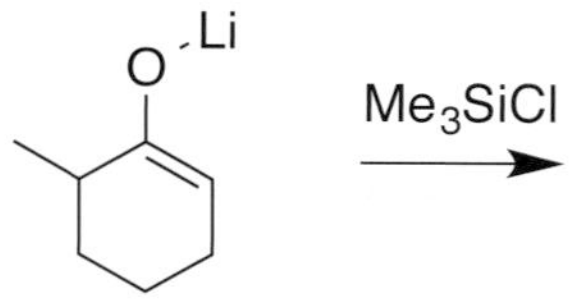

C-based electrophiles preferentially add to enolates at *carbon / oxygen*.

However, in *polar protic / aprotic / polar aprotic* solvents that do not solvate oxygen anions well then it is possible to favor *O / C*-alkylation using *hard / soft* electrophiles (hard electrophiles have *diffuse / concentrated* positive charges).

Draw the *O*-alkylation products of the following reactions.

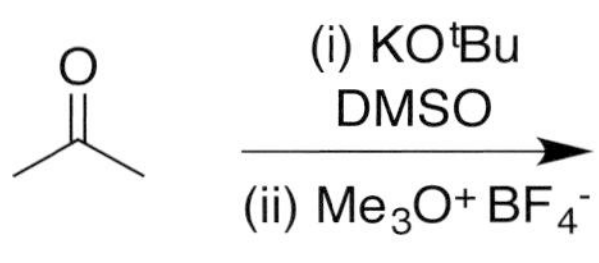
O
(i) KO^{t}Bu
DMSO
(ii) $Me_3O^+ BF_4^-$

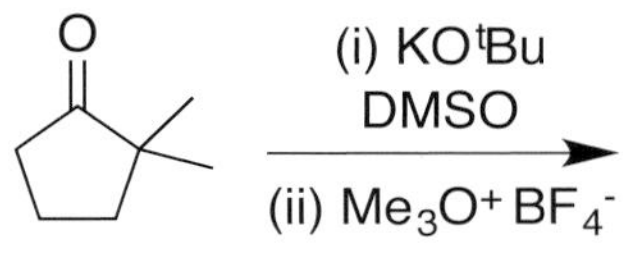
O
(i) KO^{t}Bu
DMSO
(ii) $Me_3O^+ BF_4^-$

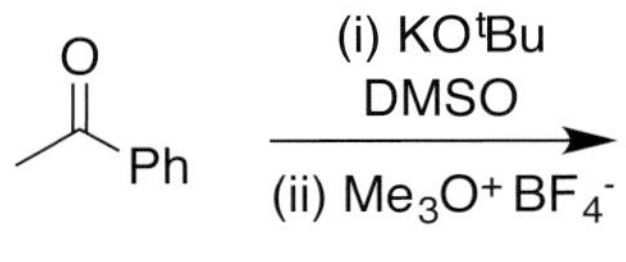
O
Ph
(i) KO^{t}Bu
DMSO
(ii) $Me_3O^+ BF_4^-$

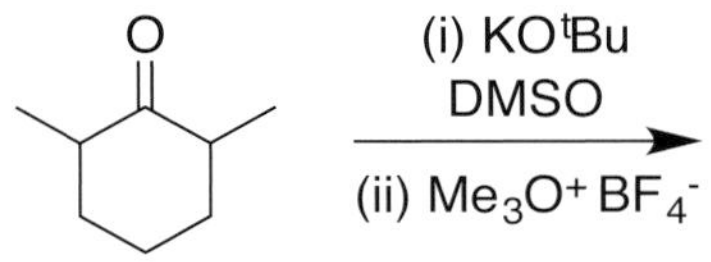
O
(i) KO^{t}Bu
DMSO
(ii) $Me_3O^+ BF_4^-$

Simple electrophiles tend to add to the *C*-atoms of enol ethers, then the best nucleophile available will remove the silyl group.

Draw mechanisms for the following reactions.

Me_3Si
O
$+H^+$
H_2O
$-H^+$
$-HOSiMe_3$

C-protonated form

Me_3Si
O
O
$+H^+$
H_2O
$-H^+$
$-HOSiMe_3$

C-protonated form

addition of a PhS⁺ electrophile

Me₃Si—O → CISPh / -Cl⁻ → → H₂O / -H⁺ / -HOSiMe₃ →

_____
thioether silyloxonium ion

_____
thioether

Reactions of dihydropyran with alcohols in the presence of anhydrous acid gives THP-protected (THP tetrahydropyran) alcohols.

The functional group in THP ethers is a(n) *thioether / acetal / orthoformate*; it *is / is not* chiral leading to diastereomeric products if the R group is chiral.

protonation then quench of the oxonium ion with an alcohol

O → +H⁺ → → ROH / -H⁺ →

dihydropyran

_____
C-protonated form

_____
THP-protected alcohol

This process can be reversed by treating the product with *aqueous / anhydrous* acid.

OR → +H⁺ → → -ROH →

THP ether

_____

_____

-H⁺ →

_____

C α-Alkylation Of Carbonyl Compounds Under Near-neutral Conditions

Enamines From Ketones and Aldehydes

α-Alkylation can be achieved via formation of enamines, then reaction of these with electrophiles.

Donation of *N*-electron density in enamines through the alkene and through the α-carbon to electrophiles results in *imines / iminium ions*, which are easily hydrolyzed on workup.

Show the mechanism of the following enamine-mediated alkylation.

Et—Br

OH₂

———————————————
least hindered enamine

———————————————
iminium

-H⁺, +H⁺

———————————————
tetrahedral intermediate

———————————————
ammonium intermediate

-H⁺

———————————————
protonated carbonyl

Synthesis of enamines from unsymmetrical ketones could give *1 / 2 / 3* possible product(s); the enamine with the least hindered alkene is preferred, so enamine chemistry to preferentially form the corresponding alkylated products at the *least / most* substituted α-carbon is convenient.

Formation of enamines with four groups on the alkene part is disfavored because steric clashes occur if one of the *N*-substituents is co-planar with any alkene substituent.

Show the products of the following reactions.

O
N
H
H+
(i) EtI
(ii) H3O+

enamine

4-methyl-3-hexanone

O
N
H
H+
(i)
Cl
(ii) H3O+

enamine

O
O
N
H
H+
(i) BnBr
(ii) H3O+

O
N
H
H+
(i) AcBr
(ii) H3O+

23 Reactions Of Ester Enolates With Carbonyl Compounds

from chapter(s) _____ in the recommended text

A Introduction

Focus

Halogens and alkylating agents are not the only electrophiles that can add to enolates. Enolates can be *acylated* and, even though esters are not particularly good acylating agents, they *do* tend to react with enolates. Thus an ester enolate can react with the ester it was formed from, and a mixture of two esters may cross-react under basic conditions, though a mixture of products is formed if *both* esters are enolizable.

Reasons To Care

erythromycin

doxorubicin

brefeldin A

Besides carbohydrates, nucleic acids, and proteins, living organisms produce a huge number of diverse organic molecules, "natural products", some of which have medicinal properties and a subset of these can be used as pharmaceuticals. Like carbohydrates, nucleic acids, and proteins, these natural products are assembled *in vivo* from naturally occurring building blocks. However, the building blocks used to obtain these compounds are diverse, and their assembly is augmented by a series of reactions to modify them. For instance, a common pathway that Nature follows to make natural products involves combinations of the following steps: acylation of enolates (particularly, thioenolates with thioester electrophiles), carbonyl reductions, dehydration, and addition of hydrogen across alkenes. Those steps may be performed iteratively, where some are not always used in each cycle, to build materials that display functional groups in irregular three-dimensional shapes, often evolved for specialized functions *in vivo*.

Concepts Involved

enolates • electrophilic attack • condensation reactions • thioesters

Objective

Sophomore organic chemistry, or any other course, cannot present a simple rationale for how all natural products are formed, because there is not one. However, the objective of this part of the course is to cover some of the most important reactions that are used in syntheses and biosyntheses of natural products.

B Enolates With Ester Electrophiles (Claisen Condensations)

Homocoupling Of Esters

Each of the following structures has *one or two* predominantly nucleophilic or electrophilic *C*-atom(s); circle it and indicate if it is a nucleophile or an electrophile.

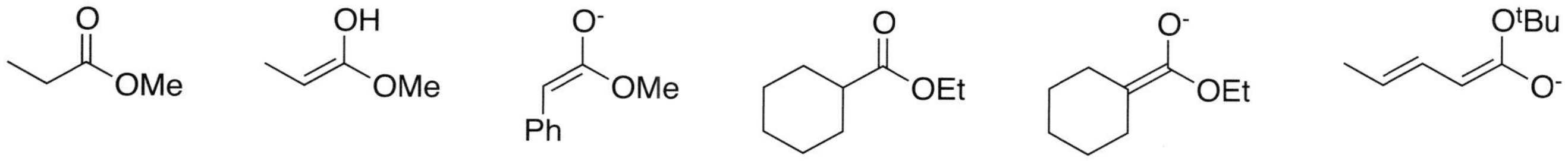

Claisen condensations involve reaction of *enolates / enamines* with esters.
Show the electron flow for this process for self-condensation of ethyl acetate.

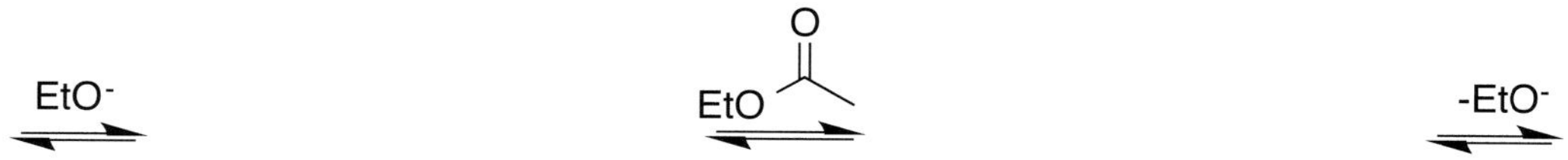

ethyl acetate	enolate	tetrahedral intermediate

1,3-dicarbonyl	enolate

In the reaction sequence above, the 1,3-dicarbonyl product is *more / less* acidic than the starting material.

The amount of base needed in these reactions is *catalytic / stoichiometric*.

Alkoxide bases are frequently used in these processes. It is desirable to use the alkoxide that corresponds to the alkoxy group in the ester to avoid *transesterification / cross-coupling / Wittig reactions*.

Give the products of the following homocoupling reactions of esters.

Ph⌒C(=O)OMe   (i) MeO⁻
                        →
                        (ii) H⁺

_____

1,3-dicarbonyl

⌃⌃C(=O)OEt   (i) EtO⁻
                        →
                        (ii) H⁺

_____

EtC(=O)O⌒=   (i) ⁻OCH₂CHCH₂
                        →
                        (ii) H⁺

_____

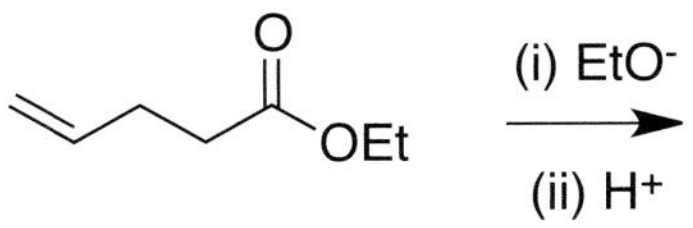

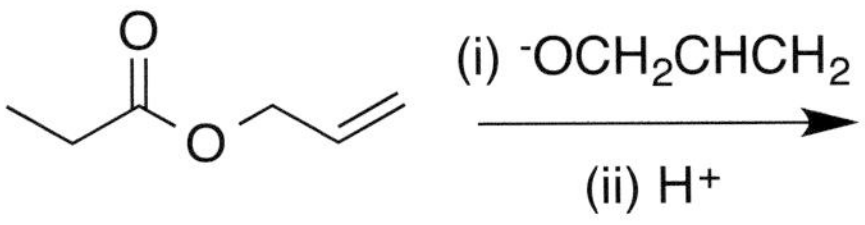

How could Claisen condensations be used to make these products?

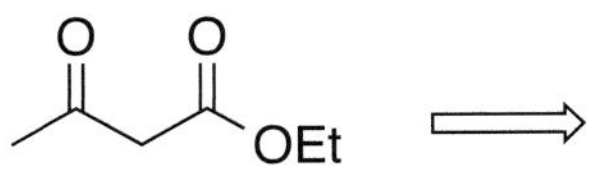

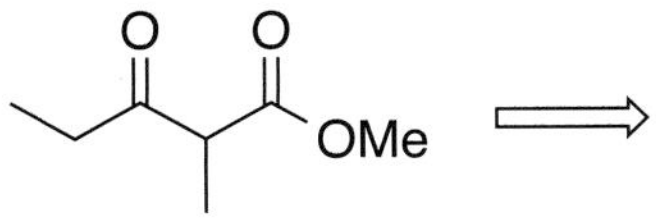

CH₃C(=O)CH₂C(=O)OEt ⟹

CH₃CH₂C(=O)CH(CH₃)C(=O)OMe ⟹

_____

Uncontrolled Cross-Claisen Condensations

The following cross coupling reaction *cannot* give predominantly one product; if only one material was desired then separation might be difficult because two of the products are constitutional isomers that probably have similar polarities and boiling points. Show all possible products of the following reaction.

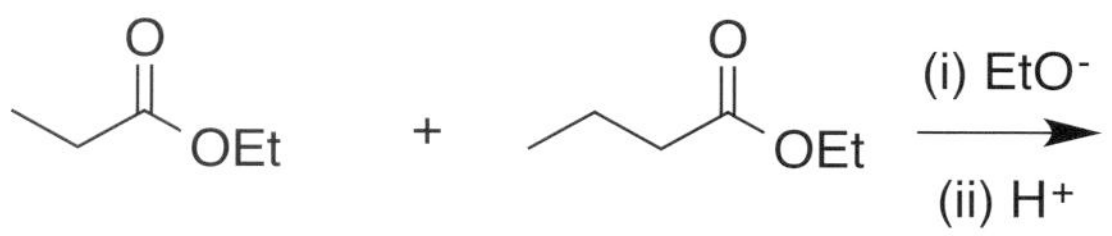

+

+

+

constitutional isomers

Controlled Cross-Claisen Condensations

Only three of the eight carbonyl compounds shown below can form enolates. Draw the enolates of those three.

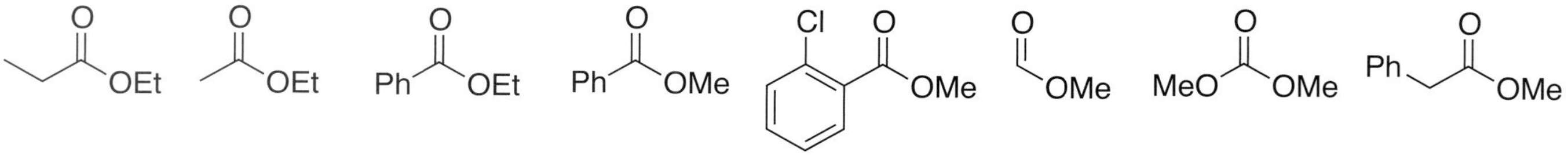

enolate 1   enolate 2   enolate 3

Cross coupling reactions between esters can give predominantly one product if *only one / two* of the components has/have enolizable carbons. *Only* three of the six reactions below can give exactly *one* cross coupling product; identify those three, and draw the products.

CH$_3$CH$_2$C(O)OEt + CH$_3$C(O)OEt →(i) EtO⁻ (ii) H⁺ **A**

Ph-C(O)OEt + CH$_3$C(O)OEt →(i) EtO⁻ (ii) H⁺ **B**

Ph-C(O)OMe + (2-Cl-C$_6$H$_4$)-C(O)OMe →(i) MeO⁻ (ii) H⁺ **C**

H-C(O)OMe + CH$_3$CH$_2$C(O)OMe →(i) MeO⁻ (ii) H⁺ **D**

MeO-C(O)-OMe + CH$_3$CH$_2$C(O)OMe →(i) MeO⁻ (ii) H⁺ **E**

Ph-CH$_2$-C(O)OMe + (2-Cl-C$_6$H$_4$)-CH$_2$-C(O)OMe →(i) MeO⁻ (ii) H⁺ **F**

_____ letter _____

_____ letter _____

_____ letter _____

Identify starting materials from which the following cross Claisen products could be made.

EtO-C(O)-CH(C$_4$H$_9$)-C(O)-OEt ⟹ _____ + _____

Ph-C(O)-CH(CO$_2$Me)-CH$_2$CH$_2$-CH=CH$_2$ ⟹ _____ + _____

Intramolecular Reactions Of Ester Enolates With Esters (Dieckmann Reactions)

Intramolecular condensations of a diester where the ester groups are identical can give predominantly one product.

Show how this 1,6-diester can undergo intramolecular cyclization to form a substituted cyclopentanone.

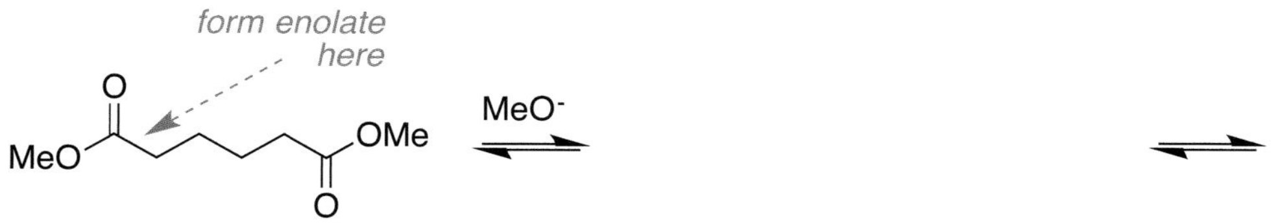

form enolate here

MeO⁻

_____   _____
enolate   enolate in conformation
                           for cyclization

-MeO⁻

_____
a cyclopentanone

Predict the products of the following reactions (the left hand one goes through a ketone enolate).

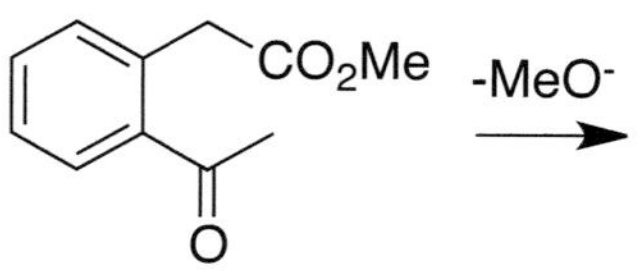

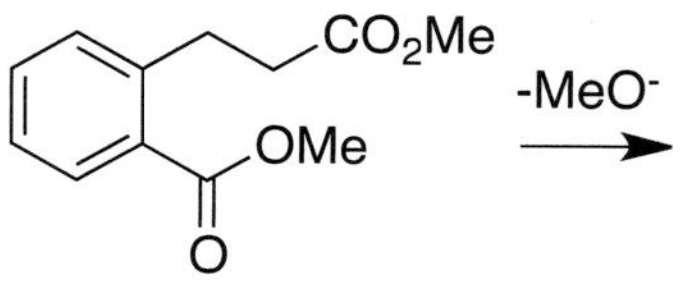

_____   _____

Spirocyclic atoms are ones that *form a single point of contact between two rings / are part of helical spiral molecules*.

Draw the product of the following reaction and encircle the spirocyclic atom.

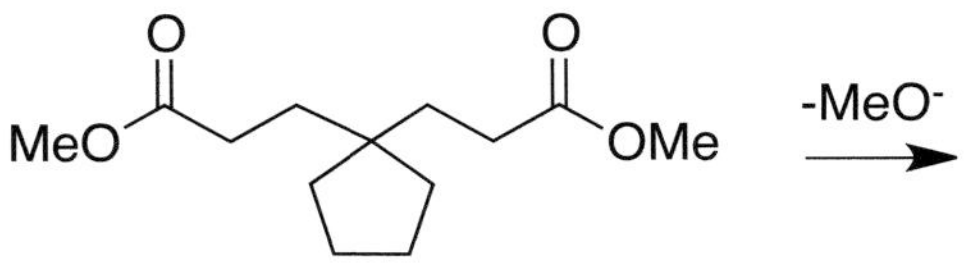

Similar cyclizations that involve two inequivalent, enolizable esters can give *only one / more than one* cross-coupling product.

These are *more / less* practical strategies to obtain cyclic products than the ones shown above because the two products would have to be separated and the yield of the desired one would be *increased / diminished* in the isolation.

Draw all the possible products of the following reactions.

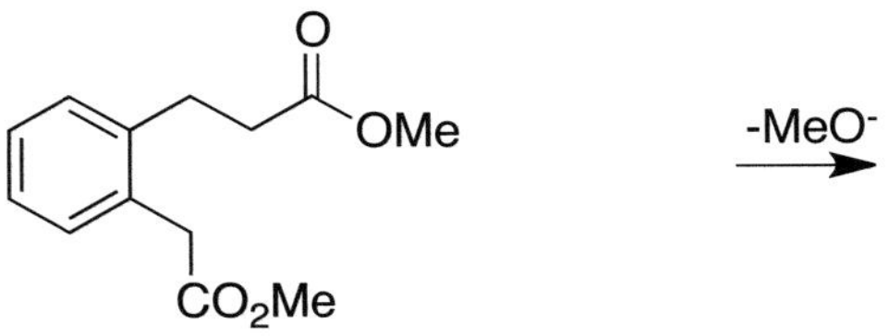

+

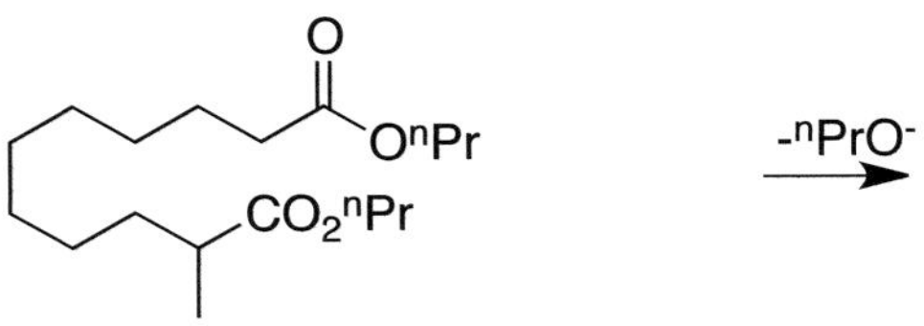

+

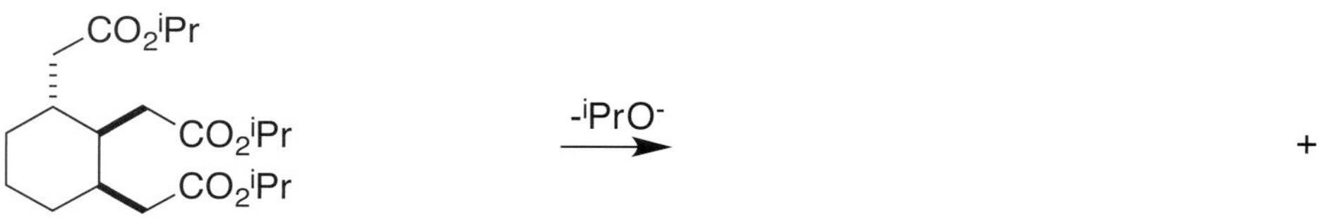

-ⁱPrO⁻ →

+

_____   _____

assume trans-fused 6,5-rings are not formed since they are less stable

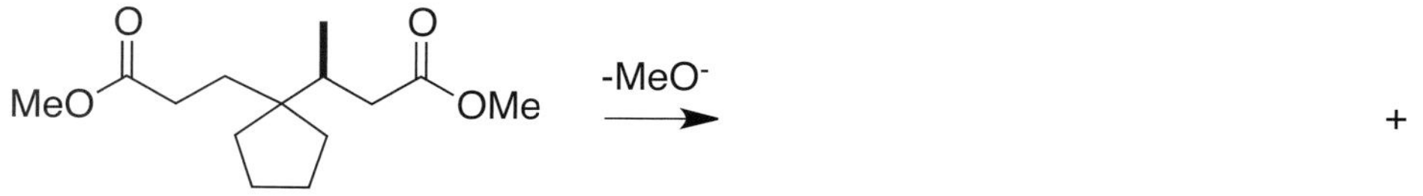

-MeO⁻ →

+

_____   _____

Check your answer to the last question has the correct stereochemistry by assigning *(R)-* or *(S)*-configuration to the starting material and to the product; the chiral center should have *the same / different* configurations.

C Decarboxylation Of 3-Oxocarboxylic Acids

From Carboxylates

β-Keto carboxylates (*eg* from Claisen reactions) tend to decompose quickly to form an enolate, with release of CO_2.

Draw arrows to show loss of carbon dioxide from 3-oxobutanoate *anion* to give the enolate of acetone.

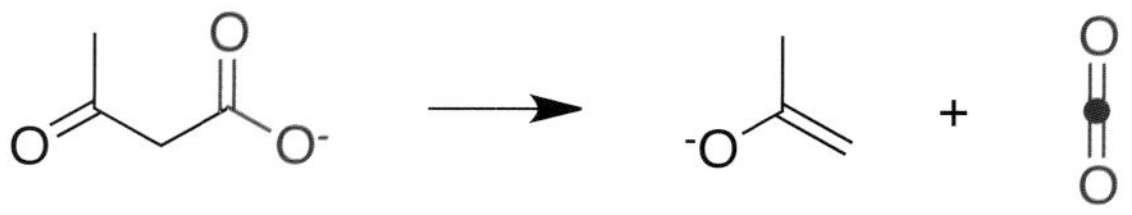

Use the concept shown above to predict the enolates formed from loss of CO_2 in the following reactions.

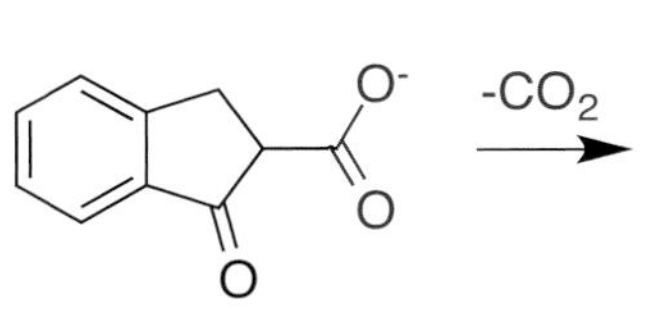

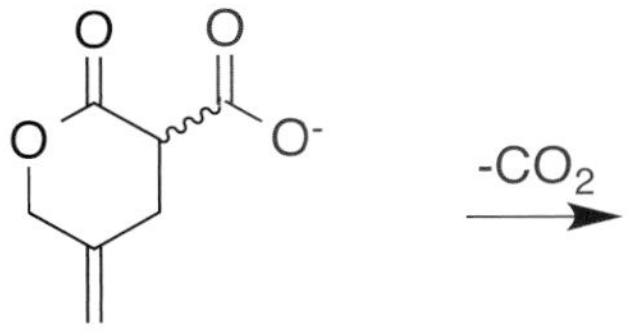

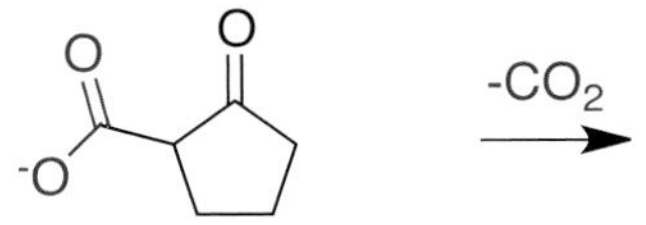

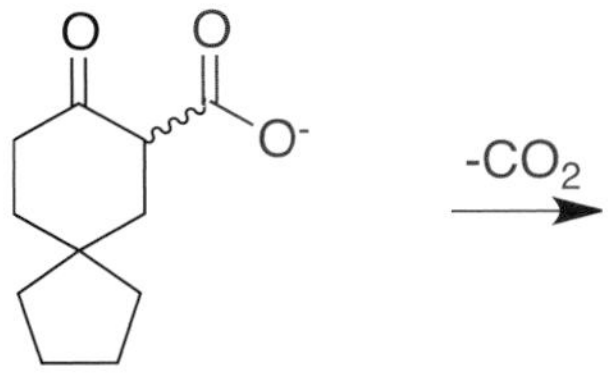

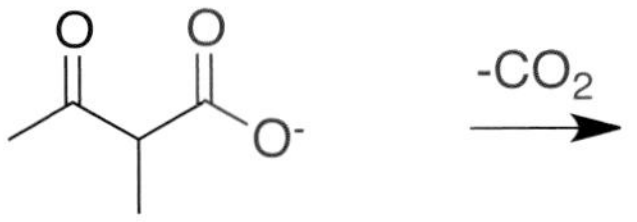

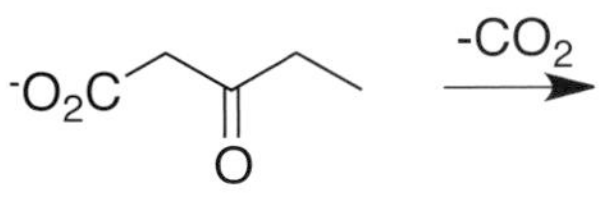

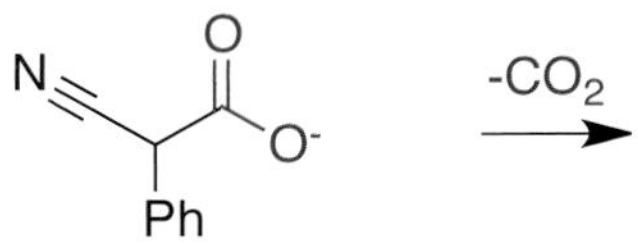

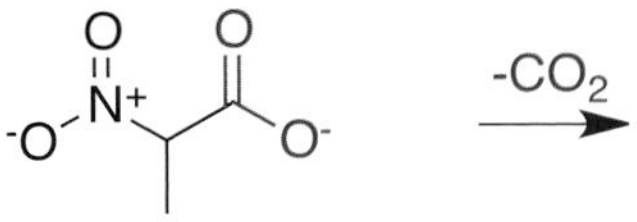

From Carboxylic Acids

Enolates and enols are similar to *carboxylic acids / carboxylates* and *carboxylic acids / carboxylates*, respectively.

Like β-keto carboxylates, β-keto *acids* can lose CO_2 but they directly generate *enols / enolates* (whereas *carboxylates* produced *enols / enolates*).

These processes are facilitated by intramolecular hydrogen bonding in the starting material that makes them possible with minimal movement of atoms.

Complete the following drawing of an intramolecularly *H*-bonded conformer of 3-oxobutanoic acid by adding arrows to illustrate loss of CO_2 with concurrent formation of the *enol* of acetone.

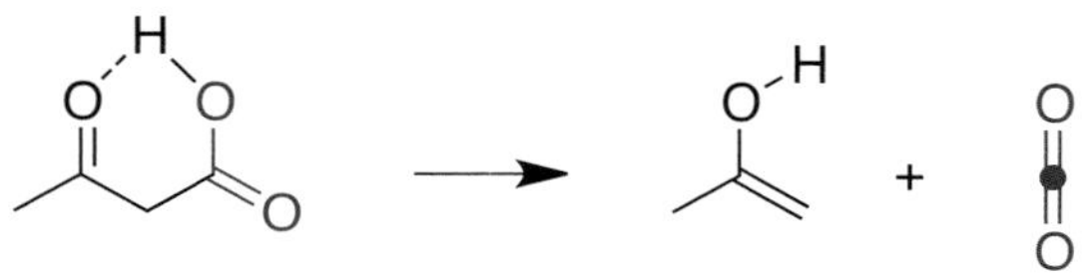

Use this concept to predict the products of the following reactions.

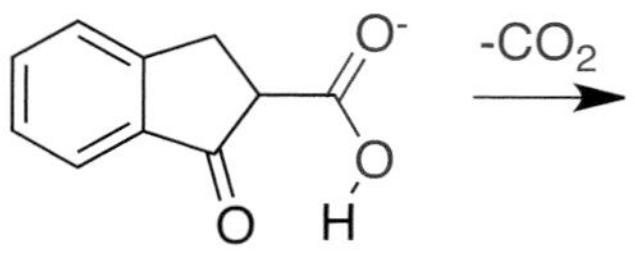

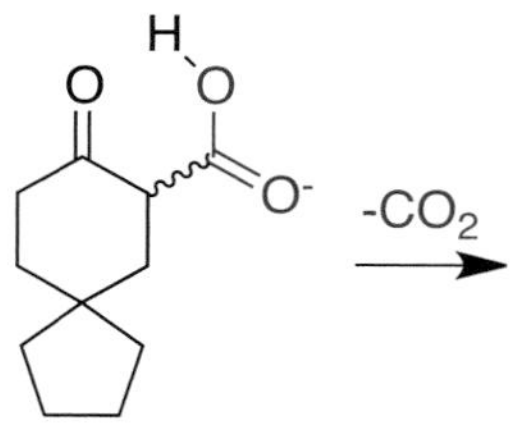

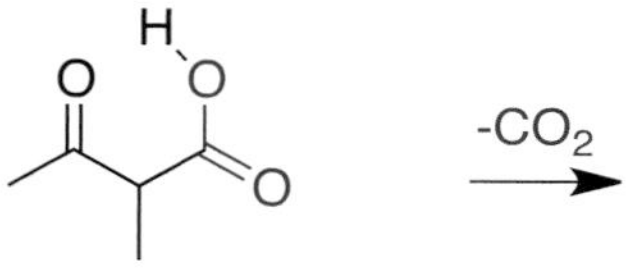

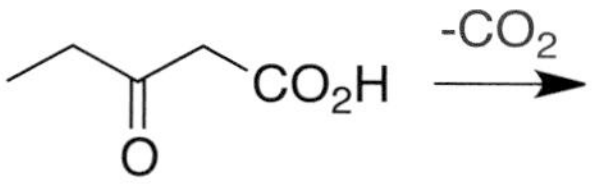

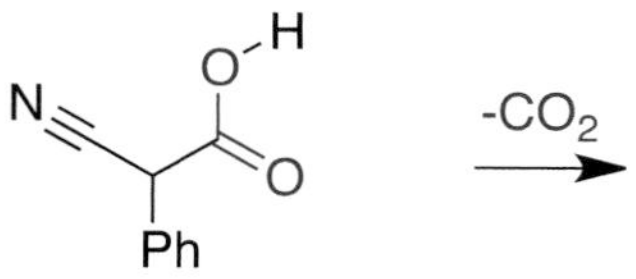

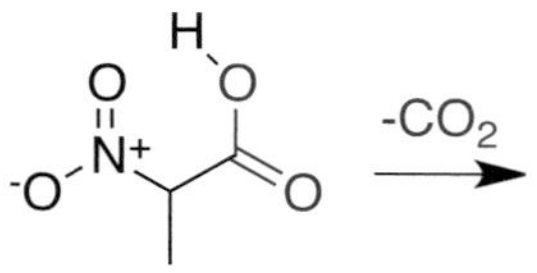

D Classical Syntheses Of Amino Acids

Draw and name the amino acid formed in each of the following syntheses.

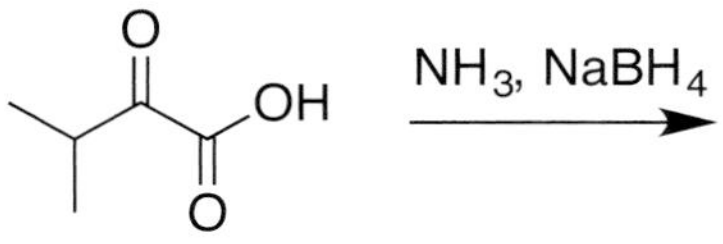
OH
NH_3, $NaBH_4$

amino acid ____________

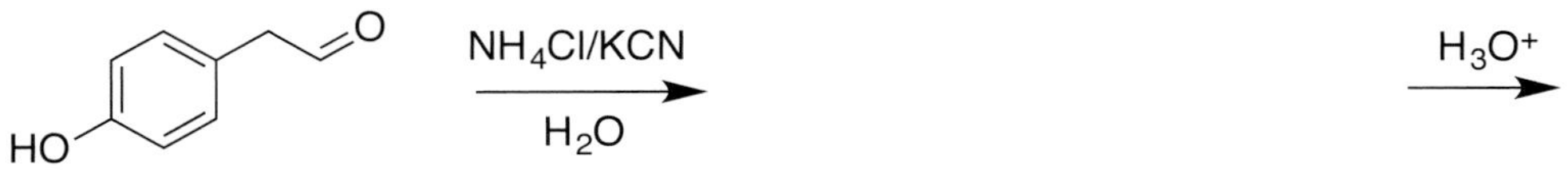
HO
NH_4Cl/KCN
H_2O
H_3O^+

amino acid ____________

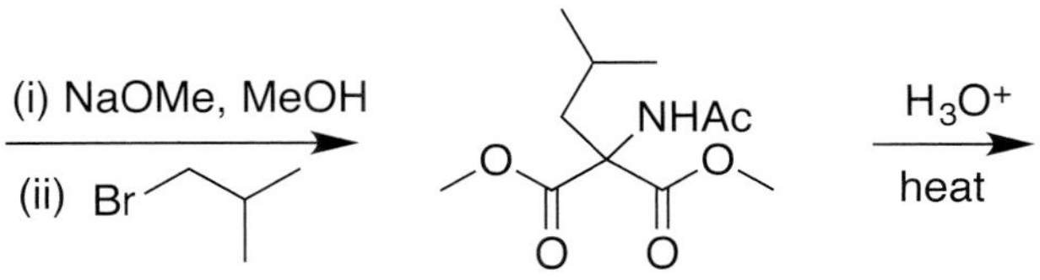
(i) NaOMe, MeOH
(ii) Br
NHAc
H_3O^+
heat

amino acid ____________

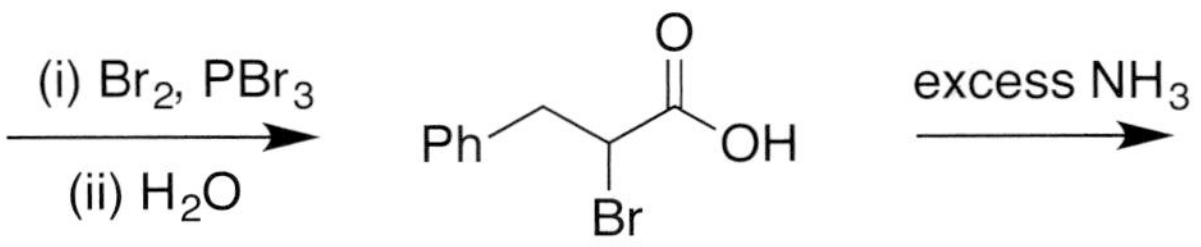
(i) Br_2, PBr_3
(ii) H_2O
Ph
OH
Br
excess NH_3

amino acid ____________

Amino acids formed in these syntheses will be *optically pure / somewhat optically active / racemates*.

Suggest a synthesis of (±)-Phe from diethyl acetamidomalonate and benzyl bromide.

Suggest a synthesis of (±)-Ala from propionic acid.

Suggest a synthesis of (±)-Pro from the following nitro compound.

E Thioesters Are More Reactive Than Esters

Nature uses *thio*esters for intracellular acylation.

The pKa of thioethanol is 10. whereas that of ethanol is 1.9. EtSH is therefore a *stronger / weaker* acid than ethanol, EtS⁻ is a *better / worse* leaving group than EtO⁻, and thioesters will undergo reactions in cells under *milder / harsher* conditions than esters would.

Look up the structures of coenzyme A and acyl-CoA and write them below.

_____

coenzyme A or CoASH

_____

acyl coenzyme A or acyl-CoA

The leaving group in these molecules is *huge / small* compared to acyl.

Thioesters are *better / worse* electrophiles than esters.

Nature's Equivalent To Ester-ester Condensations

Malonyl-CoA is the intracellular equivalent of malonic esters in the lab. This transesterifies with endogenous thiols and the product reacts with thioesters, then reacts with thioesters in a reaction driven by loss of CO_2 from the malonate derivative. Outline this process in general terms.

malonyl-CoA	transthioesterification product	enolate of thioester

product

Fatty acids are constructed by hydridic reduction of the carbonyl in the products, followed by combinations of dehydration and hydrogenation reactions.

Draw an outline of this process in general terms in the space below.

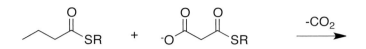

+

$-CO_2$

_____

ketone
reduction

show
Si-face addition
of hydride

dehydration

$-H_2O$

_____   _____

hydrogenation

$+H_2$

_____

24 Aldol and Aldol Condensation Reactions

from chapter(s) _____ in the recommended text

A Introduction

Focus

The last section was about reactions of ester enolates with esters that give 1,3-dicarbonyl compounds. This one is primarily about analogous reactions of aldehyde or ketone enolates with aldehydes or ketones, and it mirrors transformations of esters, but one oxidation state below them.

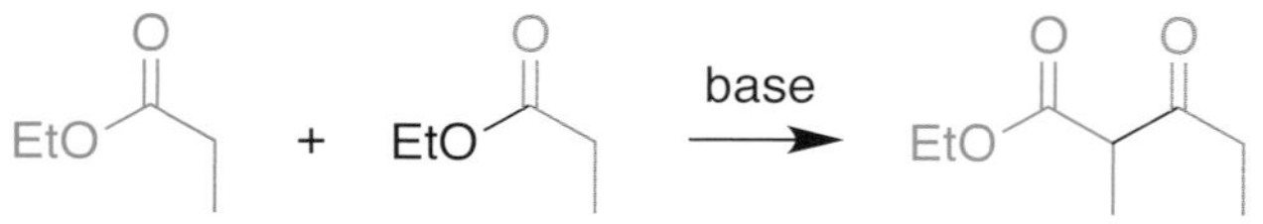

esters condensing with esters: Claisen

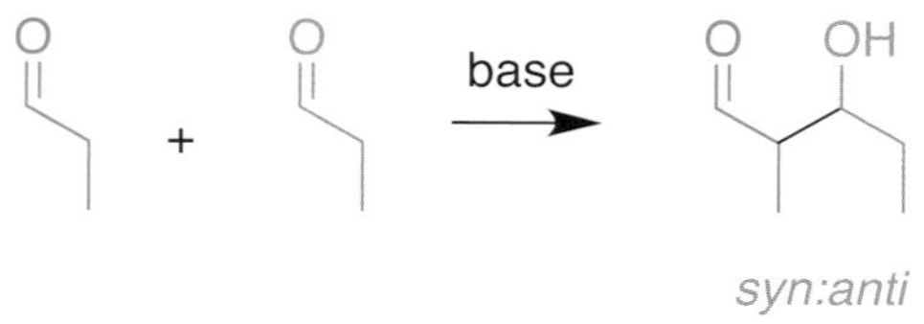

aldehydes condensing with aldehydes: aldol

syn:anti

Aldol reactions are inherently more complicated than condensations between esters for several reasons. Firstly, mixtures of diastereomers can be formed (*syn* and *anti*) because there are two chiral centers in most aldol products, not one as in most ester/ester condensations. Secondly, the aldol product may dehydrate to α,β-unsaturated carbonyl compounds.

Reasons To Care

Both aldol and ester condensations are useful in construction of larger carbon skeletons in natural products.

Concepts Involved

enols and enolates • ester-ester condensations • stereochemistry • alkene hydration reactions (reversed)

Objective

To illustrate that aldol reactions are not hard to learn for students who already understand ester condensations. Aldol reactions have some different characteristics, but these are logical, and not as important as appreciating the parallel shown in the diagram above.

B Acidities Of Carbonyl Compounds

Aldehydes and ketones (and other carbonyl compounds) may act as electrophiles, and, if they have acidic α-C*H* atoms, as nucleophiles too. Each of the following structures has at least one carbon that is nucleophilic or electrophilic; circle that center(s) in each case and indicate if it is a nucleophile or an electrophile.

Draw the following compounds in the spaces provided, in order of increasing acidity of their α-C*H*s based on the pKa values indicated: *N*,*N*-dimethylpropionamide (~30), ethyl acetate (24.), ethanal (17.0), acetone (19.2), ethanonitrile (2).

*increasingly acidic αC*H_

These compounds are *more / less* acidic than water (pKa *ca* 16).

Electron withdrawing groups (EWGs) increase the acidity of α-C*H*s in a compound by stabilizing its deprotonated form. Two EWGs can provide more stabilization than only one EWG. Arrange the following doubly activated compounds in order of increasing acidities of the α-C*H*s.

EWG¹ EWG²   where EWG¹ = EWG² = CO_2Et; COMe; NO_2
                and where EWG¹, EWG² = MeCO, CHO; MeCO, CO_2Et

*increasingly acidic αC*H_

Some of these compounds are *more / less* acidic than water. In the presence of one equivalent of hydroxide they exist mainly in their *protonated / deprotonated* forms.

C Aldol Reactions

An *aldol reaction* occurs when a carbonyl compound (aldehyde or ketone) in the enol or enolate form, *ie* acting as a(n) *nucleophile / electrophile* combines with a second carbonyl compound acting as a(n) *nucleophile / electrophile*.

Show the aldol products of the following reactions (without dehydration).

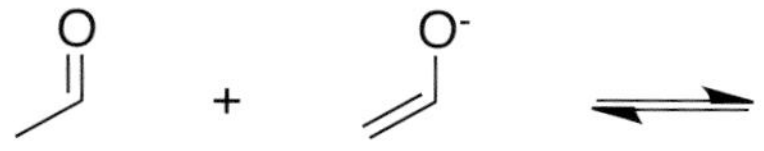

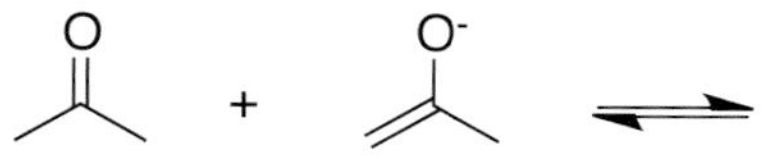

Enolates are produced from carbonyl compounds under basic conditions. Consequently, aldol reactions such as the ones above may occur simply by adding base to the carbonyl; some of the carbonyl is converted to the enolate form that may add to molecules that have not yet enolized. Thus these types of reactions may be expressed in the following way (show products).

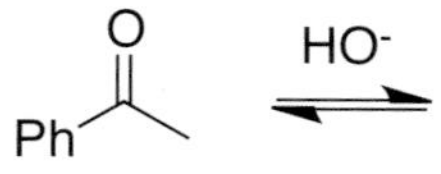

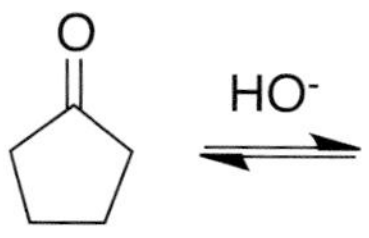

These are *homo- / hetero*-coupling reactions because they involve combinations of the same units.

Substituted enolates can react with their parent carbonyl compounds to give two diastereomers: *syn* and *anti* (and their enantiomers). Draw the *syn*- and *anti*-isomers of the following aldol reactions. These diastereomers will be formed in *equal / unequal* amounts because the products, and the transition states that precede product formation, have the *same / different* free energies.

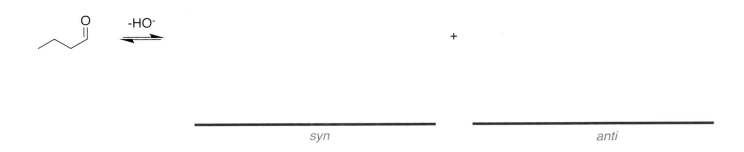

+

_____   _____
         syn   *anti*

Draw enantiomers of the products above. The ratio of the enantiomeric *syn* products in this reaction will be *exactly / more than / less than* 1:1. The ratio of the *syn* and *anti*-forms of the two products above will be *the same / different* (as) to the enantiomers drawn below.

+

_____   _____
         syn   *anti*

In reactions such as these, it is common to draw just one set of *syn* and *anti* diastereomers, and ignore their enantiomers. Using this approach, draw the aldol products of the following reaction.

-HO⁻

+

_____   _____
         syn   *anti*

Intramolecular Aldol Reactions

Intramolecular aldol reactions can occur between two ketone or aldehyde groups in *the same molecule / different molecules*. Draw the products of the following intramolecular reactions.

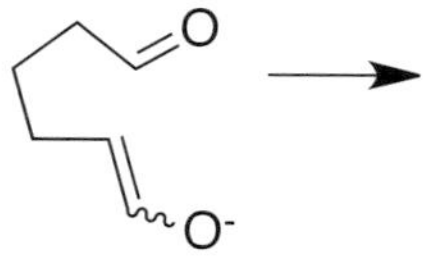

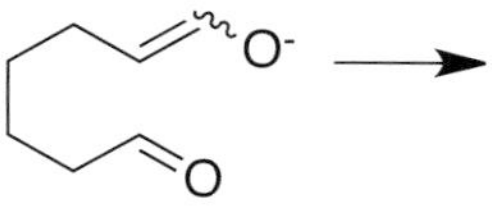

In organic chemistry it is often helpful to draw starting materials in conformations that are predisposed to give products. Try this for the following cyclization reaction.

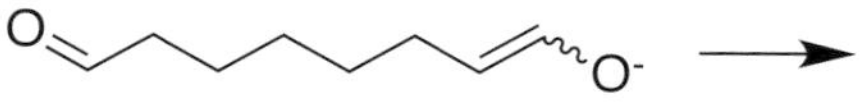

starting material re-drawn   *product*

Predict the dialdehyde starting materials that were used to form these cyclic products via aldol reactions.

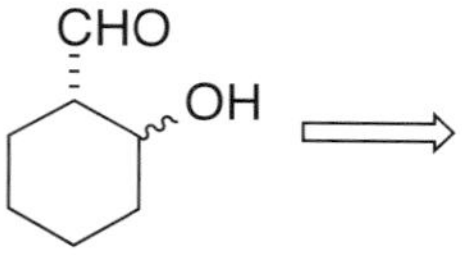

CHO

OH

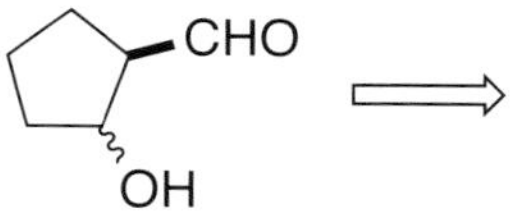

CHO

OH

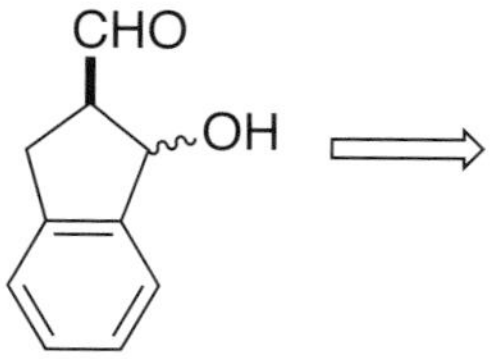

CHO

OH

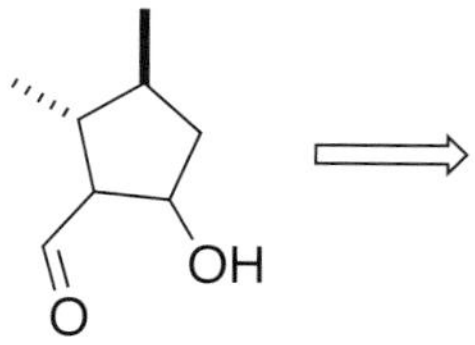

OH

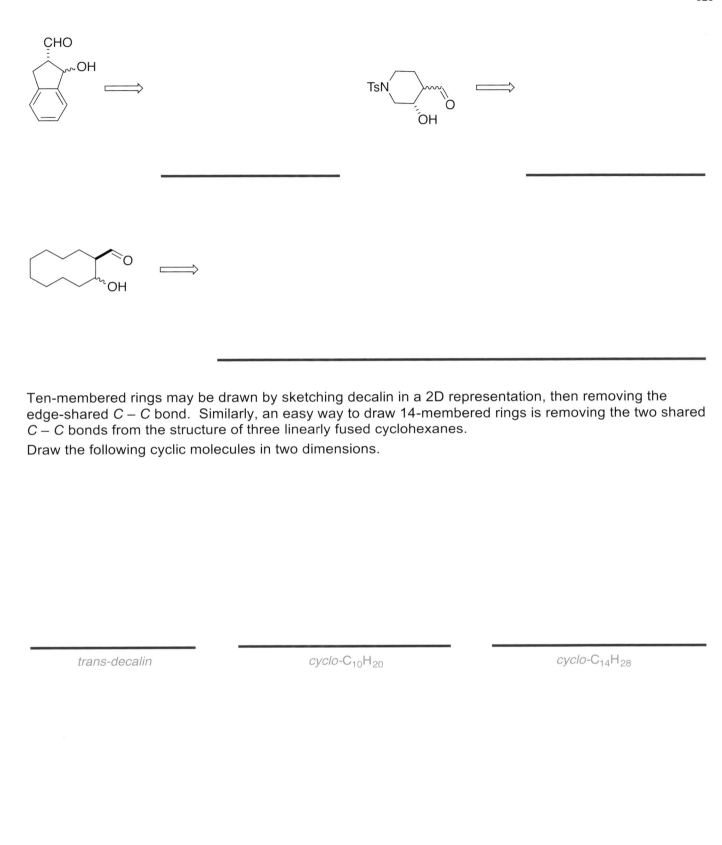

Ten-membered rings may be drawn by sketching decalin in a 2D representation, then removing the edge-shared $C - C$ bond. Similarly, an easy way to draw 14-membered rings is removing the two shared $C - C$ bonds from the structure of three linearly fused cyclohexanes.

Draw the following cyclic molecules in two dimensions.

trans-decalin   cyclo-$C_{10}H_{20}$ cyclo-$C_{14}H_{28}$

cyclo-$C_{18}H_{36}$ cyclo-$C_{22}H_{44}$

324

Under reversible conditions, a cyclization process at equilibrium favors the thermodynamic product. Illustrate why base treatment of 2,-cyclohexadione leads to 3-hydroxyl-3-methylcyclopentanone in preference to (2-hydroxy-2-methylcyclopropyl)ethanone.

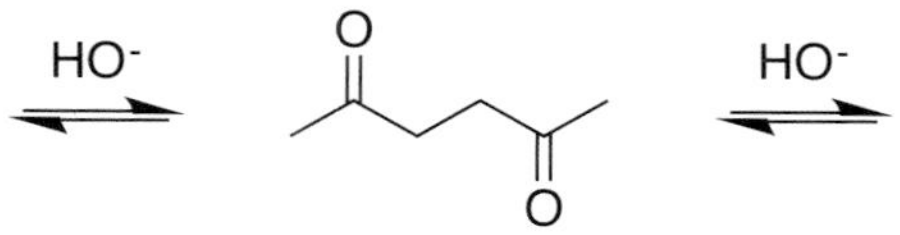

$$HO^- \rightleftharpoons \quad \rightleftharpoons HO^-$$

---

internal enolate
(extended conformation)

⇅

---

terminal enolate
(extended conformation)

⇅

---

internal enolate
(conformation to give cyclopropane)

⇅

---

terminal enolate
(conformation to give cyclopentane)

⇅

---

kinetic alkoxide

---

thermodynamic alkoxide

By analogy with the questions on the previous page, explain why 3-hydroxyl-3-methylcycloheptanone is *not* the predominant product from base mediated cyclization of 2,7-octanedione.

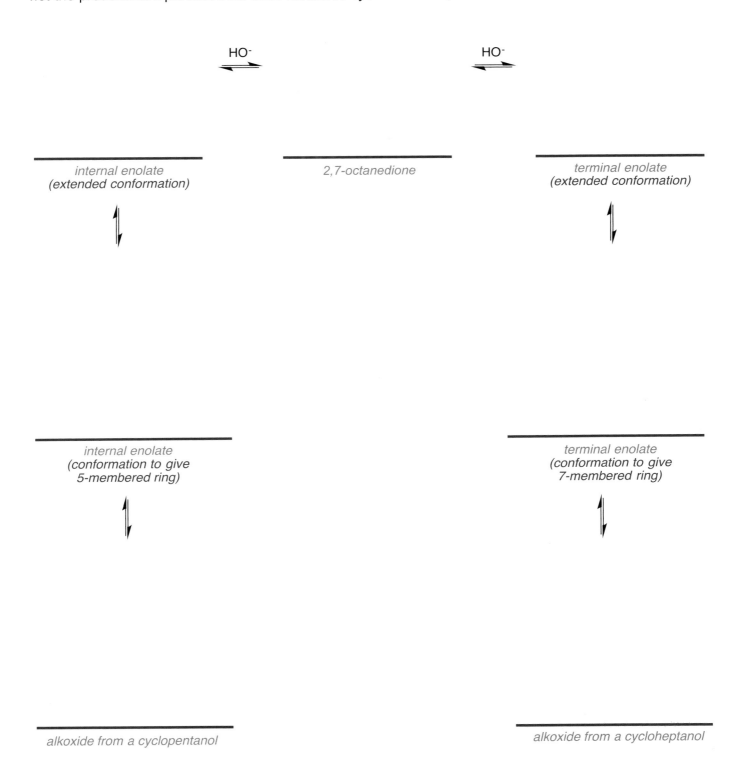

HO⁻

HO⁻

internal enolate
(extended conformation)

2,7-octanedione

terminal enolate
(extended conformation)

internal enolate
(conformation to give
5-membered ring)

terminal enolate
(conformation to give
7-membered ring)

alkoxide from a cyclopentanol

alkoxide from a cycloheptanol

3-Hydroxyl-3-methylcycloheptanone is *not* the predominant product from base mediated cyclization of 2,7-octanedione because it is the *kinetic product / thermodynamic product / neither of these*.

Predict the alcohol products (after aqueous work-up) of the following *intramolecular* aldol reactions. It may help to first: (i) count the carbon atoms, (ii) deduce which two become connected to give favorable ring sizes; and, (iii) re-draw the starting material with those atoms close to each other.

$\xrightarrow{\text{HO}^-}$

_____
starting material re-drawn

_____
product
(edge shared
7 and 5-membered rings)

$\xrightarrow{\text{HO}^-}$

_____
starting material re-drawn

_____
product

$\xrightarrow{\text{HO}^-}$

_____
starting material re-drawn

_____
favored product

$\xrightarrow{\text{HO}^-}$

_____
starting material re-drawn

_____
favored product

D   Dehydration Of Aldol Products: Aldol Condensations

Homocouplings

Draw the aldol product that would form in the following reaction, then show a mechanism to yield the dehydration product.

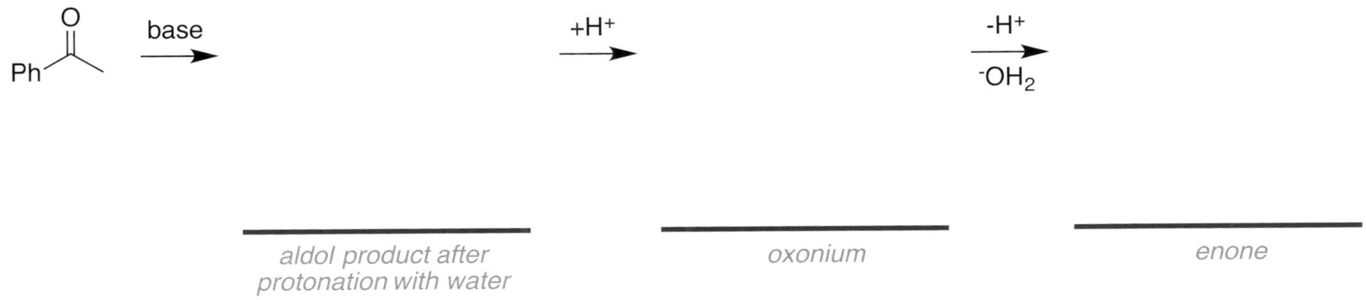

Ph — (C=O) — CH3   **base** →   **+H⁺** →   **-H⁺** / **⁻OH₂** →

_____   _____   _____
aldol product after   *oxonium*   *enone*
protonation with water

Similarly, draw the product from base-mediated self-condensation of one molecule of acetone with one molecule of itself, then acid-mediated dehydration to give an enone.

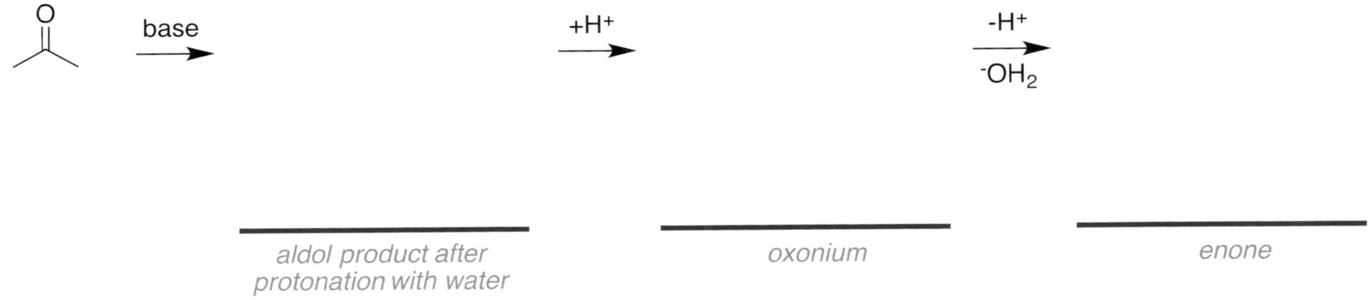

(acetone)   **base** →   **+H⁺** →   **-H⁺** / **⁻OH₂** →

_____   _____   _____
aldol product after   *oxonium*   *enone*
protonation with water

Cross Condensations

Featuring One Enolizable Component

Some *intermolecular* reactions between two different carbonyl compounds can give only one aldol condensation product and only one possible dehydration product. Show the product that may arise via coupling of the following carbonyl compounds.

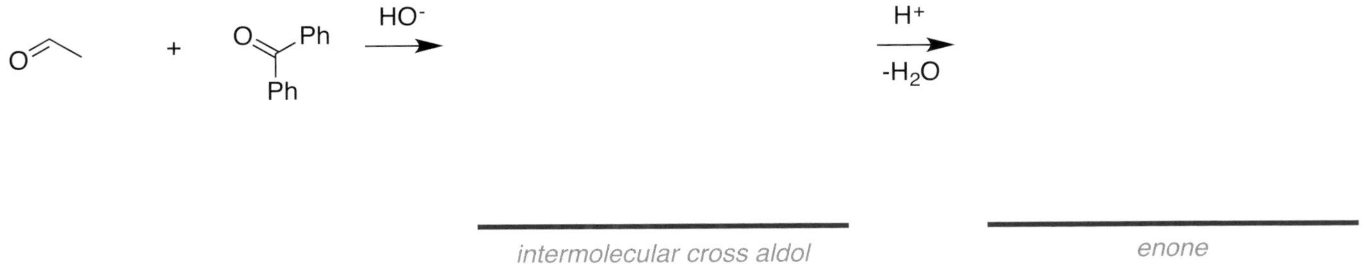

(acetaldehyde)   +   (benzophenone: O=C(Ph)(Ph))   **HO⁻** →   **H⁺** / **-H₂O** →

_____   _____
intermolecular cross aldol   *enone*

328

Ethanal is a *more / less* reactive electrophile than benzophenone, so the reaction above will tend to lead to self-condensation of the aldehyde, but there are no such ambiguities for the following reactions; show the products.

—————————————
intermolecular aldol

—————————————
dehydration to enone

—————————————
intermolecular aldol

—————————————
dehydration to enone

One / two / three different enolates can be formed from the starting materials in these transformations. In general, *highly selective* cross-coupling reactions occur when *one / both* of the components is/are enolizable.

If only one of the components can be enolized then only *two* products are possible: one from self-combination and the other from *cross coupling*. Show this for the reaction of ethanal with benzaldehyde.

base
⟶

————————————— + —————————————
benzaldehyde   *ethanal*

————————————— + —————————————
homocoupling product   *heterocoupling product*
                                (ie cross coupling)

It is possible to suppress *homocoupling* and favor formation of the cross-coupling product by using one carbonyl component in excess, and adding the other one to it slowly. To achieve this the component used in excess would be *benzaldehyde / ethanal* and the one added slowly to this would be *benzaldehyde / ethanal*.

Aldol cross-coupling reactions of aldehydes are extremely difficult to control if the aldehydes are similarly enolizable and reactive. Only in some of the cases below can reaction conditions be designed to predominantly afford the cross-coupling product. Draw the corresponding product *for only those cases.*

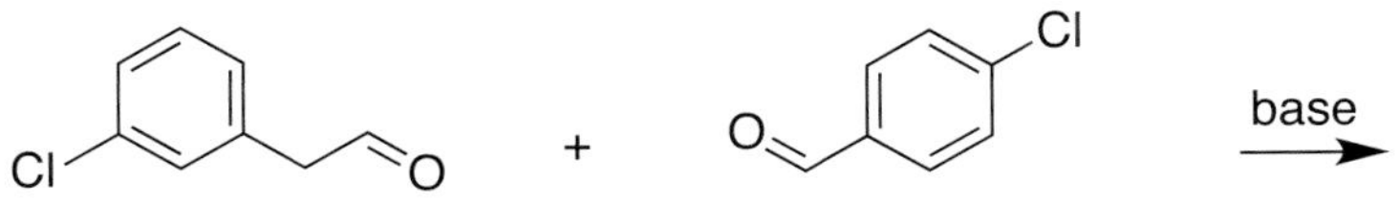

(3-chlorophenyl)acetaldehyde + 4-chlorobenzaldehyde →(base)

_____

heterocoupling product
(ie cross coupling)

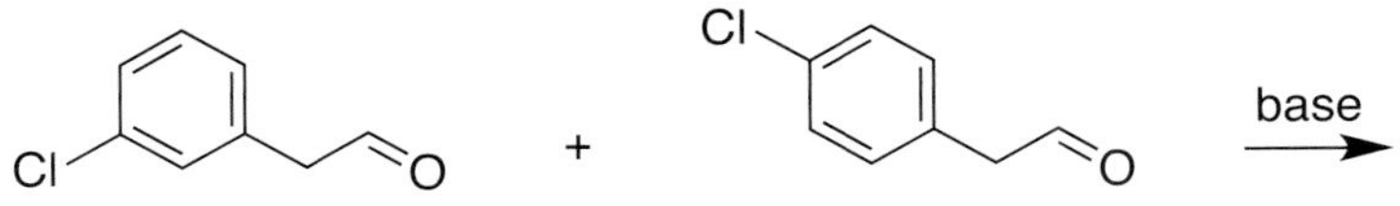

(3-chlorophenyl)acetaldehyde + (4-chlorophenyl)acetaldehyde →(base)

_____

heterocoupling product
(ie cross coupling)

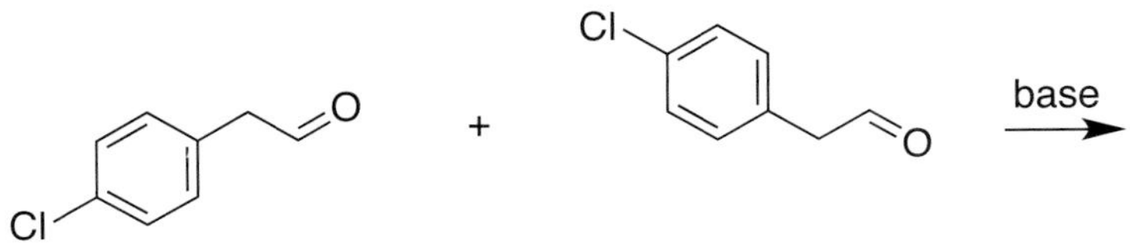

(4-chlorophenyl)acetaldehyde + (4-chlorophenyl)acetaldehyde →(base)

_____

homocoupling product

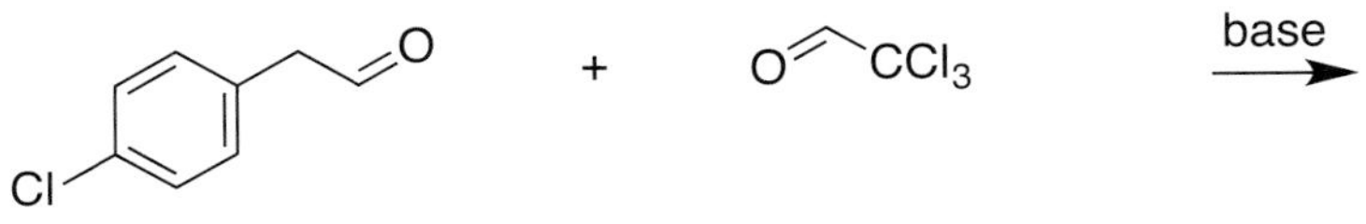

(4-chlorophenyl)acetaldehyde + Cl₃C–CHO →(base)

_____

heterocoupling product
(ie cross coupling)

Aldol Condensations Are Hard To Control When Two Enolizable Compounds Are Used

When two different enolizable aldehydes are mixed in the presence of base then either could be both the nucleophile and the electrophile resulting in two self- and two cross-aldol reactions. Show the products (without indicating relative stereochemistry, or show their enantiomers, *ie* use squiggly lines).

base →

\+   \+

---
homocoupling product 1

---
homocoupling product 2
(two diastereomers)

\+

---
heterocoupling product 1

---
heterocoupling product 2
(two diastereomers)

base →

\+   \+

---
homocoupling product 1

---
homocoupling product 2
(two diastereomers)

\+

---
heterocoupling product 1

---
heterocoupling product 2
(two diastereomers)

Intramolecular Condensations

The predominant products formed in these types of reactions result from formation of unstrained rings, usually - or 6-membered. Draw the predominant product you would expect from each of the following intramolecular aldol-dehydration reactions.

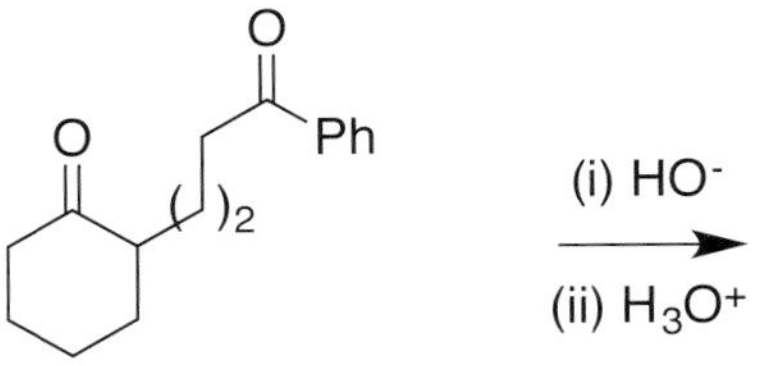

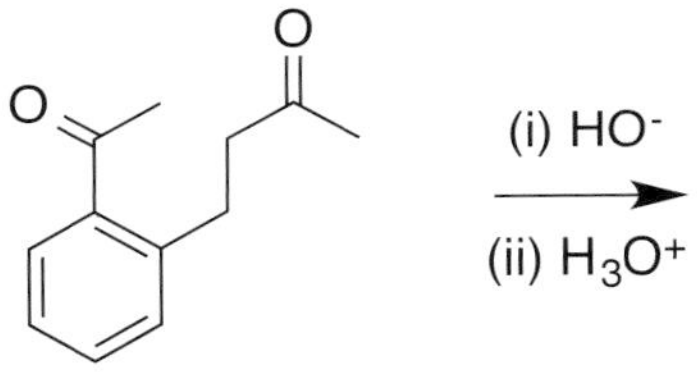

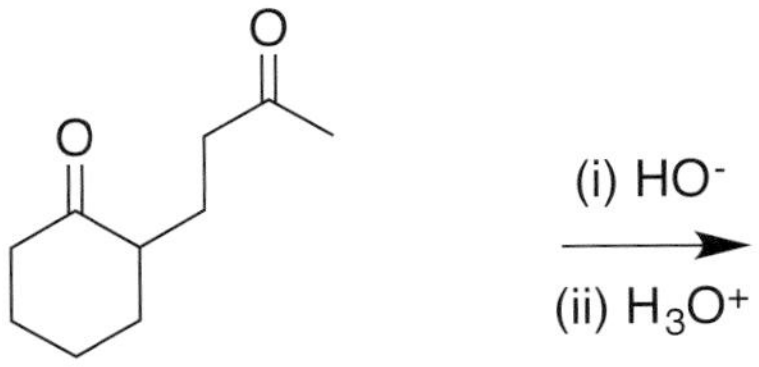

(i) HO⁻

(ii) H_3O^+

(i) HO⁻

(ii) H_3O^+

(i) HO⁻

(ii) H_3O^+

25 Conjugate Additions

from chapter(s) _____ in the recommended text

A Introduction

Focus

Esters, aldehydes, and ketones can act as electrophiles at their carbonyl atoms, and, if they have α-C$\underline{H}$ atoms, as enolate nucleophiles. α,β-Unsaturated carbonyl compounds can act as electrophiles at the carbonyl group *and* at the β-carbon. Moreover, when α,β-unsaturated carbonyl compounds react with

saturated carbonyls   *unsaturated carbonyls in conjugate additions*

nucleophiles at the β-carbon this produces an enolate that may then combine with another electrophile.

Thiols, amines, alkoxides, and even peroxides readily undergo conjugate addition reactions. In cases where the nucleophile is a delocalized enolate, the enolate that is produced may combine with other electrophiles in both inter and intramolecular reactions.

Electron deficient aromatic systems can also accommodate nucleophiles in conjugate addition reactions. The rate determining step in these processes is disruption of the aromaticity. Conjugate additions of this kind are given a special name: nucleophilic aromatic substitutions, S$_N$Ar reactions.

Reasons To Care

α,β-Unsaturated carbonyl compounds are formed after ester-ester couplings, reduction and dehydration, or after aldol reactions followed by dehydration. Their ability to undergo conjugate additions reactions adds a useful facet to their reactivity profiles.

Concepts Involved

ester-ester condensations • aldol reactions and aldol condensations • epoxidation

Objective

This section illustrates how α,β-unsaturated carbonyl compounds have two electrophilic centers, and a masked enolate that is exposed when a conjugate addition occurs.

333

B Polarization Of α,β-Unsaturated Carbonyl Compounds

Draw resonance structures of the following alkenes that put a negative charge on the most electronegative atom of the electron-withdrawing group (EWG).

The *positive* charge of these resonance structures *is / is not* always on the β-carbon; the charge simply indicates how the polarity of the substrate kinetically drives nucleophiles to add at this position.

In molecular orbital theory, the *HOMO / LUMO* at that β-carbon would have a large coefficient (*ie* a big orbital).

Enolates are formed by adding nucleophiles to the β-carbon hence the products are *more / less* stable than ones which could conceivably be formed in similar reactions of non-activated alkenes.

C Mechanism Of Conjugate Addition

Anionic nucleophiles add to α,β-unsaturated carbonyl compounds to give enolates directly, and these are then protonated (usually when water is added to quench the reaction) to give the products.

Draw curly arrows and the missing structures to complete this mechanism.

_____
enolate

If the nucleophile is neutral, then the mechanism must involve loss of a proton from the nucleophilic site after the addition, and gain of a proton to protonate the enolate.

Show the following mechanisms of the following conjugate additions of a generic *neutral* nucleophile.

_____
enolate

D Examples Of Conjugate Additions

Amines And Thiols

Other conjugate additions typically involve thiolates and amines. The products can be referred to as 1,4-addition products because the *nucleophile / proton* adds to the 4-position, and the *nucleophile / proton* adds to the oxygen giving an enolate.

Draw mechanisms for the following conjugate additions.

_____   _____
    enolate intermediate   *1,4-addition product*

_____   _____
    enolate intermediate   *1,4-addition product*

Predict the products of the following *conjugate* addition reactions to alkenes substituted with EWGs that are *not* aldehydes or ketones.

_____

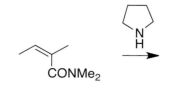

$$\xrightarrow{}$$

CO_2Me $\xrightarrow[\text{-H}^+]{\text{H}_2\text{O}}$
CO_2Me

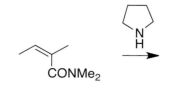

NH_2   +   CO_2Me $\xrightarrow{}$

excess

H_2N   CN $\xrightarrow{\text{-H}^+}$

Enzyme-mediated Conjugate Additions

Predict the products of the following enzyme-mediated conjugate addition reactions.

^-O_2C ⟍⟋ CO_2^- + NH_3 → β-methylaspartase

_____

^-O_2C ⟍⟋ CO_2^- + OH_2 → fumerase

_____

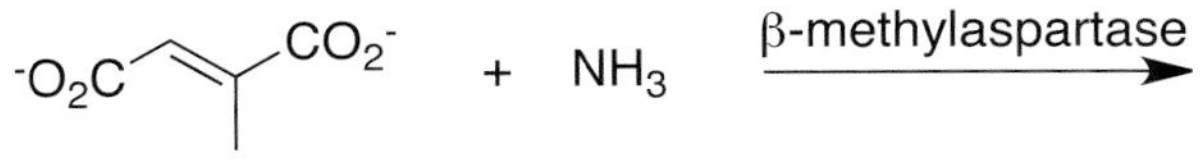

S-product

Thiol nucleophiles can undergo conjugate addition reactions of cysteine-containing peptides and proteins. Give a mechanistic explanation below to show how Cys-nucleophiles could mediate *cis-trans* isomerization of the substrate shown via a reversible conjugate addition.

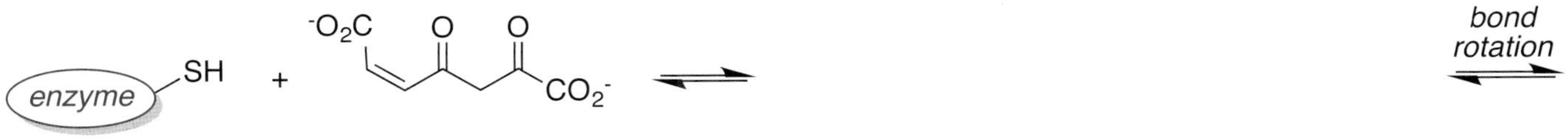

enzyme SH + ^-O_2C ⟍⟋ O O CO_2^- ⇌ → *bond rotation*

_____

adduct

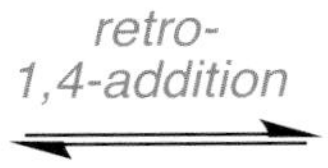

retro-1,4-addition

_____   _____

rotamer of initial adduct   *isomerized product*

Stabilized C-Anion Nucleophiles

Stabilized enolates undergo conjugated addition reactions with electron deficient alkenes. For each of these reactions, the base is required in *catalytic / stoichiometric* quantities.

Draw the products of the following reactions.

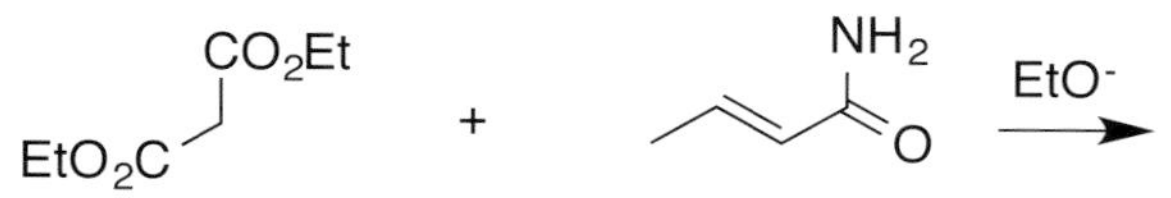

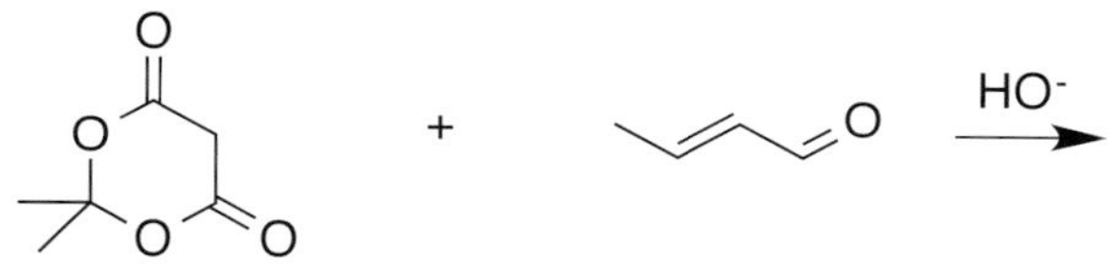

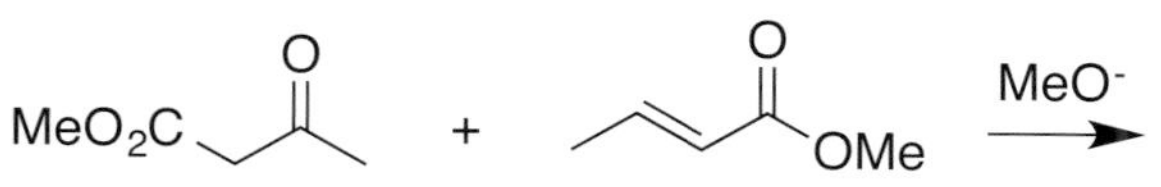

Organometallic Agents In Laboratory Chemistry

Cuprates (R$_2$CuLi) are typical nucleophiles for conjugate additions in synthetic chemistry; they are sources of "soft" R$^-$ groups that do not add to aldehydes or ketones.

Complete the following diagrams showing illustrative curly arrows.

Me
Cu
Me   Li
——→
-MeCu

H$_3$O$^+$
——→

_____   _____
    enolate intermediate   *1,4-addition product*

Show the product of the following reaction.

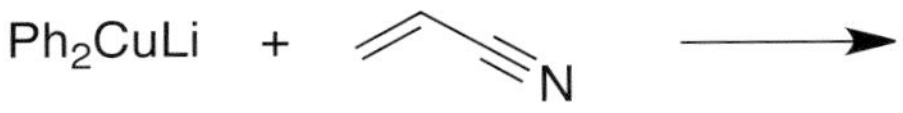

Ph$_2$CuLi   +   ——→

_____

E Conjugate Addition Then Aldol Condensation

In the following example the conjugate addition product cyclizes via an intramolecular aldol reaction. *Note* under appropriate basic conditions all the possible enolates are in equilibrium.

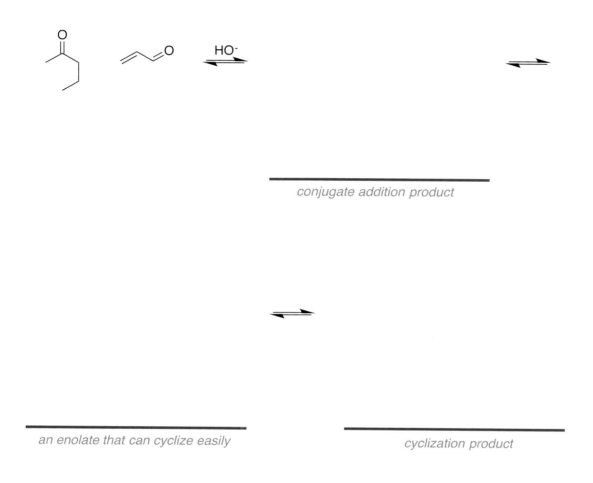

conjugate addition product

an enolate that can cyclize easily

cyclization product

cyclic aldol/dehydration product

Predict the products of the following reactions.

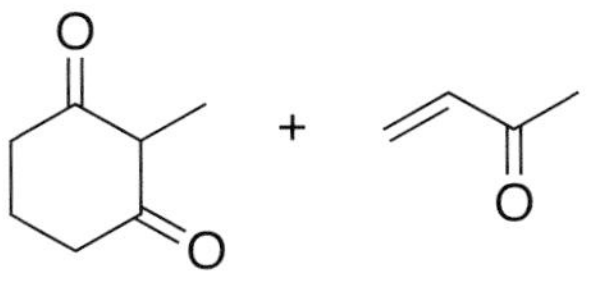

HO⁻

⇌

_____
enolate from conjugate addition

_____
terminal enolate

HO⁻

H⁺
-H₂O

_____
intramolecular cyclization product

_____
enone

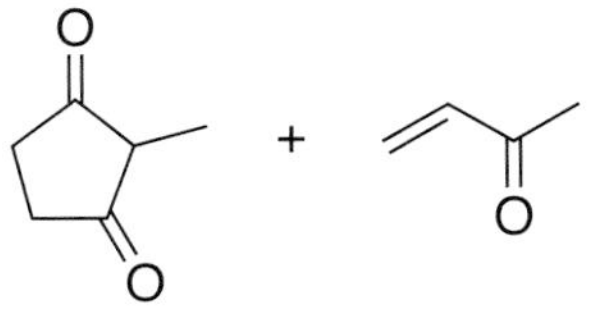

HO⁻

⇌

_____
enolate from conjugate addition

_____
terminal enolate

HO⁻

H⁺
-H₂O

_____
intramolecular cyclization product

_____
enone

The whole process outlined above can be performed in one pot (the *Robinson Annulation*). Show the products of the following reactions.

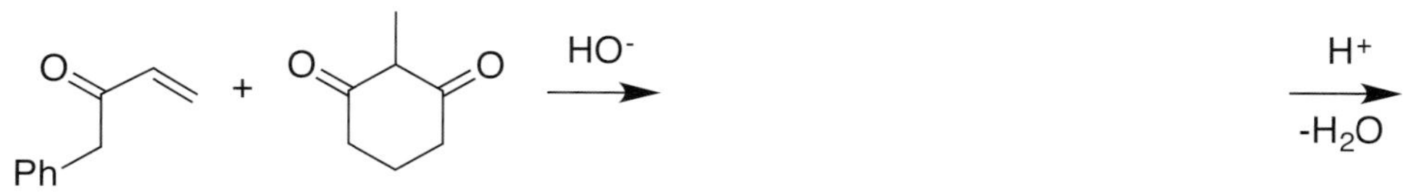

HO⁻ →

H⁺
−H₂O →

_____ intramolecular cyclization product _____ enone

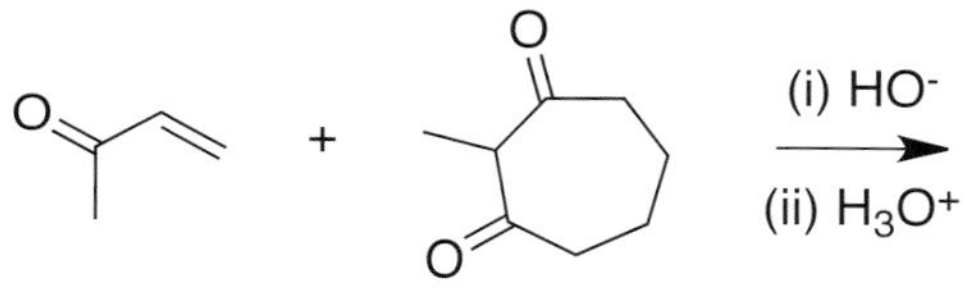

(i) HO⁻
(ii) H₃O⁺

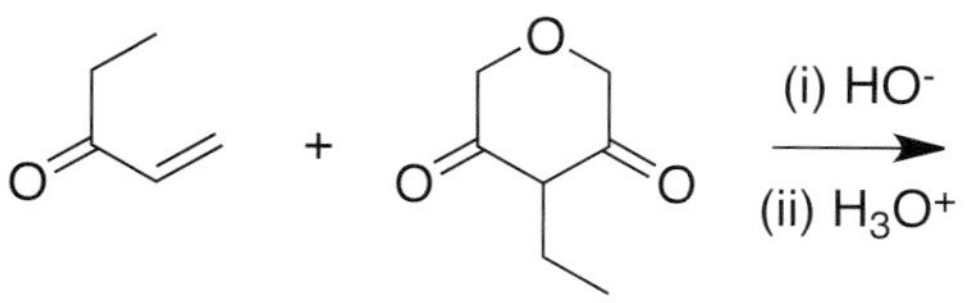

_____

(i) HO⁻
(ii) H₃O⁺

_____

F Nucleophilic Epoxidation

Just as hydrazine is more nucleophilic than ammonia, the hydroperoxide anion is more nucleophilic than hydroxide; this is called the *α-effect / β-effect*.

Hydrogen peroxide is also *less / more* acidic than water (pK$_a$ 11.6 and 1.4, respectively) so the hydroperoxide anion forms in aqueous solutions of hydrogen peroxide and base.

Activated alkenes in this medium may add hydroperoxide to give an enolate; the enolate then acts as a *C*-nucleophile to displace hydroxide. Complete the following mechanisms showing clear curly arrows.

_____
enolate intermediate

_____
epoxide

_____
enolate

_____
epoxide

_____
enolate intermediate

It *is / is not* possible to form the *cis*-epoxide of the product above via this route.

G Addition Elimination Reactions

Addition-elimination reactions of activated alkenes are mechanistically similar to those outlined above, except the enolate displaces a β-leaving group. Complete the mechanisms of the following reactions using clear curly arrows to depict the electron flow.

-HF

_____
enolate

_____
product

-Cl⁻

_____
enolate

_____
product

-HCl

_____
enolate

_____
product

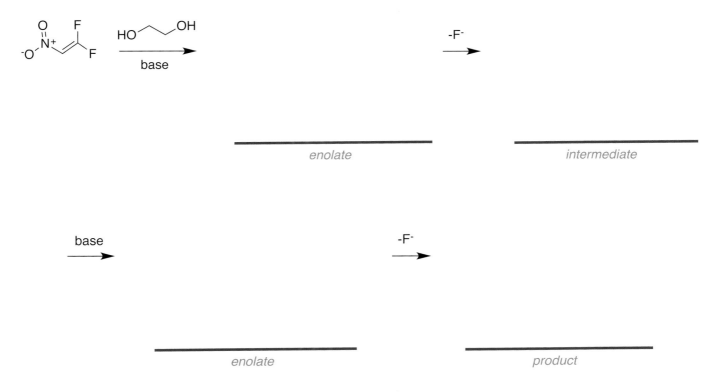

enolate   _intermediate_

enolate   _product_

Formation Of α-Bromo Enones

The following reaction is not quite the same, but is mechanistically related. Fill in the gaps.

dibromide intermediate   _enolate_

-HBr

monobrominated product

H Nucleophilic Aromatic Substitution

Nucleophilic aromatic substitution reactions are denoted as S_N2 / S_NAr / S_N2 / S_N1 processes.

They involve *fast / rate-limiting* addition of nucleophiles giving *cationic / anionic* intermediates with one sp^3 / sp^2 / sp hybridized *C*-atom.

Draw this addition process for attack of cyanide on 2-fluoropyridine, and arrows to indicate how 2-cyanopyridine can be produced via expulsion of fluoride from the intermediate.

Draw all the resonance structures for the intermediate formed by addition of thioethoxide to:

2-chloropyridine

3-chloropyridine

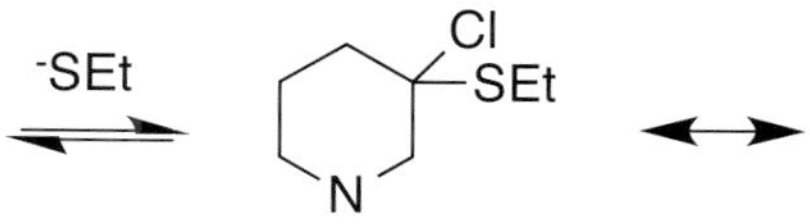

4-Chloropyridine in these types of reactions will behave similar to the *2- / 3-* isomer.

Addition occurs fastest for the *2- and 4- / 3-*isomers because the intermediates have negative charges on the *N*-atoms.

Draw the intermediates (as most stable resonance form) and products for the following S$_N$Ar reactions. One *does not proceed* under convenient conditions, and the other two may be ranked as *slow*, and *fast*. Show that ranking in each case.

2-chloro-1,3-pyrimidine reacted with cyanide

_____
intermediate

_____
product

slow /fast

4-bromo-1,3-pyrimidine reacted with azide

_____
intermediate

_____
product

slow /fast

chlorobenzene reacted with phenoxide

_____
intermediate

_____
product

slow /fast